D1200420

LATE-PLEISTOCENE ENVIRONMENTS OF NORTH PACIFIC NORTH AMERICA

The beginning of a pollen-environmental record. Sitka spruce pollen floating on the surface of an Alaskan kettle pond formed only several years previously by glacier recession.

AMERICAN GEOGRAPHICAL SOCIETY • SPECIAL PUBLICATION NO. 35

Late-Pleistocene Environments of North Pacific North America

An Elaboration of Late-Glacial and Postglacial Climatic, Physiographic, and Biotic Changes

By

CALVIN J. HEUSSER

Research Associate
American Geographical Society

Published under the Patronage of the
LOUISE A. BOYD PUBLISHING FUND

AMERICAN GEOGRAPHICAL SOCIETY
BROADWAY AT 156TH STREET • NEW YORK, N. Y.
1960

LIBRARY OF CONGRESS CATALOG CARD NUMBER 60-53557

PRINTED IN THE UNITED STATES OF AMERICA
BY THE LANE PRESS, BURLINGTON, VT.

To my field companions

FOREWORD

The science of palynology has come a long way since the presentation of the first paper on modern pollen analysis by Lennart von Post at Oslo in 1916. Like many sciences it was initiated as a rather narrow discipline and consisted largely of interpretation of pollen diagrams in terms of vegetational history. While this is the basic principle of palynology, it was soon recognized that aside from the immediate paleoecology involved, a number of other disciplines could be coordinated and integrated with the interpretation of the basic data. These include climate, chronology, glaciation, plant geography, geology, archeology, human history, paleontology, and others. In fact, the integration of these disciplines has been responsible for palynology developing into a most valuable, interesting, and recognized important field of science.

A thorough knowledge and understanding of the phytosociological relationships of the species represented in the pollen-bearing sections are most essential, as this is the basis for logical interpretations of the other phases of palynology. The interpretation of vegetational history from the pollen profiles must be done with full cognizance of the sources of error inherent in the method, which are discussed in this monograph. Because of these sources of error and the many variables involved between the time the pollen is shed and a small sample from a given horizon of a certain site is microscopically analyzed, the interpretations cannot be precise. Thus only general, long-range, regional patterns and trends are depicted.

Through my long-time acquaintance with the author, Dr. Calvin J. Heusser, first as my student and then as my colleague mutually interested in problems of Pleistocene climate and vegetation in western North America, and particularly the Pacific Northwest and the North Pacific region, I sincerely believe that no one is better qualified through training, study, and experience to put together the many facets of the palynological story of the "Late-Pleistocene Environments of North Pacific North America." Dr. Heusser has very ingeniously employed the many tools available in interpreting his data to the best advantage in order to present a lucid and comprehensive picture of the vegetation along the North Pacific coast during the late-glacial and postglacial millennia. He has thoroughly checked the pertinent literature in order to take advantage of researches of other workers that might throw light on the over-all problem at hand.

The area involved covers a vast latitudinal range and contains a large number of species of diverse ecological characteristics. An assemblage of such diverse species adds support to climatic interpretations. If a species with a wide geographic range portrays the same paleic climatic trends in different climatic areas and in association with species of different phytosociologic relations, its value as a climatic indicator is strengthened. In the Willamette Valley of western Oregon, for example, an influx of ponderosa pine at the expense of Douglas fir indicates warming and/or drying, while in eastern Oregon its expansion and partial replacement of grasses, chenopods, and composites indicates a cooler and/or moister climate.

An important consideration and an inherent source of error in depicting paleic climates and other trends from pollen profiles may be the failure to recognize normal forest succession resulting from reaction of the vegetation upon the environment without macroclimatic change. Many palynologists tend to ignore this ecological concept and attribute all vegetational change largely to climatic fluctuation. In a deglaciated region recently freed of ice, lack of soil, organic material, and propagules of many species prevent the immediate invasion by an assemblage of plants in direct response to climate. Thus, in the Pacific Northwest, the ubiquitous lodgepole pine has been the pioneer postglacial invader, probably because it was able to thrive close to the glacier and under rather severe environmental conditions, including a cold, damp climate. Its initial regional postglacial invasion of denuded terrain was a matter of expediency; no other arboreal species were at hand. As time progressed other more aggressive, longer-lived, and more shade-tolerant species were able to migrate and replace lodgepole. The predominance of the tree in the regional forest complex during the early postglacial, however, indicates a cool, wet climate.

The marine climate of the North Pacific Coast poses another problem in interpreting paleic climatic patterns and trends from pollen diagrams. The heavy annual precipitation does not approach a critical minimum, so that a wide fluctuation in the precipitation can take place without reaching the threshold of moisture requirement for most arboreal species. Thus, one must assume that only long-range trends of significant magnitude in the pollen profiles can be assigned to moisture fluctuations.

Radiocarbon dating is one of the most important recent developments of significance to palynology, particularly with respect to late-glacial and postglacial sediments. Radiocarbon assay affords a fairly consistent and logical chronology. Dates so determined for key strata in this paper have enabled Dr. Heusser to correlate and coordinate the climate and chronology over much of the area studied.

The radiocarbon dates for bottom sediments containing forest tree pollen from muskegs in southeastern Alaska and the occurrence of tree pollen in the lower levels of muskegs along the Alaska Highway in British Columbia and the Yukon refute the assumption of some palynologists and ecologists that postglacial forest migration began at the southern terminus of the glacier and proceeded northward in the wake of the retreating ice. An abundance of forest tree pollen in the lower levels of peat sections, as much as seven meters deep along the Alaska Highway on the east slope of the Rocky Mountains, indicates that there were ice-free areas between the Cordilleran and Keewatin ice that supported forests during the Late Wisconsin glaciation. It would seem to have been impossible for vegetation to migrate from proglacial sites south of the glacier in time to be represented by pollen in the lower levels of such deep muskegs. This is in accord with Hultén's theory of refugia in west-central Yukon and central Alaska, and this writer's theory that forests did persist in ice-free areas between the Cordilleran and Keewatin ice and served as centers of migration in late-glacial time. Dr. Heusser's work strongly supports the belief that forests persisted in a number of other refugia, which accounts for forest tree pollen in early postglacial sediments, probably at least 10,000 years old, at these high latitudes.

Palynologists and others interested in late-glacial and postglacial vegetation, climate, and chronology will greatly appreciate, and profit by, the time and effort that Dr. Heusser has taken in bringing together in this monograph a great deal of information concerning these problems and their interpretation. He is to be highly commended for a job well done—one involving arduous field work with many problems of transportation; long tedious hours of routine work in the preparation and microscopic study of the sediments for the pollen diagrams; the study and collating of literature encompassing a broad range of disciplines—resulting in a cogent, well-written, and logical monograph. It has been a pleasure and honor for me to write this brief foreword for an outstanding publication in a field in which I have been interested for thirty years.

Henry P. Hansen
Professor of Palynology
Oregon State College

February 1960

PREFACE

This study began during the summer of 1950 when as a graduate student at Oregon State College I started work on the late-Pleistocene history of the climate in the region of the Juneau Ice Field, Alaska. During eight successive field seasons, which lasted through the summer of 1958, collections and observations were extended to other parts of Alaska and southward along the North Pacific coast to California. Most of the field work, however, was carried out between June and September 1956 and was done expressly to provide as full a coverage of the Pacific Coast Conifer Forest as practicable. Sixty-seven sections taken in 1956 form the groundwork for this study. In addition, 11 sections reported previously have been restudied and are included here. Although only 78 sections are diagramed and discussed in the pages that follow, the conclusions presented are based on 114 sections, the total number gathered in the course of field work.

Most of the program was supported by the U. S. Office of Naval Research, largely through a separate contract arranged by the Geography Branch but also as part of a contract for the Juneau Ice Field Research Project. Additional support was given by the Society of the Sigma Xi, American Philosophical Society, Arctic Institute of North America, National Science Foundation, and the American Geographical Society. To all these organizations, I am extremely grateful for aid and encouragement.

Assistance was provided by numerous persons as well as other organizations and is also gratefully acknowledged. Professor Henry P. Hansen, whose pioneering palynological studies in the Pacific Northwest are classic works, advised me at Oregon State College. He has been a constant source of help and counsel and suggested localities for sampling in Oregon and California. In the preparation for the major field program during 1956, Don J. Miller of the Alaskan Geology Branch, U. S. Geological Survey, gave invaluable advice for finding sampling sites for the study of marine terraces in the Katalla, Yakataga, and Lituya Bay districts, Alaska. He also made available his unpublished data on these districts and helped in many other ways. Dr. George B. Rigg, Professor Emeritus at the University of Washington, gave freely of his time and expert knowledge regarding the location of sites in western Washington. Professor Donald B. Lawrence of the University of Minnesota and William O. Field of the American Geographical Society have shown many courtesies.

Particular thanks are due field companions Professor Albert C. Hawbecker of Fresno State College, California (in 1956), Stephen L. Den Hartog (in 1954), and Robert Peters (in 1955). Their willingness to work long hours, often under uncomfortably wet and cold conditions, will always be remembered with appreciation.

The field program on Kodiak and Afognak Islands, Alaska, was made possible through the facilities of the Kodiak Naval Air Station. On the southwestern Kenai Peninsula, Alaska, James W. Scott, Forester of the U. S. Bureau of Land Management, arranged for air travel to the Windy Bay and Port Chatham sites. He was also very helpful in pointing out localities about Homer, providing ground transportation, and indicating the range limits of a number of important tree species. About Girdwood and on the eastern part of the Kenai, Robert Goodwin kindly made transportation available for reaching field stations. The Phillips Petroleum Company, by way of its drilling operation at Icy Cape, Alaska, enabled the collection of the Munday Creek section. The U. S. Forest Service, particularly through Alva W. Blackerby, Harold E. Andersen, Clyde Maycock, and Dr. Raymond F. Taylor, greatly facilitated the field work in the Juneau area and at several other localities in southeastern Alaska, as well as on the eastern part of the Kenai, near Cordova, and at Alaganik. The British Columbia Forest Service, through R. L. Schmidt and P. Young, provided ground transportation around Prince Rupert. The Alice Lake Logging Company, Ltd., aided in securing the Harbledown Island section. Most sites were reached by bush planes of Cordova Airlines, Juneau Air Taxi Service, Pacific Western Airlines, and B. C. Airlines. An especial note of appreciation is recorded in recognition of the skilled flying and assistance of Kenneth Loken, Juneau Air Taxi Service.

Collections of nonvascular cryptogams have been identified by Dr. Howard A. Crum of the National Museum of Canada. The marine character of the sediments underlying the Sarkar Lake, Alaska, profiles was kindly confirmed by Allyn G. Smith, research malacologist of the California Academy of Sciences. Fresh pollen of certain California conifers was generously supplied by Miss Jean Mac G. Boyd and Mrs. Marie Kelly of Mendocino City and by Professor Donald V. Hemphill of Pacific Union College. Lamont Geological Observatory determined the radiocarbon ages of a number of Alaskan and British Columbian samples, although most determinations were handled by Isotopes Inc., Westwood, New Jersey. Certain pieces of information were furnished by Professor Harold J. Lutz of Yale University, Howard H. Waldron of the U. S. Geological Survey, Professor Ewart M. Baldwin of the University of Oregon, the Port Orford Chamber of Commerce, and the Oregon Coast Ad Club.

The manuscript was edited by Rhoda L. Heinecke, Editorial Assistant of the Society's *Geographical Review*. Her literary skill brought order to many a tangled paragraph, and her good taste and judgment added a measure of coherence and continuity to the entire work. Professor Henry P. Hansen read the manuscript, placing particular emphasis on the sections dealing with vegetation and palynology, and made a number of valuable comments. Don J. Miller gave the geological parts of the manuscript a critical reading. He helped to clarify several important points bearing on interpretation and called attention to some pertinent geological literature. The stratigraphic diagrams were completed with the assistance of Norman Swanston, and most of the maps were drawn by Rolf Rehm. The Society's Library made available the greater part of the source literature. The manuscript was prepared by Florence Belli and Margaret Young. Mrs. Young also prepared the index.

Publication has been made possible through the patronage of the Louise A. Boyd Publishing Fund. This act of benevolence on the part of Miss Boyd is an honor for me and extremely gratifying.

It is a pleasure to record a word of appreciation to the Director of the American

Geographical Society, Dr. Charles B. Hitchcock, for the freedom given me to follow the demands of this research program and for his interest in the publication of the results. And, finally, my gratitude goes to my wife, Grace Harrington Heusser, who has been a true source of inspiration and has helped much more than she realizes.

C. J. H.
American Geographical Society

March 1960

CONTENTS

ABBREVIATIONS

Since most of the measurements given in the text are necessarily approximations, the abbreviation *ca*, meaning "nearly," "roughly," "approximately," and so forth, is used almost consistently with units of measurement. Other abbreviations used and their meanings are:

B. P.	Before Present
cm	centimeter(s)
dm	decimeter(s)
ft	foot (feet)
in	inch(es)
m	meter(s)
mi	mile(s)
ml	milliliter(s)
mu	micron(s)
sp.	species singular
spp.	species plural
sq mi	square mile(s)
subsp.	subspecies
var.	variety
yr	year(s)
/century	per century

ABSTRACT

North Pacific coastal America from Washington to southwestern Alaska was mantled almost completely by a glacier complex ca 11,000 B. P. Late-glacial ice had begun to recede from the Puget Lowland terminal moraine in western Washington at least as early as 14,000 B. P., but an important readvance occurred ca 11,300 B. P. Large-scale postglacial recession was in progress by ca 10,500 B. P. at latitude 49°N in southern British Columbia; by ca 10,000 B. P. near latitude 54°N in northern British Columbia and southeastern Alaska; and by 9000 B. P. near latitude 60°N in south-central Alaska. These conclusions are based largely on the radiocarbon dating of the basal fractions of peat deposits situated on this coast.

Since late-Pleistocene glacier recession began, North Pacific America has undergone a series of climatic, physiographic, and biotic changes. Some of these environmental changes have occurred slowly over relatively long periods of time and have been of variable intensity; others have been sudden and often violent but of short duration. The natural vicissitudes that have taken place since ice retreat have been determined by a study of the pollen and peat stratigraphy of 114 sections collected from muskegs, bogs, and lakes situated between Kodiak Island, Alaska, and northern California. Radiocarbon dating, for the most part, is the basis for the chronologies of the environmental changes.

A late-glacial sequence, considered equivalent to Older Dryas, Alleröd, and Younger Dryas of the European chronology, is recognized only on the Olympic Peninsula of western Washington. A lodgepole pine (*Pinus contorta*) parkland prevails during a cold interval (Older Dryas) following the recession of Vashon ice. Forests of mountain hemlock (*Tsuga mertensiana*) and fir (*Abies*), indicative of some warming, become established ca 12,500 B. P. (Alleröd). Subsequently ca 11,500 B. P., the climate becomes cold as revealed by a reversion to lodgepole pine parkland (Younger Dryas) and by ice advance. Sections northwestward of the Olympic Peninsula contain only the closing late-glacial interval (Younger Dryas). They disclose a park tundra composed of willow (*Salix*) and alder (*Alnus*) with lodgepole pine in British Columbia and southeastern Alaska; in south-central Alaska, tundra of heath (Ericales), willow, and sedge (Cyperaceae) develops about Prince William Sound; and on the Kenai Peninsula tundra is constituted by birch (*Betula*) and willow with sedge and fern (Polypodiaceae). No late-glacial data are available from southwestern Alaska.

Postglacial time on the North Pacific coast, ensuing between ca 10,500 B. P. and 9000 B. P., is subdivided into three major intervals which resemble those categorized by von Post. This sequence shows a cold, moist climate during the opening interval, drying and warming later reaching a temperature maximum (Hypsithermal), and a return to a climate marked by cooling and rising humidity, which has fluctuated to the present. The hypsithermal interval in some Alaskan sections contains what appears to be a warm and moist equivalent of the Atlantic time of Blytt and Sernander. The duration of each of these intervals is dependent on the latitude of the site. The Postglacial in southeastern Alaska, which has been more intensively studied, has its beginning ca 10,000 B. P. and the limits of the Hypsithermal are at ca 8000 and 3500 B. P. The vegetation succession from which the postglacial environments are interpreted also depends on the latitude of the site.

Lodgepole pine and alder are prominent components of early-postglacial vegetation between Washington and southeastern Alaska. Northwesterly, in south-central and southwestern Alaska, fern and sedge are notable. Alder is less conspicuous and umbellifers more so westward along the Gulf of Alaska. No record was obtained from Oregon and California where the sections begin during the Hypsithermal. During early-postglacial time, coastal tundra is increasingly manifest at higher latitudes.

A gradual rise of conifer forest over the length of the Hypsithermal occurs southeasterly from Prince William Sound. Southwest of the sound, alder and birch are most noteworthy and on the Kenai Peninsula are found with grass (Gramineae) and sedge. Mountain hemlock, accompanied by alder, appears in Prince William Sound. It is a minor constituent of the forest in the Alexander Archipelago, and in coastal British Columbia and Washington early in the interval, the species gains only a transitory prominence, often with fir. Sitka spruce (*Picea sitchensis*) and western hemlock (*Tsuga heterophylla*), in the company of alder, are the principal conifers from Icy Cape, Alaska, to northern British Columbia. This assemblage develops also in Oregon. In southern British Columbia and Washington, however, these trees become mixed with Douglas fir (*Pseudotsuga menziesii*), western white pine (*Pinus monticola*), and alder. In parts of Washington, oak (*Quercus*) reaches maximum numbers. California vegetation is a mosaic of grass, composites (Compositae), alder, and Bishop pine (*Pinus muricata*).

A *Grenzhorizont*, particularly striking in southeastern Alaska and British Columbia muskeg, marks the boundary between the Hypsithermal and Late Postglacial in many of the sections. In southeastern Alaska it is radiocarbon dated at ca 3500 B. P. Ligneous peat, preserved from the Hypsithermal when forest had invaded muskeg, underlies sphagnum that regenerated during the Late Postglacial at the expense of the forest. Heath also forms a part of the regeneration complex at this time. In addition, lodgepole pine, released from competition with upland-forest trees, becomes established on the muskeg.

Western hemlock, with Sitka spruce and often with mountain hemlock, becomes luxuriant from southeastern Alaska to Oregon during the Late Postglacial. In Prince William Sound, mountain hemlock is the principal tree, and western hemlock rises in proportion during this interval. Sitka spruce is a late-postglacial migrant along the ocean coast of the Kenai Peninsula and on Afognak and Kodiak Islands. On the Cook Inlet side of the Kenai, white and black spruces (*Picea glauca* and *P. mariana*) appear, having migrated from the interior of Alaska. In California, alder and Bolander pine (*Pinus bolanderi*) gain in number, although grass and composites remain noteworthy components of the vegetation.

During the Alaskan Postglacial at least five major volcanic eruptions are recorded, as indicated by ash horizons embedded in the peat sections. The oldest is of Mt. Edgecumbe in the southeastern "panhandle," and the youngest is of Mt. Katmai in the Aleutian Range. The three remaining eruptions are in the Aleutian Range and Wrangell Mountains. The major postglacial eruptions southward are those of Glacier Peak in Washington and Mt. Mazama in Oregon.

A brackish-water phase in the postglacial history of coastal lakes in Alaska, Washington, and Oregon is dated between ca 6500 and 4000 B. P. This transgression is thought to represent a eustatic sea-level change that occurred during the Hypsithermal. Postglacial changes in land and sea-level relations resulting from differential uplift are measured and dated about Katalla, Lituya Bay, and Juneau, Alaska.

Pollen-stratigraphical and chronological correlations of environmental changes are attempted with other areas in the United States and with Hawaii, Japan, New Zealand, Fuego-Patagonia, Tristan da Cunha, and the British Isles. The quality and quantity of data available at these places, however, are mostly insufficient to permit refined correlations. A general parallelism is in evidence but synchronism is apparent only in certain instances.

Phytogeographical aspects take into account the existence and location of ice-age "nunataks" or refugia and the patterns of migration. Refugia appear to have been located (1) south of the ice limit, (2) on the higher parts of Vancouver Island, (3) in the Queen Charlotte Islands, (4) in the Alexander Archipelago, (5) at places between Icy Point and the mouth of the Copper River, (6) around Prince William Sound, and (7) on the Kenai Peninsula. Plants have migrated from some if not all of these and from refugia in the continental interior. Pollen data from the Kenai Peninsula are significant in that they supply evidence that the locus indicated by Hultén for his Western American Coast Radiants did in fact exist.

Passing consideration is given to the antiquity of man and the routes he followed in his generally accepted immigration from Asia. Although most anthropologists believe that early man traveled southward along the Rocky Mountain front, favor is attached to pre-Wisconsin coastal migration via the Aleutian Islands and archipelagoes of Alaska and British Columbia. Because the dates referable to postglacial man north of the southern limit of the ice sheet do not extend back earlier than ca 5000 B. P., it would seem that his migration has been northward from unglaciated southern North America, where his antiquity is greater than five millennia and a cultural relationship is probable.

LATE-PLEISTOCENE ENVIRONMENTS OF NORTH PACIFIC NORTH AMERICA

Chapter I

INTRODUCTION

The North Pacific coast of North America is a bleak and gloomy edge of the continent, where the forces of nature are dynamic and often violent. Low-pressure storms are frequent invaders from off the ocean, tracking inland over the western cordillera and bringing heavy rains and cloudiness during the greater part of the year. In winter at high elevations in the northern mountains, blizzard conditions prevail and deep snows accumulate that persist throughout the summer. The cyclonic disturbances are commonly associated with squalls and atmospheric turbulence, causing floods over the low-lying areas and strong tide rips through the islands and fiord networks of southeastern Alaska and British Columbia. Where cold water wells up from the ocean depths, particularly along the California and Oregon coasts, daytime offshore fogs form in summer, move landward by night, and retreat under a diurnal meteorological control. Along this sector, storm winds, mostly in winter, have pitched up massive sand dunes and sped their destructive migration along broad alleys many miles inland.

The western cordillera constitutes the arcuate spine of the North Pacific coast. This rugged mountainous rim is formed largely of granite, interrupted by volcanoes and eruptive material, as well as sedimentary and metamorphic rock. The altitudes of many of the summits are more than 10,000 ft: Mt. St. Elias, situated above the head of Icy Bay, Alaska, rises 18,008, loftiest of the coastal peaks. Volcanoes appear in the Aleutian Range and in the Wrangell, Coast, and Cascade Mountains. Many of them are known to have been active intermittently through historic time, and several continue to smoke and spew ashes. Most spectacular of all the eruptions was that from the Mt. Katmai area in 1912. All the high peaks are perpetually snow clad and scarred by avalanches. Their upper slopes are brewing grounds for clouds and snowstorms at all seasons of the year.

The cordilleran barrier hems in long, narrow stretches of coast between the river valleys. Many of the rivers have cut deeply into the ranges and have managed to maintain their courses over past episodes of mountain building. Rivers northward along the coast, the Stikine, Taku, Alsek, and Copper, for example, are charged with tremendous amounts of glacial rock flour. Where they reach sea level on a falling tide, their milky waters trace great distances oceanward. Their sources are the valley glaciers and ice fields that mantle the northern ranges for thousands of square miles. Some of the glaciers, such as the Grand Pacific-Melbern system of upper Glacier Bay, Alaska, are intermontane. Others, exemplified by the Malaspina and Bering Glaciers, Alaska, are strongly developed piedmont types that have resulted from valley glaciers flowing out onto the coastal plain and more or less stagnating.

Almost everywhere within the glacial border, in the lowlands and in the high country, the grandeur of ice-age sculpture is evident. Without doubt Pleistocene glaciation has been the greatest natural force, both direct and indirect, acting upon this coast and giving rise to its present landscape. Ice moving through the valley systems, gouging, quarrying, and smoothing, has created a classic glacial topography. Morainal remnants and erratic boulders perched on mountain slopes and summits and bedrock scratched by overriding ice that has long since disappeared can be found far above the valley floors. The magnificent fiords of southeastern Alaska and British Columbia, among the finest in the world, are mostly glaciated valleys drowned to great depths by marine waters. These features attest to the power and size of what is termed the Cordilleran Glacier Complex of ice-age time. The dynamics of the Pleistocene are further accentuated by active volcanoes that poured forth lavas and emitted molten ejectamenta while the complex of ice fields and glaciers dominated the landscape. Moreover, at certain places, changes in land–sea-level relations are known to have amounted to hundreds and even thousands of feet since the epoch began. Such were the vicissitudes of the Pleistocene, many phenomena of which are known to have been repeated again and again.

During the interglacial, interstadial, and interfluctuational, as well as the late-glacial and postglacial intervals, when the environment was mollified, plants invaded and migrated along this coast from outside the glacial border. Environmental stability was never achieved indefinitely, however, because under returning climatic and glacial stress, the vegetation was overcome repeatedly to varying degrees and excluded, perhaps totally, from the area glaciated. Some evidence suggests that certain biota found refuge in localities that were not, owing to peculiar physiographic, climatic, or other circumstances, overridden by ice. The existing plant distribution has attained its present status to a great extent since the last ice age. Whether it too, like its ancestral types, is destined to be changed by a future glaciation over its high-latitude parts is as yet unknown. In view of the past record, however, every indication seems to be toward cyclical succession and a swing from the present, moderately glacial to a pronounced glacial environment. The vegetation that now abounds should be looked upon as representing an interglacial age of the Pleistocene.

The forest of the North Pacific coast is perhaps the grandest on the North American continent, if not in the world. Ancient stands contain western red cedar, Sitka spruce, and Douglas fir, among other trees, that have grown to tremendous sizes. Some specimens from the State of Washington are over 20 ft in diameter and some have gained heights well over 200. Along the California coast, giant redwoods have measured more than 20 ft through and 300 tall. The tallest tree, located on the North Dyerville Flats, is ca 12 ft in diameter and 364 in height. The finest development of the coastal forest is between southern British Columbia and southern Oregon. Because of the predominance of coniferous species, the name Pacific Coast Conifer Forest is often applied to it.

The forest is paramountly evergreen and dense. The interior is seldom penetrated by sunlight and in the dim light, a misty quality pervades the atmosphere. Yellow, gray, and green mosses and lichens ensheath the trunks and branches and hang like pendant shrouds from the trees and shrubs. On the floor, with decaying humus, rotten fallen timber, and other organic litter, these cryptogams form a thick, wet, spongy cover. Dead snags—the result of past burning, insect and fungus infestation, and overmaturity—stand amid the living trees. In the dark interior, the damp air is heavy with the musty odor of mold that has generated from rotting organic debris. The sound of rushing water from snow-fed and glacier-fed streams nearly always can be heard.

Most of the trees along the open ocean are deformed, scraggly lodgepole pine and Sitka spruce, stripped of almost all their branches by sand blast and salt spray. Inland along the channels and waterways, by contrast, trees are thrifty and appear to form continuous forest from tidewater to timber line. Much of the forest in actuality is a narrow band close to sea level and only stringers follow the streams to a more continuous belt on the mountain slopes below the arctic-alpine tundra. Behind the timbered fringe in northern British Columbia and southern Alaska, scrubby-plant barrens, called muskeg, usually dominate the flats and low slopes of poor drainage, their surfaces interrupted by pit ponds and small lakes. They are a significant vegetation type, since their history, as will be seen, dates back in some cases to as early as the Late-glacial. During postglacial time, many became engulfed by forest but later were able to encroach upon it under conditions of climatic change.

It is apparent from the tension displayed between forest and muskeg that the vegetation established on this coast since ice-age glaciers melted has never been static. Primarily under the control of climate, timber lines on the mountains and along the edges of muskeg have fluctuated at least since the opening of the Postglacial. Species have migrated both up and down the coast, as well as from and into the interior. They have advanced and retreated as climates became favorable or unfavorable. Secondary successions, created by earth movements, eustatic sea-level changes, vulcanism, mountain glaciation, earth slides, floods, fires, insect and fungus depradation, and man, have further altered the vegetation.

The North Pacific coast is indeed a region of dynamic change. In the ca 11,000 yr since ice-age glaciers began to waste away on the lowlands and retreat up into the cordillera of southeastern Alaska and British Columbia, land–sea-level relations have been altered in amounts of more than 500 ft in the area around Juneau, Alaska, 750 in the vicinity of the lower Fraser River, British Columbia, and possibly as much as 1500 to 1700 about Lituya Bay, Alaska. Many glaciers, such as the Mendenhall near Juneau, which now terminates nearly 5 mi from salt water, formerly calved icebergs directly into the tide possibly as recently as the early part of the Hypsithermal. Southern Alaska has witnessed at least three major volcanic eruptions in the Aleutian Range. Mt. Edgecumbe in the Alaskan "panhandle" erupted ca 9000 yr ago and Glacier Peak in the northern Cascades of Washington ca 6700 yr ago. Icy Bay was completely filled by ice until the beginning of the present century. Glacier Bay, which was fully occupied by glaciers in the latter part of the eighteenth century, has been opened to more than 60 mi in the ca 200 yr since then. Two buried forest layers at Muir Inlet in Glacier Bay indicate previous ice advances ca 7000 and ca 2000 yr ago. Changes are continuing down to the present, some gradual and almost unobserved, others periodic and violent, such as the 1899 earthquakes in Yakutat Bay and the very recent earthquake of 9 July 1958 at Lituya Bay. Crustal movement causing the latter was instrumental in creating a wave of water with such power that the forest to an elevation of more than 1700 ft on a shoulder bordering Gilbert Inlet was completely washed away.

These late-Pleistocene environmental changes, of both a physical and biological nature, are interpreted in the pages that follow. They have been dealt with in the course of investigating the palynology and peat stratigraphy of muskeg, lake, and bog deposits situated between Karluk on Kodiak Island, Alaska, and Fort Bragg, California (Figs. 1–5). This study has as its major objective the reconstruction of late-Pleistocene vegetation and associated climatic and physiographic changes in the region of the Pacific Coastal Forest. It includes an elaboration of glacial and land–sea-level variations and of vulcanism; the determination of plant-migration patterns during the Late Pleistocene, taking into account biota, relative number of the various migrants, succession, and rates of migration; the establishment of a chronology founded on radiocarbon dating and stratigraphic correlations; and a correlation with other environments and chronologies developed in both the Northern and Southern Hemispheres, thereby contributing to the existing knowledge of the late-Pleistocene history of the earth.

This research is best categorized as an investigation in historical plant geography, although it is closely allied to historical geology and paleoclimatology, among other fields. Wulff (1950) clearly defines this branch of phytogeography as "the study of the distribution of species of plants now existing and, on the basis of their present and past areas, the elucidation of the origin and history of development of floras, which, in turn, gives us a key to an understanding of the earth's history." The methods employed in studying the North Pacific coast have evolved mainly since the outset of the present century and have become classic approaches, particularly for the solution of many biogeographical problems of the Pleistocene.

The length of coast treated coincides almost completely with the extent of the Pacific Coastal Forest and covers ca 21°33′ of latitude and ca 32°06′ of longitude, a distance of ca 2500 mi. In addition, another ca 2500 mi were reconnoitered in an unsuccessful search for suitable sampling sites. This included reconnaissance about Port Nellie Juan and Bligh Island in Prince William Sound, at McKinley Lake near Alaganik, on the flats near Yakutat, at Dundas Bay in southeastern Alaska, in the vicinity of Port Alberni on Vancouver Island, at Floras Lake in Oregon, and near Mendocino City, California. It was the intention to gather peat sections from the west side of Vancouver Island, but poor flying conditions precluded this, and sites on the east side were chosen instead. The Washington and Oregon coasts were examined less intensely than other sectors since Dr. Henry P. Hansen of Oregon State College had already achieved coverage as far south as Bandon (Hansen 1947a). Sections from California are unfortunately few and do not penetrate farther into the past than the latter part of the Hypsithermal; work here must be considered only exploratory.

In this monographic treatment of the development of the North Pacific coastal environments during the Late Pleistocene, it is necessary to use terms in the parlance of the subject matter. A discussion of these follows.

Pleistocene, following the suggestion by Flint (1957), is here understood to be all

FIG. 1. Sketch map showing general locations of sampling sites and areal coverage of Figs. 2–5.

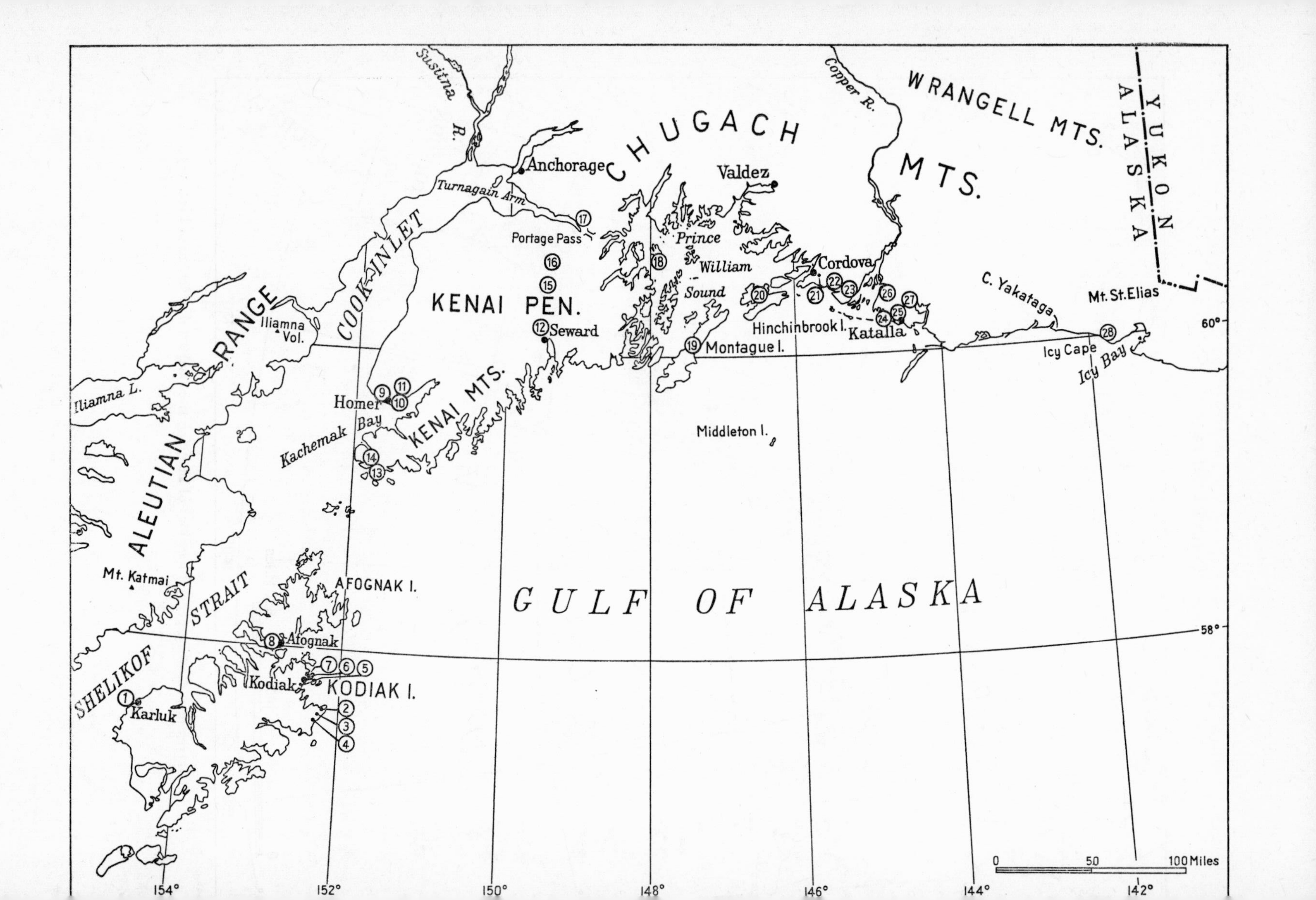
YUKON
ALASKA
WRANGELL MTS.
CHUGACH MTS.
Copper R.
Susitna R.
Anchorage
Turnagain Arm
Portage Pass
Valdez
Prince William Sound
Cordova
Hinchinbrook I.
Katalla
C. Yakataga
Mt. St. Elias
Icy Cape
Icy Bay
Montague I.
Middleton I.
KENAI PEN.
Seward
KENAI MTS.
COOK INLET
Homer
Kachemak Bay
Iliamna Vol.
Iliamna L.
ALEUTIAN RANGE
Mt. Katmai
SHELIKOF STRAIT
AFOGNAK I.
Afognak
Kodiak
KODIAK I.
Karluk
GULF OF ALASKA
60°
58°
154°
152°
150°
148°
146°
144°
142°
0
50
100 Miles
1
2
3
4
5
6
7
8
9
10
11
12
13
14
15
16
17
18
19
20
21
22
23
24
25
26
27
28

Fig. 3. Sketch map showing locations of sampling sites in Alaskan Southeastern District and part of northern British Columbia.

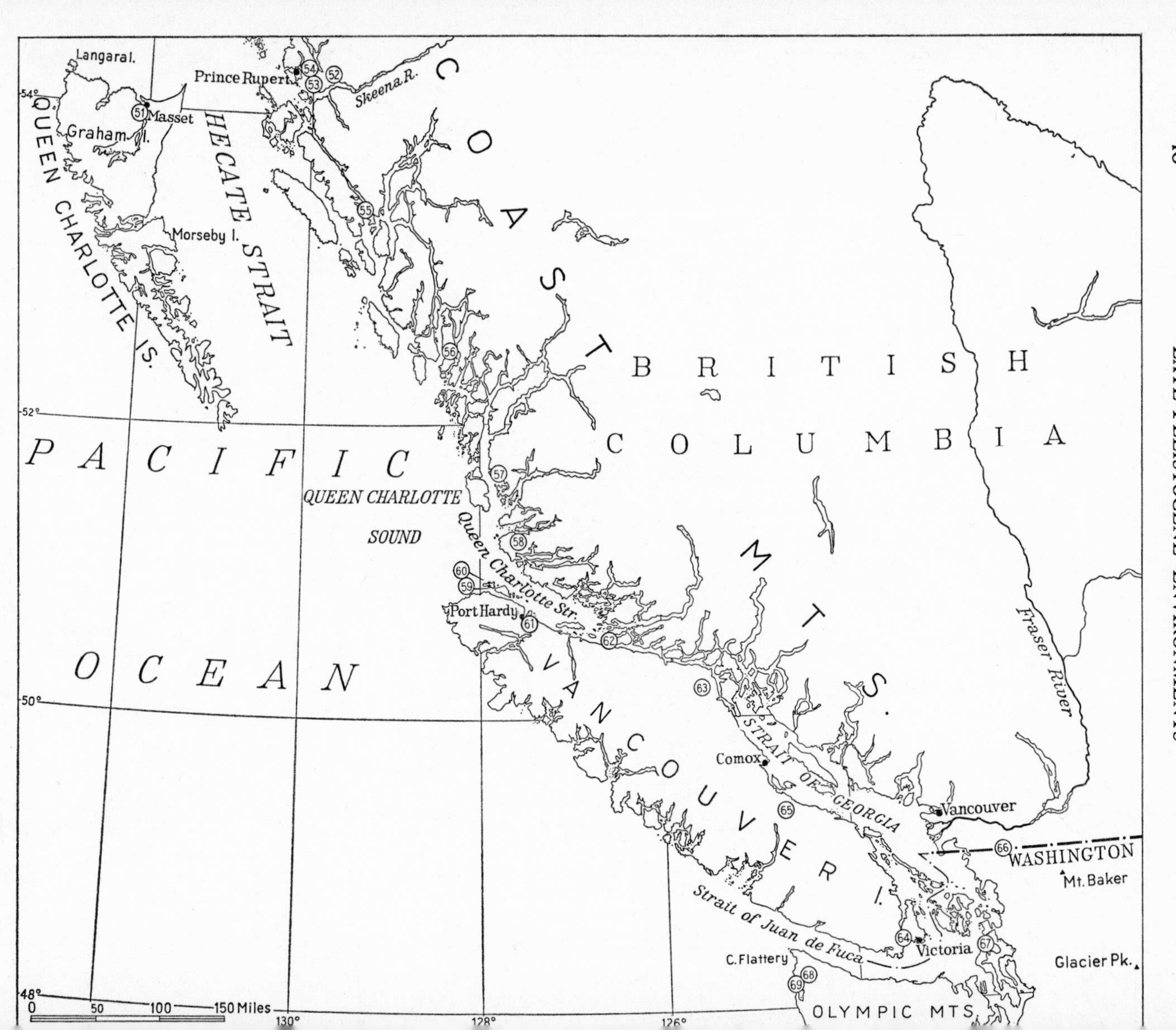
COAST MTS.
BRITISH COLUMBIA
Fraser River
WASHINGTON
Mt. Baker
Glacier Pk.
Vancouver
Victoria
OLYMPIC MTS.
STRAIT OF GEORGIA
Comox
VANCOUVER I.
Strait of Juan de Fuca
C. Flattery
Queen Charlotte Str.
Port Hardy
QUEEN CHARLOTTE SOUND
PACIFIC OCEAN
Skeena R.
Prince Rupert
HECATE STRAIT
Morseby I.
Masset
Graham I.
Langara I.
QUEEN CHARLOTTE IS.
54°
52°
50°
48°
126°
128°
130°
0 50 100 150 Miles
51 52 53 54 55 56 57 58 59 60 61 62 63 64 65 66 67 68 69

FIG. 5. Sketch map showing locations of sampling sites in Washington, Oregon, and California and part of southern British Columbia. Hachured line approximates the position of the glacier boundary.

of post-Pliocene time or a division of epoch rank of the Cenozoic Era. This usage avoids the controversial terms "Recent" and "Post Pleistocene." The Late Pleistocene is treated as an interval of variable duration and has ensued since ice of the last glacial subage receded from the surfaces under consideration. In Alaska, northern British Columbia, and parts of southern British Columbia and Washington, the Late Pleistocene appears to have been equivalent mostly to the Post Valders or the Post Late Wisconsin of the midwestern United States glacial-stratigraphic column. In the Puget Sound region of Washington, the last subage seems best correlated with the maximum of the Early Wisconsin in the Midwest.

Late Pleistocene is subdivided into the Late-glacial and the Postglacial. The Late-glacial is recognized as that interval during which the amelioration of climate following the last ice age was interrupted by a temporary reversion to cold conditions. Subsequently, during the Postglacial, climate steadily improved through the Hypsithermal. The latter term, recently proposed by Deevey and Flint (1957) to replace the faulty terms "thermal maximum" and "climatic optimum," represents a time when mean annual temperatures were higher than those of the present. On the North Pacific coast the duration of these intervals has varied according to latitude. The Early Postglacial here follows the Late-glacial but precedes the Hypsithermal; Late Postglacial is all of post-hypsithermal time. The terms interglacial and interstadial refer to deposits laid down between glacial ages and subages; interfluctuational refers to material laid down between minor glacier advances during the Late Pleistocene.

Plant nomenclature follows Hultén (1941–1950) unless authorities are given; in the text, binomials and subspecific scientific names of seed plants, ferns, and fern allies not occurring in Alaska, and therefore not included by Hultén, are followed by the pertinent authorities. These are valid, so far as I am aware, according to the International Rules of Botanical Nomenclature. The manuals by Anderson (1943–1947, 1949, 1950), the British Columbia Provincial Museum (1921), Henry (1915), Piper (1906), Peck (1941), and Jepson (1925) and recent journal papers have been used freely in order to bring all the names up-to-date. Authorities where applicable have been given only in the text and do not appear on the stratigraphic diagrams.

The English system of measurement is followed for distance and altitude, and the metric system is adhered to in strictly palynological and stratigraphical matters.

Finally, a few words should be written about the presentation of material in the text. A description of the physiographic events, climate, and vegetation, including a review of the pertinent literature, follows the Introduction and precedes the section on palynology. This arrangement is made because it is felt that these pages contain information necessary for an understanding of the late-Pleistocene palynology. In the palynological section, the history, principles, and methods of study are presented, and the results of the North Pacific work are discussed. A glossary of terms considered unfamiliar to the lay reader appears at the back.

Chapter II

LATE-PLEISTOCENE PHYSIOGRAPHIC EVENTS

The Late Pleistocene has been an interval during which the processes of gradation, diastrophism, and vulcanism have been intensely active on this coast. The degradational work of ice, running water, and ocean waves, tides, and currents has vigorously corraded the land surfaces while aggradation of the degraded material has resulted in extensive valley filling and the formation of shore and offshore features. The land forms produced in this way have been further modified by earth movement, so that marine till and former strand lines and deltas lie differentially elevated. Moreover, volcanoes have erupted, ejecting pyroclastic material onto the landscape with attendant alteration of the terrain, both locally and at considerable distances from the seat of activity.

Since the reconstruction of glacier variations, land–sea-level changes, and episodes of vulcanism during the Late Pleistocene is an integral part of this paper, this section is intended to review and discuss the evidence and conclusions previously reported regarding late-Pleistocene physiographic events.

GLACIATION

The loftiness of the Pacific Mountain System and the influence of storms moving in from the ocean have created the vast array of ice fields and glaciers that abound over the region (Plates I, II). The present extent of ice, however, occupies only a part of the cordillera that was overrun by glaciers during the ice ages. At the height of glaciation, a mass of interconnected piedmont and valley glaciers and an ice sheet extended from the Alaskan Aleutian Islands to the Cascades north of the Columbia River in Washington. This Cordilleran Glacier Complex, as it is called, was 2350 mi long and from Vancouver Island to the eastern side of the Rocky Mountains was 550 mi wide (Flint 1957). Although details have not been worked out, the complex probably achieved dimensions close to these several times during the Pleistocene. Even possibly as early as the Middle Miocene, glaciers were active over part of the region, as is indicated on the Alaskan coast near Yakataga (Miller 1957b).

During the last maximum at least, glaciers of the Cordilleran Complex flowed toward the interior of the continent and toward the Pacific. The Gulf of Alaska region was a dumping ground for ice that passed oceanward from Shelikof Strait, Cook Inlet, Prince William Sound, Copper River, and the bays eastward to Cross Sound. The intermontane valleys in the Aleutian Range and the Kenai, Chugach, and St. Elias Mountains became choked by glaciers, although it is generally unknown to what extent the ice reached oceanward. Middleton Island, located in the gulf over 50 mi from the nearest land mass, Montague Island, was originally thought to have been glaciated (Dawson 1893). Glacial material, in a tilted-bedrock sequence and considered to be Late Pliocene or Early Pleistocene in age, is now interpreted by

Miller (1953) as having been derived under marine conditions from a floating ice shelf or from icebergs or both.

Although considerable ice presumably came off the gulf border, one stretch of coast appears not to have contributed greatly. East of the lower Copper River valley, observations by Martin (1908) bring him to conclude that Martin River Glacier was only 600 to 700 ft higher at its maximum than it is now and along with Bering Glacier underwent little, if any, further extension during the last glaciation. However, it appears that evidence to indicate ice discharge into the ocean may be beneath marine and estuarine deposits that were laid down and have emerged since glaciation. Nevertheless, on the basis of the lateral extent of the glaciers, only a relatively small quantity of ice appears to have come from this sector.

Kodiak Island and its neighbors comprised a locus for glaciation, particularly the high central part of Kodiak (Capps 1937). The ice moved outward radially to tidewater and is thought to have coalesced with glaciers coming off the Aleutian Range and from Cook Inlet and the Kenai. Several sources of evidence support this concept: (1) The deeply eroded valleys and fiords logically require glaciers of considerable size and erosive power to produce them and the local upland seems insufficient to generate such glaciers. (2) Because of the directional alignment of the fiords separating the islands, and the presence on southwestern Kodiak of pebbles of volcanic rock formed by fine-grained aphanitic and a variety of porphyritic lavas, types present on the Alaska Peninsula, it seems evident that ice originating in the Aleutian Range crossed parts of the islands. (3) The two deeply glaciated north–south arms of Tonki Bay on eastern Afognak Island, in the vicinity of an upland less than 2000 ft in altitude, strongly indicate at least partial excavation by glaciers coming eastward and southward from Cook Inlet and the Kenai Peninsula.

The upper heights of the islands appear to have stood above the ice that on northwestern Kodiak and on nearby Afognak had a thickness of some 2000 ft. The limited amount of glacial debris present is thought to be a consequence of the intensity of glaciation whereby most materials were carried out into the ocean. A broad, shallow submarine platform on the south, east, and north of Kodiak indicates the fringe where dumping was greatest and also indicates that glaciers pushed out southeasterly into the ocean for some 50 mi.

On the Kenai Mountains the maximum ice coverage was represented by an extensive system of alpine glaciers (Martin, Johnson, and Grant 1915). The entire area, however, was not overridden. Glaciers drained into Prince William Sound to the east and into the gulf and Cook Inlet (via the Kenai Lowland) to the south and west. The oldest glaciation recognized on the southwestern Kenai is the Caribou Hills and is represented by drift and ice features in the heights of this upland (Krinsley 1953). The youngest major glaciation, the Naptowne, is revealed by end moraines along the northern, eastern, and southern margins of the Caribou Hills. At its maximum, it covered their eastern slopes to an elevation of 1600 ft, occupied what is now Tustumena Lake, and extended west to a point midway in the course of the Kasilof River, which drains the lake. In Kachemak Bay, this ice reached north to Anchor Point, ca 15 mi northwest of Homer, and is presumed to have coalesced with ice from the

Aleutian Range (Krinsley 1953). Elsewhere on the Kenai Lowland, the Naptowne is represented by a conspicuous end moraine that crosses the Sterling Highway near the settlement of Naptowne and by moraines in front of the valleys heading in glaciers in the Kenai Mountains (Karlstrom 1953).

Karlstrom (1957) correlates the Naptowne with the Wisconsin of the North American continental chronology, and the Skilak glaciation of Cook Inlet and the Kenai is identified with the Mankato (Valders) subage. The Skilak is dated by him at ca 12,900 ± 300 B. P. (Before Present) (Rubin and Alexander 1958). Several dates have been given for late- or post-Skilak glaciation (Broecker, Kulp, and Tucek 1956) but the oldest is 10,370 ± 350 B. P. (Rubin and Alexander 1958).

The former limits of glaciation in Prince William Sound and the lower Copper River are described by Tarr and Martin (1914). They state that the low-lying islands were completely overridden, and unaffected areas appear to be largest on the islands near the entrance to the sound. Hinchinbrook Island was only covered in part during the last glaciation. Along its southwestern slopes near Hinchinbrook Entrance, Tarr and Martin made a number of observations but locate till and other evidence of glaciation at altitudes no higher than 440 ft, although the island has a maximum elevation of 1546. They believe that the heights of Hawkins and Montague Islands as well were not overridden. According to Grant and Higgins (1910), Knight Island was not affected above 2400 ft by the Prince William Sound piedmont glacier, although Latouche Island may have been barely overridden. The investigations of Tarr and Martin (1914) further disclose that during its maximum the ice had a slope of 60 ft to the mile between the northern headlands of the sound and Hinchinbrook Island. This ice scoured the submarine topography to depths that are now at 1200 to 2400 ft below sea level. The most prominent channel runs from the neighborhood of Valdez Arm to Hinchinbrook Entrance, a distance of ca 40 mi, and is 7 to 10 mi wide with depths ranging from 1200 to 1500 ft.

Many of the foothills in the vicinity of the Copper River mouth do not appear to have been crossed by ice. Near Alaganik, Tarr and Martin (1914) are unable to find any indications of glaciation, such as striae on the bedrock or erratics. They believe that the rock pinnacles standing beyond the mountain front were formed by wave action before the Copper River delta sediments surrounding them were deposited. These formations would have been toppled if ice had traveled over this terrain. The western limit of this driftless area lies 8 mi west of the Copper River—its eastern limit is difficult to establish.

Martin (1908) states that driftless tracts also occur in the Controller Bay region. This fact was recently confirmed by the field studies of Don J. Miller of the U. S. Geological Survey (personal communication). Miller has been unable to recognize any glacial features at a number of localities between the Copper River and Icy Point near Cross Sound. These include the south end of Ragged Mountain near Katalla, the vicinity of Bering Lake, the Suckling Hills, the narrow strip west of Icy Cape, and much of the ocean border between Yakutat Bay and Icy Point. Most of these places are, however, associated with marine terraces, and the absence of evidence may be a consequence of emergence since glaciation. Nevertheless, there should be some marine till at least where streams have dissected the terraces, but none has been observed in the areas carefully studied by Miller.

The fiord coasts of southeastern Alaska and British Columbia owe much of their character to glaciers that developed along the axes of both the Coast Mountains and the Insular Mountains. Four developmental phases of glaciation—alpine, intense alpine, mountain ice sheet, and continental ice sheet—are described for northern British Columbia (Kerr 1934). They are applicable to southeastern Alaska and comparable to those recognized in southwestern British Columbia (Davis and Mathews 1944). During the initial alpine phase, glaciers were restricted to the high elevations but during the intense alpine glaciation, ice occupied the valley systems. When such valleys as the Stikine and Taku were filled, this latter phase was prominent. With successive thickening, the mountain-ice-sheet phase was reached and outward flow took place, especially westward to the Pacific. Ultimately a continental ice sheet was attained, and it is generally considered that all but the uppermost peaks were buried at this time and little ice movement occurred. This final phase differs in the latter respect from those preceding in which considerable movement was exhibited. It is also thought that topography influenced the direction and movement of the ice during the first three phases, whereas during the final one development was controlled by climate.

During its maximum the Cordilleran Ice Sheet or Glacier Complex reached to the Pacific Ocean. In Alaska the main routes are represented by Lynn Canal-Chatham Strait, Cross Sound-Icy Strait, Stephens Passage-Frederick Sound, and Clarence Strait-Dixon Entrance (Flint *et al.* 1945). Buddington and Chapin (1929) summarize the thickness of the ice at a number of points: at the head of Portland Canal, 6000 ft; south of the Stikine River and east of Wrangell, 5000; near Thomas Bay north of Petersburg, 5000; along the Whiting River east of Stephens Passage, 4500; and in the Eagle River region near Juneau, 5400. In the Alexander Archipelago thickness appears to have been at least 3500 ft on Etolin Island; on Kupreanof Island over 3000; on Kasaan Peninsula on the east side of Prince of Wales Island over 2840; over 2100 on the west side of Chichagof Island and over 2800, although under 4000, on the east side; and on Yakobi Island, south of Cross Sound, over 2300. Recently, Miller (1952) investigated the upper limit of glaciation in the Juneau Ice Field north of the Taku River valley. He is of the opinion that it is between 5600 and 6000 ft on the nunataks in the interior of the field and between 5000 and 5500 ft on the margin. These levels agree with those indicated on the "Glacial Map of Canada" (Wilson 1958). The data presented by Buddington and Chapin (1929) and by Miller (1952) are based on the elevations of ice-traversed, rounded summits; of horned peaks presumably standing as nunataks at the time of continental glaciation; and of highest erratics and lowest, weathered bedrock exhibiting no glacially displaced joints.

The extent of the latest ice-age glaciation and the multiplicity of glaciations are not known for southeastern Alaska. From the work of Dawson (1880) and Armstrong and Tipper (1948), which discloses two major advances of the Cordilleran Complex in north-central British Columbia, it is probable the same advances are recorded in Alaska. Armstrong and Tipper suggest that the greatest accumulation areas for glaciers in the Coast Mountains of British Columbia lie opposite Queen Charlotte Sound and Dixon Entrance. This seems likely, as these authors point out that no orographic barriers stand in the way of the ocean storms. In the vicinity of Dixon Entrance, William H. Mathews of the University of British Columbia (personal communication) found evidence of glaciation as far westward as Langara Island in the Queen Charlotte Islands. He was unable to verify the existence of overriding ice on Forrester Island, situated ca 18 mi west of Dall Island in the Alexander Archipelago, although Buddington and Chapin (1929) state that ice moved through Bucareli Bay, 26 mi north of Forrester Island.

The Queen Charlotte Islands, according to Dawson (1880), show little or no indication that ice from the mainland passed over them. Erratics found along the northern and eastern shores of Graham Island show that ice from the mainland or neighboring islands reached only the lowlands of the Queen Charlottes. During the maximum it is probable, however, that ice of the Cordilleran Complex passed through Skidegate Inlet-Skidegate Channel into the Pacific. There seems to have been little opportunity for glaciers from the mainland to pile up against the islands, in view of the broad exits represented by Dixon Entrance and Queen Charlotte Sound.

Ice from the Queen Charlotte Ranges flowed predominantly westward and eastward. The glacial grooving and scouring along the waterways separating Graham, Moresby, and Kunghit Islands point to such movement. Upper Masset Inlet (eastern embayment on the northern Graham Island coast) as well as the islands west of the mouth of Masset Sound (connecting the inlet with Dixon Entrance) show signs of glaciation. Some parts of the islands, on the other hand, are devoid of any such signs. MacKenzie (1916) concludes that glaciation was either absent or quite local in the vicinity of Yakoun Lake, on south-central Graham Island. Valleys tributary to the lake are V-shaped and only moderately, if at all, ice eroded. Yakoun is at 500-ft elevation and is of preglacial origin with its islets never having been overridden. Slopes and summits in the Queen Charlotte Ranges are only partly glaciated above 3000 ft.

The field work carried out by Dolmage (1922, 1923), Dawson (1887), Gunning (1929), Bancroft (1913), Clapp (1912), and Armstrong and Brown (1954), among others, uncovered the pattern of glaciation for coastal British Columbia. The valleys of the Skeena and Fraser Rivers and those valleys now drowned (fiords), such as Douglas and Dean Channels and Knight, Bute, and Jervis Inlets, were some of the major alleys of egress for the Coast Mountains glaciers. Ice traveled oceanward via Dixon Entrance and Hecate Strait-Queen Charlotte Sound along the northern coast. Toward the south, ice from the Vancouver Island Ranges drained southwestward toward the ocean and also northeastward toward the continent. Northeastward, the ice became united with that from the Coast Mountains and filled the interlying trough. Seymour Arch divided the flow northwestward via Queen Charlotte Strait into Queen Charlotte Sound; southeastward, the flow was deflected through the Strait of Georgia where it joined the Fraser valley ice, sending one lobe into the Puget Trough and another out the Strait of Juan de Fuca.

The thickness of this ice was ca 8000 ft over most of the southern British Columbia Coast Mountains, but ca 7000 over their northern area (Wilson 1958). On northern

Vancouver Island, Gunning (1929) finds glacial drift to an altitude of 5000 ft, and Mathews (1958) locates erratics and striae up to 7150 in the Mt. Garibaldi map area of southwestern British Columbia. Armstrong and Brown (1954) state that at least two major episodes, indicated by two tills separated by interglacial deposits, occurred in most of British Columbia. Armstrong (1956) dates an advance in the lower Fraser valley at 11,300 ± 300 B. P. and considers it equivalent to the Mankato subage, which since has been replaced by the Valders (Wright and Rubin 1956 and others). He believes this advance here consisted only of valley glaciers that moved southwestward from the Coast and Cascade Mountains and terminated a few miles south of the Canadian boundary. The ice sheet immediately preceding the Valders, however, had much greater proportions, and advanced a considerable distance south of the boundary, into the Puget Sound area.

This forerunner of the Valders is known as the Vashon and in the Puget Sound lowland is tentatively correlated with the Early Wisconsin of the central United States (Waldron, Mullineaux, and Crandell 1957). The Vashon is the youngest of the two glaciations recognized by Willis (1898) and Bretz (1913) and of the four recently described by Crandell, Mullineaux, and Waldron (1958). Its age is greater than the 13,650 ± 550 B. P. date for basal peat in Lake Washington near Seattle (Rigg and Gould 1957). According to Crandell, Mullineaux, and Waldron (1958) and Waldron, Mullineaux, and Crandell (1957), Vashon glaciation is older than 14,000 B. P., which these authors consider the approximate time this ice began to waste.

During the maximum in the Puget Sound area, the ice extended along the eastern side of the Olympic Mountains, where the end moraine travels from Lake Cushman southward to ca 15 mi west of Shelton and then southeastward and eastward, its southernmost limit ca 12 south of Olympia (Bretz 1913). This limit is the farthest south ice of the Cordilleran Complex reached west of the Cascades. Upon recession, lakes formed along the front and drainage was principally via the Chehalis River valley westward to Grays Harbor and the Pacific Ocean.

Along its western flank the lobe was associated with glaciers from the Olympics and on the east with those from the Cascades north of the Columbia River. Bretz (1913) describes till from the Olympics overlying pre-Vashon till along Hood Canal and mentions the dominance of Canadian ice as indicated by granite erratics present for 25 mi upriver in the Elwha valley south of Port Angeles. Danner (1955) states these are at 2000-ft elevation and elsewhere as high as 3000. According to Bretz there is no evidence to show that the Puget lobe was pushed back into the Cascades as it was in the Olympics. Mackin (1941) is of the opinion on the basis of his studies of the glacial geology of the Snoqualmie-Cedar area that the last mountain glaciation in this part of the Cascades is the correlative of the Vashon. On the eastern side of the mountains, Page (1939) presents evidence for three ages or subages. Since the recent studies by Armstrong (1956) show the Valders to be represented only by valley glaciation, Page's youngest till may be its equivalent. His middle till is possibly Vashon in age and the oldest till may be Pre-Vashon.

Glaciers from the Olympic Mountains and the Vancouver Island Ranges combined with piedmont ice moving westward from the Strait of Georgia filled the Strait of Juan de Fuca to a depth of at least 3000 ft (Danner 1955). Glaciers moved over the lower mountains of the northwestern Olympic Peninsula and out to the ocean across Cape Flattery. Danner states that it is uncertain how far south they advanced. Granite boulders occur south to the Hoh River but were probably carried there by melt-water. Arnold (1906) marks the limit of the Pleistocene 6 mi south of the mouth of the Ozette River.

South of the Columbia River the areas of glaciation are discontinuous along the Cascade Mountains and in the Klamath Mountains and Sierra Nevada (Flint *et al.* 1945). Along the coast no direct effects are manifest south of the northern Olympic Peninsula. Mention should be made of the studies of former mountain glaciation in the Klamath Mountains by Hershey (1900, 1903) and Holway (1911, 1914). No glaciers are known to exist at present, and the glacial geology of this mountain complex has been but little explored. This early work reveals, however, that glaciers reached at least 15 mi in length, and two episodes of glaciation occurred. Correlation of these with other areas has not been attempted.

Since the melting of Wisconsin-age ice, advances of lesser rank have been reconstructed along the North Pacific coast. Karlstrom (1957) recognizes a multiplicity of glacier variations in the Cook Inlet region since the recession of the Skilak about 10,370 B. P. In Glacier Bay, there appear to have been several post-Valders advances (Preston *et al.* 1955, Cooper 1937). On the Icy Bay-Yakutat Bay coast, Plafker and Miller (1958) date an advance that culminated between 600 and 920 A.D. in Icy Bay and between 970 and 1290 in Yakutat Bay. Subsequent recession began before 1400 and ended ca 1700. More recently glaciers have moved forward all along this coast. Most advances culminated no later than the early or mid-1800's, although special cases like Taku Glacier near Juneau reveal ice still pushing outward in 1959 (William O. Field, American Geographical Society, personal communication).

LAND–SEA-LEVEL VARIATIONS

The position of the sea upon the land has been variable all along the North Pacific coast. The histories of the land–sea-level variations have likewise differed. Along the glaciated part, the time of deglaciation serves as a datum, although the Postglacial, as previously mentioned, has not been of uniform duration. Compared with the unglaciated strip, however, its history is better known. The exact causes underlying the shore-line changes have not been determined, and it is likely the changes have resulted from the interplay of several factors.

Flint (1957) enumerates and discusses the major causes of the variations. Perhaps the most important is (1) glaciation, which is a response to climatic changes, in turn modified by various factors. During the glacial ages and subages when ice is piled up on the continents, sea level would theoretically be lower; during the interglacials when a good deal of the ice has melted, it would be relatively higher, if no other controls come into play. Foremost of these additional controls is (2) tectonic activity. Crustal movements, both continental and suboceanic, alter the size and shape of the ocean basins. Such action can result in either a rise or fall of sea level. Other contributing causes are (3) sedimentation along with outpouring of submarine lava on the ocean floors, (4) temperature change effecting an expansion or contraction of sea water, (5) isostatic adjustment to the loads of water on the ocean basins and on the continents, and (6) decantation of water from epicontinental seas to the deep oceans as a result of crustal uplift.

Marine features that are both emerged and submerged, revealing previous positions of sea level with respect to the land, are generally widespread along the North Pacific coast. Most striking are the wave-cut or wave-built terraces or platforms that stand as much as hundreds of feet above the ocean, particularly along the California, Oregon, and Washington coasts and between the Copper River mouth and Icy Point. The inner edges of these terraces are often bordered by steep former sea bluffs and cliffs, some of which reveal wave-notched bases and abandoned sea caves. In addition, sea stacks have on occasion been found and also disclose the former presence of the ocean. Marine deposits upon the terraces consist largely of sand and gravel along with varying amounts of fossils. The mineralogy of these materials has recently been studied by Bradley (1957), who is accordingly able to trace their origins. Elevated deltas and beaches, like those in the Juneau region (Plate III), represent former levels of the sea. In such glaciated segments of the coast, they are comprised of both marine and glaciofluvial sediments. These regions also display fossiliferous marine till at different altitudes. Some of the emerged terraces have submerged counterparts that must have been developed during intervals of lower sea level, as, for example, those studied by Emery (1958) in California.

Twenhofel (1952) reviews the general status of shore-line changes along Pacific coastal Alaska. He finds a relative uplift in evidence at most places but with indications of some submergence in Yakutat and Glacier Bays and a general drowning in the region of Prince William Sound and the Copper River delta. Specific information is available from many sectors. On western Kodiak Island, Maddren (1919) reports a beach deposit containing marine shells, between two tills, at an elevation of 30 to 50 ft. On the northeastern end of the island beyond the village of Kodiak, I observed what appear to be marine terraces up to an altitude of 130 ft. Martin, Johnson, and Grant (1915) mention a marine shell bed at an elevation of 30 ft on the north side of Kachemak Bay, Kenai Peninsula. According to Twenhofel (1952), D. J. Miller noted a sea-level change of ca 100 ft along the west shore of Cook Inlet. On Middleton Island, Miller (1953) describes wave-cut surfaces at six levels between sea level and ca 100-ft altitude. In Prince William Sound (Plate IV) recent submergence is as much as 10 ft below sea level as shown by submerged freshwater peat and trees *in situ* (Grant and Higgins 1910, Dachnowski-Stokes 1941). Submergence is also noted from peats to a depth of 40 ft below sea level in the vicinity of the lower Copper River and to a depth of 30 ft at Bering Lake near Controller Bay (Tarr and Martin 1914).

From the mouth of the Copper River to Icy Point, however, elevated marine features indicate extensive changes in land–sea-level relations. Glacial marine sediments, considered to be Miocene and possibly Early Pliocene in age, are elevated to at least 8400 ft in the Robinson Mountains near Yakataga (Miller 1957b). Near Yakutat Bay in the Malaspina Glacier vicinity, 2000 to 5000 ft of Pliocene (probably Early Pliocene) and older glacial marine sediments rest at elevations up to 5000 ft or more in the Chaix Hills, Samovar Hills, and Pinnacle Pass Hills (Russell 1893, Plafker and Miller 1957).

Marine terraces were measured and described by D. J. Miller (personal communication) from the Katalla district at two or three levels less than 100 ft in elevation at the town; to ca 25 in the lower half of the Katalla River valley; two or more levels below 200 and probably no higher than 100 at the northeast and southwest ends of Kayak Island; and at two levels up to 200 and possibly more in the neighborhood of Cape Suckling. Martin (1908) describes marine beds to a maximum elevation of ca 100 ft on Wingham Island. Eastward in the Yakataga district D. J. Miller (personal communication) finds three major and two minor terraces with strand lines at altitudes of ca 15, 40, 130, 230, and 950 ft. On the west side of Icy Bay, Taliaferro (1932) records a recent rising of the land amounting to 25 ft.

Findings in Yakutat Bay point to differential changes. At the head of Russell Fiord trees buried *in situ* in glacial gravel are over 3 ft below the high-tide level (Tarr and Martin 1912). At the time of the 1899 earthquakes, on the other hand, the southeastern side of Yakutat Bay rose a maximum of 10 ft and the northwestern as much as 47 while parts of the shore line sank (Tarr and Martin 1906, 1912). These amounts are greater than the displacement, 21.5 ft horizontally and 3.5 vertically, measured at the northeastern end of Crillon Lake by Tocher and Miller (1959) following the 1958 earthquake. Gravel reported by Tarr (1909) up to an altitude of 500 ft in the vicinity of Yakutat Bay may be marine. Blackwelder (1907) is of the opinion that the coast between the Alsek River and Yakutat Bay has been raised ca 100 ft since glaciation.

Mertie (1933) describes a series of terraces to ca 1700-ft elevation farther southeast about Lituya Bay. More recently D. J. Miller (personal communication) reported on these in considerable detail. Along one transect southeast of the bay, five were encountered with strand lines at ca 20, 40, 120, 280, and 750 ft (Plate V). Northwest of the bay, Miller finds a sequence of three major terraces with strand lines at ca 15, 85 to 130, and 260 to 400 ft or more. The highest terrace occurs at a general altitude of 1500 to 1700 ft.

In southeastern Alaska the maximum elevation of marine fossils is 500 ft, where they occur in till on Douglas Island near Juneau (Twenhofel 1952). Kerr (1936b) discovered marine deposits at ca 400 ft near the terminus of Tulsequah Glacier in nearby British Columbia. He (Kerr 1948a) mentions what may be marine terraces at altitudes as much as 600 ft in the Tulsequah valley and at 300 in the Taku valley below Wright Glacier. In the Stikine River valley south of the Taku, Buddington and Chapin (1929) report fossils at an altitude of 175 to 200 ft, 40 mi above the mouth. They also mention fossiliferous gravel and blue clay on Gravina Island near Ketchikan at ca 80 ft above sea level. East of Hyder at the head of Portland Canal, McConnell (1913) locates marine clay containing fossils to an altitude of nearly 350 ft, and similar sediments, though lacking fossils, reach to 485. Schofield and Hanson (1922) and Hanson (1923) also note what appear to be marine sediments to 450-ft altitude in this district.

Wave-cut benches, situated at and above the high-tide level, are discussed by

Buddington (1927) and Buddington and Chapin (1929). These benches appear to be locally developed on the islands and on the mainland. Examples occur on the south sides of Taku Inlet and Holkham Bay; the southeastern side of Cornwallis Peninsula, Kuiu Island; at Totem Bay, Kupreanof Island; at Rocky Bay, Etolin Island; and near Dolomi, Prince of Wales Island. The abandoned benches reflect recent changes in the relationship between the land and sea. It is likely they were formed when sea level was higher during the Hypsithermal.

Extensive evidence continues to be found along the British Columbia coast. About the mouth of the Skeena River, Dolmage (1923) states that stratifed marine gravel, clay-sandstone, and sandy clay occur from 20 ft up to 200 above sea level. These are mostly on the western side of Porcher Island and on Tugwell Island but are also on the adjacent mainland northward to Port Simpson. On Graham Island, Queen Charlotte Islands, I observed two distinct beds of marine mollusks ca 25 and 5 ft above high tide at Mary Point on Virago Sound. Dawson (1880) considers northeastern Graham Island to be a broad terrace that was covered by the sea at an elevation of 200 to 300 ft while glaciation was in progress. He also mentions a wave-cut terrace at 26 ft on Skidegate Inlet, bordering the southeastern sector of the island.

Dolmage (1921) describes unconsolidated sand, gravel, and clay of probable marine origin at an elevation of 50 ft on the west coast of Vancouver Island. In the Alberni area, MacKenzie (1923) finds stratified sand, gravel, and clay, also probably marine, to 400 ft. Related to these latter observations are those by Clapp (1912) on southern Vancouver Island, where the land is 200 to 400 ft higher since glaciers retreated from the Strait of Juan de Fuca. Also related are Clapp's (1914) observations of fossil beds at least 400 ft in altitude in the vicinity of Nanaimo, on Texada Island, and near Vancouver; likewise McConnell (1914) notes marine shells on Texada at a height of 424 ft above sea level. Marine sediments are indicated to altitudes of 500 and 525 ft about Campbell River and Courtenay, respectively (Wilson 1958). In the Fraser River delta map area, Johnston (1923) finds deltaic deposits up to 650-ft elevation, and Armstrong and Brown (1954) locate marine terraces and beach gravels up to 750. Marine shells, including forms that lived in 10 to 40 fathoms of water, occur up to 575 ft, and what possibly might be, at least in part, marine sand and gravel are located up to 1200.

The Puget Sound lowland displays marine fossils and features at various altitudes (Bretz 1913). The highest shell deposits are found on Orcas Island in the San Juan Islands at 290 ft. In Seattle they occur between 195 and 210 ft, and north of Seattle they range from 190 to 250. Along the southern shore of the Strait of Juan de Fuca, Arnold (1906) finds Pleistocene deposits occurring as terraces at 200 to 300 ft in elevation from Port Angeles eastward to Port Townsend; near Point of Arches on the northwestern Olympic Peninsula, marine fossils are intercalated in sand and gravel at 35 ft. Arnold states that a raised terrace, from ca 50 ft to 250 or 300, is found in the coastal region of the Olympic Peninsula. Wave-cut terraces and niches at the bases of sea cliffs indicate a recent fall of sea level. During early post-Vashon time, Puget Sound and Grays Harbor were connected by tidewater via the Chehalis River drainage, and the Olympic Peninsula formed an island (Bretz 1913).

A comprehensive investigation of shore-line changes on the Washington and Oregon coasts has been published recently by Cooper (1958b). Fluctuations of sea level have been extensive, as shown by terraces emerged to at least 1500 ft in elevation. The interval of submergence prior to the formation of these land forms is thought to have occurred during the Late Pliocene or Early Pleistocene. Cooper finds one terrace to be especially distinct over much of the coast. Its strand line is at ca 100-ft elevation, but, owing to local deformation, some parts are over 200 and others are at or below sea level. In northwestern Oregon, terraces appear at 200 ft or more above sea level (Diller 1896) and in southwestern Oregon, a series ranges up to 1500 (Diller 1902). This latter sequence is described in detail through a section 12 mi north of Port Orford. The lowest of this series extends to an elevation of less than 200 ft and a width from 1 to over 4 mi. The next level at 500 ft is distinct but not extensive, whereas the third at 1000 is generally the most prominent on the coast and is relatively wide and over 1 mi broad. The highest at 1500 ft is several miles across. North of the Coquille River, the 500-ft terrace is most extensive; at Port Orford a 300-ft level is well developed; and just north of the Rogue River, the most conspicuous is at 1500 ft. South of the Rogue River, a prominent terrace, at least 1 mi wide, runs between 850 and 925 ft above sea level and may be correlated with the 1000-ft one developed elsewhere. Another fairly prominent level is near 250 ft. Smaller terraces occur at 1500, 1140, 600, and 400 ft.

Diller (1902) also describes marine features in northwestern California. In the neighborhood of the Smith River mouth and Crescent City, the coastal plain is represented by a broad terrace at less than 50-ft elevation; others are at 700, 1350, and 1450. Near the Klamath River a terrace is formed between 700 and 800 ft, and also about Humboldt Bay near Eureka terracing is evident. To the north of the bay on lower Mad River, major terraces show up from 200 ft to over 500 and south of the bay near the Eel River mouth, they appear at 600 to 700, near 1000, and just below 2000. Below the Eel River along the coast to San Francisco Bay, the most readily seen terrace rests between 900 and 1000 ft along the southern part of the Humboldt County coast. It is the most persistently encountered level south of the Umpqua River in Oregon. Fenneman (1931) states that wave-cut terraces occur commonly from 50 mi north of San Francisco to Cape Mendocino. Three of Pleistocene age are reported by Weaver (1949) northwest of San Francisco, one at 375 ft above mean sea level on Point Reyes and two on the adjacent mainland at 120 and from 10 to 50.

It is difficult to assess and measure the principal causes underlying these changes in level. The causes, as pointed out by Flint (1957), are manifold, and the determination of the degree each has contributed to bring about land–sea-level fluctuations is a complex problem. Along a coast such as this where continental glaciation was active over the northern end but not at the southern, isostatic adjustment to ice load and melting can be considered only partly effective. Eustasy, on the other hand, was evidently an important factor along the entire coast. Crustal movement or tectonic activity, other than isostatic adjustment, has also been a noteworthy factor causing shore-line changes all along the ocean front.

Certain changes can be measured and attributed to definite causes, although specific cases are infrequently encountered. Examples are the fluctuations about Yakutat Bay and Crillon Lake associated, respectively, with the 1899 and 1958 earthquakes. Another is the recent local subsidence about Prince William Sound, almost certainly a consequence of crustal downwarping, where standing trunks of dead trees are partly submerged beneath high-tide level.

St. Amand (1957) reviews data on the measurable contemporary changes along the North Pacific parts of Alaska and British Columbia. Observations in southeastern Alaska over a period of 31 to 34 yr and based on tide gauges, sea level, and differences between levelings show that Ketchikan has remained relatively stationary and Sitka has risen at a rate of 1.9 ft/century; Funter Bay on northern Admiralty Island, at 5.8; William Henry Bay on Lynn Canal, at 7.4; Haines at 7.9; and Skagway at 6.3. From these and other data, St. Amand concludes that upwarping between southeastern Alaska and southern Yukon Territory is taking place with maximum vertical movement at Haines.

VULCANISM

North Pacific coastal North America occupies part of the great volcanic belt that encircles the Pacific Ocean. Volcanoes are scattered along the Aleutian Range, in the Wrangell Mountains, on Kruzof Island in the Alexander Archipelago, in the Coast Mountains, and in the Cascades. They have erupted at various times through the Late Pleistocene, under conditions of glaciation as well as during ice-free intervals. One of the volcanoes to erupt recently in this arc is Mt. Spurr (11,069 ft) in the Aleutian Range, which had an ash eruption in 1954 (Powers 1958). Mt. Spurr was active in July, 1953, and at this time caused a 0.25-in layer of ash to be deposited at Anchorage over 80 mi distant (Muller, Juhle, and Coulter 1954).

Thirty additional volcanoes occur in the Aleutian Range (Powers 1958), but only those in the vicinity of Shelikof Strait and Cook Inlet will receive mention here. Southwestward from Spurr, Black (6000 ft) and Double (6400) volcanoes are encountered, both probably having no historical activity. Redoubt (11,200 ft), the highest in the range, was active in 1778, 1819, 1902, and 1933, emitting steam or steam and ash clouds. Iliamna (10,085 ft) was observed to be active in 1768, 1786, 1876, 1933, 1948, and 1952–1953, and in 1867 had an ash eruption. Augustine (3970 ft) showed activity in 1812, an ash eruption in 1883, and a lava eruption in 1935. Douglas (7064 ft) has been steaming intermittently. The group comprised by Fourpeaked (6903 ft), Unnamed (2800), Kukak (6710), Steller (6900), Denison (7200), and Knife Peak (7000) appear not to have been active historically. Those remaining, Katmai (7500 ft), Trident (6300), Novarupta (2700), and Mageik (7500), were all active in 1912. Mageik had additional ash eruptions, in 1927, 1936, and 1953, and exhibited activity in 1929 and 1946. Trident has also had subsequent activity as recently as 1953.

The most dramatic and spectacular eruptions in the Aleutian Range in recent times were those of Katmai along with its neighbors, Novarupta and Mageik, in 1912. According to Powers (1958), the first was an explosion of pumice and rock from Novarupta while at or about this time the collapse of the top of Katmai occurred. Subsequently Katmai had its main eruption. They are recorded by three separate ash falls at Kodiak, ca 100 mi distant. These falls are now settled or compacted and mostly under vegetative cover, but originally the first consisted of ca 5-in thick rather coarse, gray ash, the second was a 4-in layer made up of fine reddish-brown ash, and the third was ca 1-in thick fine, gray ash (Griggs 1922). Some parts of Kodiak received as much as 1 ft of ash and small amounts fell at points as far as 1500 mi from the Katmai area.

In the Wrangell Mountains, volcanoes are Mts. Blackburn (16,523 ft), Sanford (16,208), Wrangell (14,006), and Jarvis (12,700). Mt. Wrangell is the only remaining active volcano—the other three are extinct. At the present time steam and ash rise from the Wrangell summit on occasion, and an eruption is known to have taken place within the last century (Black 1958). An important eruption apparently from somewhere in the Wrangell Mountains took place some time ago. This is indicated by the 2-ft ash layer bedded ca 7 ft below the surface of a peat deposit located along the upper White River on the northern side of the mountains (Capps 1916). The ash is estimated to be at least several centuries, and as much as 1400 yr, in age and to cover 140,000 sq mi. This eruption is believed to be comparable to or greater than that of Katmai, based on the amounts of ash ejected.

Mt. Edgecumbe in southeastern Alaska erupted in the Early Postglacial (Knopf 1912). It is one of several volcanic cones on Kruzof Island. According to Reed (1958), Edgecumbe ash covers an extensive area to the north and east of Chichagof and Baranof Islands. Remaining areas of Pleistocene vulcanism in the panhandle of Alaska are in the Coast Mountains and eastward. Wright (1906) reports lava and ash in the Unuk River region. These are so recent that in the early part of the century patches of the ash covered the glaciers as much as 8 to 10 mi from the source.

Northward, in the Iskut River area, Kerr (1948b) describes Hoodoo Mountain, which he believes was active up to some time within the last several centuries. It appears to have erupted early onto glaciated surfaces while it was surrounded by ice to 3500 ft in elevation. Later flows occurred during an interglacial time. Pleistocene lavas also are found along the upper Stikine River and along the Iskut upriver from Hoodoo Mountain. Northward in the Tuya-Teslin area of British Columbia, flat-topped volcanoes called "tuyas" occur. These appear to have originated from eruptions into lakes in the Cordilleran Glacier Complex that had been thawed by volcanic heat (Mathews 1947).

Northeast of Prince Rupert along the Nass River and a tributary, the Tseax River, is a lava flow that is probably as recent as 300 yr (Hanson 1923). The flow came from a crater northeast of Lava Lake, from which Tseax River drains, and the lake is a result of the lava blocking the river drainage. Apparently only a single flow, 20 mi in length, took place, followed by an eruption of scoriae. Southward on the British Columbia coast, stratified volcanic tuff and some flows of postglacial age occur along Mathieson Channel and on Bardswell, Price, and Swindle Islands (Dolmage 1922). No craters or volcanic cones are associated with this rock.

At the southern end of the Coast Mountains, the Mt. Garibaldi area north of Vancouver is a well-known site of vulcanism. Mathews (1951b, 1952a and b, 1958) in a series of papers indicates that the volcanic rock is largely, if not entirely, Pleistocene. Many of the eruptions appear to have been in contact with glaciers, much in the same manner as those previously mentioned in northern British Columbia. Vulcanism has been associated notably with Mt. Garibaldi, The Table, Clinker Mountain, The Black Tusk, and The Cinder Cone. It appears to have terminated with the wastage of the last ice sheet or glacier complex. Burwash (1914) and Brock (1928) present previous information regarding volcanoes and vulcanism in this area and in the Coast Mountains to the northwest.

The northern Cascade Mountains in Washington exhibit well-known volcanoes. Mts. Baker, Rainier, St. Helens (9671 ft), and Adams (12,307), and Glacier Peak are most prominent. All except Mt. Adams are known to have been active during postglacial time (Matthes 1914; Diller 1915; Verhoogen 1937; Coombs 1939; Lawrence 1938, 1941, 1948; Williams 1948). Mt. Baker's recent eruptions are dated 1843, 1854, 1858, and 1870; those of Mt. St. Helens, 1802 and several times between 1831 and 1854; and Mt. Hood ca 1800.

A prominent eruption during the Postglacial was that of Glacier Peak, whose ash is spread over Puget Sound, the eastern Olympic Peninsula, and eastward over northern Washington, Idaho, Montana, southern British Columbia, and southwestern Alberta (Rigg and Gould 1957). The eruption is radiocarbon dated between 6500 ± 200 and 6950 ± 200 B. P. and is assigned an average age of 6700 yr. As this ash is found in late-Pleistocene peat deposits throughout the above area, it serves as an excellent time marker in stratigraphic studies.

Volcanoes stand along the Oregon Cascades and south into California. They are described by many authors, most notably by Williams (1932, 1942, 1948). From the Columbia River south into northern California, the more prominent volcanoes are Mt. Hood (11,245 ft), Mt. Jefferson (10,495), Three Sisters (over 10,000), Crater Lake, Mt. Shasta (14,162), and Lassen Peak (10,466). Technically, Crater Lake occupies the caldera of Mt. Mazama, which exploded during the Postglacial, at 6453 ± 250 B. P. (Arnold and Libby 1951). More recent vulcanism is recorded for Oregon and California. Roach (1952), working in the Nash Crater area of the middle Cascades of Oregon, finds evidence to indicate lava flows ca 1354 to 1497 A. D. He states that it is probable that the flows commenced earlier than ca 1354 and that 1497 may not represent the close of the activity. Mt. Shasta had an ash eruption as late as 1786, and Lassen Peak began to erupt in 1914, throwing out ash and lava until 1917. Lassen is the only volcano in the United States, excluding Alaska and Hawaii, that had eruptions during the twentieth century.

Chapter III

REGIONAL CLIMATE

The region encompassed along the North Pacific coast covers over 21 degrees of latitude and over 32 degrees of longitude, and yet, the general uniformity of the prevailing maritime climate is one of its striking characteristics. The Pacific Coastal Forest occupying this climatic province is an expression of its general equability, but the plant associations comprising this vegetation unit are indicative of certain variations in the over-all climatic regime.

Because of generally high mountains forming a long arc trending with the North Pacific coast and in proximity to it, the strip characterized by this cool marine climate is for the most part rather narrow. Climates transitional along its high-latitude and high-mountain continental borders are a tundra type with brief growing season and a cold, snowy forest type identified by humid winters with cool, short summers. At somewhat lower latitudes, although the forest type continues, summers are longer; the southern flank is generally warm, temperate, and rainy with dry, hot summers. Marine climate penetrates the continent along the river valleys and low passes but usually does not reach far inland. A modified form, however, is notable along the storm tracks in northern Washington and southern British Columbia.

CLASSIFICATION

The climate of this coastal strip is classified by Köppen (Köppen and Geiger 1936, Haurwitz and Austin 1944) as warm, temperate, and rainy with several subdivisions. Köppen's system is based primarily on the monthly annual means of temperature and precipitation, and although weaknesses are pointed out (Russell 1926, Jones 1932, Ackerman 1941), its broad aspects identify the province. Thornthwaite (1931) classifies North American climates on the basis of precipitation effectiveness, temperature efficiency, and seasonal distribution of effective precipitation. The boundaries for Thornthwaite's provinces are difficult to comprehend in this region, however, particularly the sharp contact across the northern Alexander Archipelago in southeastern Alaska between "taiga" to the north and "wet, microthermal" to the south. Such a boundary does not approximate the vegetation, which it should. Because of its more refined coverage and greater applicability, the Köppen system is followed.

Three subdivisions of Köppen's warm, temperate, rainy climate (C) apply at sea level (Ward and Brooks 1936a and b, Connor 1938). In addition, areas inland are penetrated by his cool and snowy forest type (D) and even his polar type (E).

The longest stretch of coast line is occupied by Cf climate and is that generally northwest of the Olympic Peninsula. Its characteristics are an average temperature of the coldest month less than 64.4°F (18°C) and greater than 26.6°F (−3°C), an average temperature of the warmest month greater than 50°F (10°C), no distinct dry season, and the driest summer month with greater than 1.2-in (3-cm) precipitation. Most of this part of the coast is governed by the subdivision Cfb, identified by cool summers with an average temperature of less than 71.6°F (22°C) for the warmest month. At more northerly and westerly coastal stations Cfc prevails, with cool, short summers and less than four months with temperatures higher than 50°F (10°C). The southern edge of Köppen's cool and snowy forest type (Dfc) crosses northern Prince William Sound and northwestern Kenai Peninsula. The essential differences between Dfc and the warm, temperate, rainy C are an average temperature for the coldest month below 26.6°F (-3°C) and an average temperature of the warmest month above 50°F (10°C).

The coast south of the Olympic Peninsula is the Csb subdivision. This is a summer-dry climate by comparison to Cfb. It receives at least three times as much precipitation in the wettest month of winter as in the driest of summer, and the driest month records less than 1.2-in (3-cm) precipitation. From the coast of central western Oregon and southward in California, a pronounced belt of fog occurs in summer. Here the seasonal change of temperature is small, and because of the fog, maximum temperature is measured in late August or even in September with June often warmer than July. Russell (1926) designates this belt of fog as a Csn subdivision on the basis of the Köppen scheme.

CLIMATIC CHARACTERISTICS

Climate and data on climatic factors have been adequately described in a number of reviews and papers. The principal sources of information on Alaska are Abbe (1906), Fitton (1930), Ward and Brooks (1936b), and Kincer (1941); on British Columbia, Connor (1938) and Kendrew and Kerr (1955); and on Washington, Oregon, and California, Ward and Brooks (1936a), Fisher (1941), Wells (1941), and Sprague (1941).

Temperature

Climatological data from selected points between Kodiak, Alaska, and Fort Bragg, California, are shown in Table 1. July average temperatures are in the 50's and 60's (F) and illustrate the uniformity of the temperature factor throughout the region in summer. Kodiak and Eureka vary by less than two degrees while the range of the July average from all stations is about ten. In winter the range of the January average is greater and amounts to ca 25 degrees. January averages in Alaska are mostly in the 20's and below freezing, whereas in British Columbia they are in the 30's and above freezing. In Washington, Oregon, and California, they are nearly all in the 40's. Kodiak and Eureka January averages vary by ca 17 degrees. A comparison of the differences between January and July averages discloses that the ranges decrease toward the south. This is illustrated by the ranges for several stations from Kodiak to Eureka: Kodiak 24.5 degrees, Sitka 22.5, Prince Rupert 21, Tatoosh Island 13.9, Newport 13.1, and Eureka 8.8.

Latitudinal differences of extreme temperatures are marked in winter but are minor in summer. Kodiak and Eureka have both measured a maximum of 85 degrees; their minima differ, however, by 32 degrees: Kodiak -12 degrees and Eureka 20

TABLE 1—CLIMATOLOGICAL DATA FOR STATIONS ON THE NORTH PACIFIC COAST. DATA FOR ALASKA ARE FROM KINCER (1941); FOR BRITISH COLUMBIA, KENDREW AND KERR (1955); FOR WASHINGTON, FISHER (1941); FOR OREGON, WELLS (1941); AND FOR CALIFORNIA, SPRAGUE (1941).

		TEMPERATURE °F					PRECIPITATION
		JANUARY AVERAGE	JULY AVERAGE	MAXIMUM	MINIMUM	GROWING SEASON DAYS	ANNUAL AVERAGE IN
Alaska	Kodiak	29.8	54.3	85	−12	160	61.5
	Seward	22.4	55.3	82	−20	132	73.7
	Cordova	27.2	54.8	87	−19	149	145.4
	Yakutat	29.3	52.8	82	5	152	129.1
	Sitka	32.4	54.9	87	− 5	159	87.1
	Juneau	27.5	56.6	89	−15	172	83.3
	Ketchikan	32.6	57.5	96	− 8	165	150.9
British Columbia	Masset	36	57	84	− 2	—	55.3
	Prince Rupert	35	56	88	− 6	198	95.6
	Port Hardy	35	56	78	6	—	64.7
	Comox	33	62	90	− 6	—	44.4
Washington	Bellingham	36.8	63.0	92	2	186	32.2
	Tatoosh Island	41.2	55.1	88	7	311	77.3
	Quinault	38.4	63.5	104	11	208	128.6
Oregon	Astoria	40.3	60.9	97	10	273	77.5
	Newport	43.7	56.8	100	1	248	66.2
	Port Orford	46.1	59.1	90	15	286	68.2
California	Crescent City	45.9	59.3	102	19	230	75.9
	Eureka	47.3	56.1	85	20	328	37.6
	Fort Bragg	—	—	—	—	279	37.2

degrees. The growing season, as one would suspect, lengthens southward; Eureka has more than twice the growing season of Kodiak.

WIND

The prevailing westerly winds, modified in winter by the Aleutian Low and in summer by the North Pacific High, are an important feature of this coast. In winter they tend to blow more frequently northward as they circulate counterclockwise about the low-pressure system. In summer, by contrast, they blow more often from the west and northwest, clockwise around the area of high pressure, because of the barometric gradient and the circulation pattern.

Despite these generalities, local conditions are variable. Topography plays a large role in altering wind direction. Mountain ranges cause the winds to be deflected, and the influence of narrow waterways between steep-sided islands creates considerable funneling of the air. Prominent river systems that drain the interior are corridors along which continental air can flow. Glaciers, particularly in Alaska, strongly affect local air movements. Winds are generally variable both in summer and winter, although in summer they are light and gales are few.

Precipitation

Rain is the foremost contributor to total annual precipitation at sea level. Snowfall becomes important to the northwest, particularly in Alaska, both at sea level and in the mountains, but also in the mountains of British Columbia and western Washington. In the coastal areas of Oregon and California snow seldom falls and when it does, it melts immediately or soon after falling. Hail, freezing rain, sleet, and fog contribute only a relatively small part of the total.

Precipitation for representative coastal stations is included in Table 1. All stations except those to the leeward of the Vancouver Island mountain chain (Comox and Bellingham) and those in southern California (Eureka and Fort Bragg) have a +55-in precipitation total. The annual average is distinctly high at Quinault on the Pacific slope of the Olympic Mountains, and in Alaska at Ketchikan, Yakutat, and Cordova. Higher amounts have been recorded, however, such as the 263.8-in annual value at Henderson Lake on the west side of Vancouver Island (British Columbia Province Department of Agriculture 1954).

Maximum precipitation occurs during fall and winter and minimum during summer. The months of minima and maxima, however, vary. Moreover, a regular precession of these times takes place northward. In Alaska, minima and maxima are, respectively, largely in June and October; in British Columbia, they are in June–July and November–December; in Washington, in July and December; in Oregon, July–August and December–January; and in California, August and January. Data are from Kincer (1941), Kendrew and Kerr (1955), Fisher (1941), Wells (1941), and Sprague (1941).

Snowfall at coastal stations in Alaska is as variable as over-all precipitation but is by and large considerable. For example, Kodiak receives ca 53 in, Cordova 140, and Sitka 43 (Ward and Brooks 1936b). In the coastal mountains, the fall is very deep and occurs throughout the year on the higher summits. British Columbia snowfall is likewise heavy. Prince Rupert has a 133.5-in record and Victoria 78.2 (Kendrew and Kerr 1955). In Washington, on the upper slopes of Mt. Olympus, LaChapelle (1959) has measured a +125-in water equivalent of snow during the accumulation period 1957–1958.

Variations in annual precipitation can be pronounced between stations only short distances apart as a result of orographic influences. Differences are illustrated by the following examples: Branscomb, in the Coast Ranges ca 12 mi northwest of Fort Bragg, California, receives 81-in precipitation compared to 37.2 at Fort Bragg (Sprague 1941); a rain shadow is apparent on Vancouver Island, shown by a 263.8-in average recorded at Henderson Lake on its west coast and a 44.4-in average at Comox on its east coast; and Telegraph Creek, on the upper Stikine River in the Coast Mountains of British Columbia, with an 8.2-in annual average is only 100 mi from Petersburg in southeastern Alaska where the average is over 106 (Connor 1938, Kincer 1941).

Sunshine, Cloudiness, and Fog

According to Ward and Brooks (1936a), the annual per cent of sunshine along the North Pacific coast is less than 40. In winter in the Pacific Northwest, it is less than

30. These same authors illustrate the intensity of daytime cloudiness for January and July. In January, extensive cloudiness (80 per cent) exists in northwestern coastal Oregon, western Washington, and the northwest tip of Vancouver Island. Almost as marked (70–80 per cent) is the cloud cover in southwestern coastal Oregon, the remainder of coastal Washington and British Columbia, and the inside islands and mainland of southeastern Alaska. The rest of the study region exhibits cloudiness for 60–70 per cent of January. In July, the most intense cloudiness (70 per cent) is over northern coastal British Columbia, the Queen Charlotte Islands, and the southeast tip of the Alaskan panhandle. Most of the remainder of the coast is covered by clouds during 60–70 per cent of July. Kincer (1941) notes that an average of 200 days each year are cloudy in Pacific coastal Alaska; Ward and Brooks (1936b) state that from October to February, the total number of clear days in this same area is only ca 30 or 40 and cloudy days average 20 per month.

Because of the difference in temperature between the cold coast and the warmer, moist winds off the ocean, fogs occur with frequency in Pacific coastal Alaska, especially in fall and winter (Ward and Brooks 1936b). On the British Columbia coast this is also true; late summer, autumn, and winter are the foggy seasons (Kendrew and Kerr 1955). Fogs are most frequent on the Washington, Oregon, and California coasts in summer (Fisher 1941, Palmer 1917, Byers 1930).

CLIMATIC CONTROLS

The position of the coast on the west side of North America subjects it to the controls of (1) the North Pacific Drift and (2) the prevailing westerly winds. The equable climate is a consequence of the coastward movement of the warm ocean stream, and the humid character results from the cooling effect of the coast on the moisture-laden winds. The North Pacific Drift is derived from the Kuroshio (Japanese) Current, which originates in the North Equatorial Current, where surface temperature is over 80 degrees (Kendrew and Kerr 1955). The Kuroshio off Japan is less warm (70 degrees in summer and 60 in winter), however, and its northeast movement becomes deflected easterly by the prevailing wind. As the North Pacific Drift, the relatively warm current travels across the ocean reaching the continent off the Washington coast. Here it divides to form a northern branch, flowing along the British Columbia coast and around the Gulf of Alaska, and a southern branch called the California Current, which moves along coastal Oregon and California.

Another significant control is represented by (3) the centers of action or the areas of high and low pressure that exert considerable influence in determining the seasonal climate and direction of wind. During the cold half of the year, the Gulf of Alaska is covered by a low-pressure trough, oriented east to west, known as the Aleutian Low (Sverdrup 1940, Kincer 1941). Polar Pacific air originates in this low-pressure area and is derived mostly from the Asiatic continental anticyclone, where the air in winter is cold and dry (Willett 1944). As the Asiatic air moves along the barometric gradient over the ocean, it is rapidly warmed and humidified and transformed into the Polar Pacific mass. The unstable nature of this air over the water is shown by low convective clouds and frequent showers. Over the land the air comes under the influence of another control, (4) the mountain barrier that follows the arc of the coast.

Heavy mountain precipitation results as the air advances inland. Frequently, because of the orographic influence and the effect of high pressure over inland Oregon and Washington, the eastward-moving storms become stagnant for days over the Gulf of Alaska. Occasionally, Polar Continental air pushes out to the coast as far south as northern California and freezing conditions result. The drop in temperature in southern Alaska on such occasions can be quite marked as indicated by the minimum temperatures in Table 1. Winter winds on the coast are for the most part southerly in keeping with the low-pressure, cyclonic storms.

The Aleutian Low is replaced by the North Pacific High during the warm part of the year. This change is effected largely by the comparatively cool ocean surface, although the area continues to be a source for Polar Pacific air masses (Willett 1944). Air flow is southward along the coast in response to the relatively low pressure over the warmed continent. Where cold water upwells in the general vicinity of Cape Mendocino, dense, low, stratus clouds form the well-known summer coastal fog of southern Oregon and California (Palmer 1917, Byers 1930). These clouds, which are driven inland by the nocturnal wind, are dissipated by insolation heating during the day; however, radiation cooling at night enables them to reappear.

CLIMATIC TRENDS OF THE LAST FEW CENTURIES

Several analyses of coastal temperature and precipitation records from the present century and in part from the late 1800's have been made. Longley (1954) has prepared curves for the 10-yr running means of mean annual temperature for five British Columbia stations: Alberni, Masset, New Westminster (near Vancouver), Prince Rupert, and Victoria. Hubley (1956) has analyzed meteorological data from Tatoosh Island near Cape Flattery, Washington. A curve of 30-yr running means of estimated and observed seasonal precipitation (September–May) for Juneau has been drawn by Robert B. Smith (personal communication).

Temperature curves from the Washington and British Columbia stations when superimposed on each other show a general similarity. The trends shown are cooling during the first and second decades, warming after the early 1920's, and a return to cooling since the early 1940's. The maximum temperature reached during the 1940's was higher than that at the opening of the century, and present cooling has not reached the level of the early 1920's. According to Hubley (1956), Juneau temperature has not shown the pronounced cooling of the 1950's revealed by the more southerly stations.

Precipitation records from Tatoosh Island and Juneau are generally comparable. Both places illustrate a primary peak reached during the first decade of the 1900's with a secondary one during the late 1940's and the 1950's. The most recent rise in precipitation began earlier at Juneau, after the late 1930's, whereas at Tatoosh Island, it began during the late 1940's.

The present trend toward lower temperature and higher precipitation is not limited to this coastal strip but appears to be widespread in western North America. Records from interior British Columbia, the Yukon, and the Northwest Territories (Longley 1954), mountainous Alberta (Heusser 1956), and Montana (Dightman and Beatty

1952) exhibit this pattern. With regard to the pre-1900 trend, however, meteorological data from the west only occasionally extend back much earlier than this century, and these early data often are of questionable value. It becomes necessary to study some measurable, climatically controlled feature in order to determine the pre-1900 changes of temperature and precipitation.

Glaciers of the coastal cordillera provide a measure of climatic trends for the last several hundred years. Their variations have been investigated and dated in a sufficient number of cases to permit climatic implications. In addition, where meteorological records have been kept nearby, the variations have been shown to be roughly proportional, although with some lag, to temperature-precipitation changes (Dightman and Beatty 1952, Hubley 1956, Heusser 1956). If it can be assumed, therefore, that relatively low annual average temperature and high precipitation are coincident with glacier advance and the converse of these conditions prevails during retreat, climatic changes can be deduced from the dated glacier variations.

The dated and measured variations of glaciers from the Olympic Mountains, the Coast Mountains of British Columbia and Alaska, and the Canadian Rocky Mountains have been summarized recently (Heusser 1957a). The earliest advance was dated during the mid-1600's and occurred in the Olympics. No advance of greater magnitude had taken place since before at least 1250. Since the 1600's, notable advances have been manifest during the early 1700's, the late 1700's-early 1800's, and the second quarter of the 1800's. Recession after 1850 has been progressive except for minor variations, particularly those during the first quarter of the 1900's. Large-scale recession took place during the 1930's, but thereafter a decrease in rate occurred during the 1940's and advances are reported for glaciers of the Olympics, the northern Cascades, and Mt. Shasta, California, among others, in the early 1950's (Hubley 1956).

The dated variations indicate a relatively ameliorated climate between at least 1250 and the early 1600's. After 1650, greater coolness and precipitation prevailed with some minor fluctuations till ca 1850. The remainder of the 1800's underwent warming with a decrease in precipitation. It is emphasized that these data are highly generalized and represent only the broad aspects of climatic change for the last several centuries. Some changes were earlier at certain places and later at others because of the influence of such factors as latitude and local physiography.

Additional sources of data from outside the coast region are of interest. Antevs (1955) mentions the prominent intervals of drought in southwestern North America occurring between 1276 and 1299 and 1573 and 1593. Schulman (1951, 1953) on the basis of tree-ring evidence notes the similarity of the climates of the Colorado River basin and southern California; maximum deficiency of rainfall since the 1300's was during the last quarter of the 1500's. Wetness during the 1300's in the basin appears equal to or even greater than the wet interval from 1905 to 1929. Brooks (1951) in his summary of the literature on western North American climate gives the eleventh, fourteenth, seventeenth, and nineteenth centuries as generally wet. The progressive increase of dryness from the late 1800's to nearly the middle of the 1900's is shown by the erratic decline from ca 1870 to ca 1945 of the level of Great Salt Lake (Ives

1954). The recent rise of the water level has brought the present surface to about the same position as it was ca 1870.

LATE-PLEISTOCENE PACIFIC COAST CLIMATE AND ATMOSPHERIC CIRCULATION

The essential features of late-Pleistocene coastal climate as brought out by the above studies and others have been (1) a rise of temperature and a decrease in humidity, during which the last ice-age glaciers wasted, and (2) a more recent interval of lower temperature and higher humidity, resulting in glacier rejuvenation and advance. These broad fluctuations are, however, made up of fluctuations of lesser magnitude, such as those that have been pointed out during recent centuries. The general climatic changes, nevertheless, appear to have been between cool-moist and warm-dry types and to have occurred not only during the Late Pleistocene but also during the succession of glacial to interglacial ages throughout the Pleistocene.

Based on the geographical locations of the limits of glaciation, former pluvial lakes, and existing climatic zones and controls, Willett (1953; personal communication, 6 May 1958) describes the probable conditions prevailing during glacial, interglacial, and postglacial times. Because of insufficient evidence, however, details of the changes and consequently of the atmospheric circulation are lacking. Climatic change is coincident with the expansion and contraction or disappearance of polar-cap circulation and the corresponding equatorward and poleward displacement of the storm tracks. When the circumpolar circulation expands, middle latitudes tend to be uniformly cool and wet while low middle latitudes experience an increase of precipitation and highest latitudes a decrease. A general advance of glaciers ensues and in high latitudes is the result of summer rather than winter conditions. When poleward contraction of the zonal climatic belts occurs, predominantly warm-dry conditions succeed in the middle and high middle latitudes and warm-wet conditions in high latitudes poleward of 60 degrees or even farther north in the case of extreme contraction. Willett states that a third pattern, one of climatic stress, is recognizable. Longitudinal maritime-continental contrasts of climate become pronounced in the same latitude when shifting of extremes of heat and cold and of wetness and dryness occurs.

During the last glaciation the paths of cyclonic storms shifted equatorward. Areas such as the Great Basin of the United States received considerable precipitation with the result that pluvial lakes occupied terrain that has been as arid as or more arid than at present (Antevs 1952). The absence of glaciation over much of interior Alaska supports Willett's belief that the polar latitudes were cold and dry during these glacial intervals. With the development of the Hypsithermal during postglacial time, climatic belts, including the prevailing westerlies and storm tracks, occupied increasingly higher latitudes and created progressively warmer conditions poleward. The last major shift has probably taken place with the reversion toward cooling and increased humidity during the Late Postglacial. If the latitudinal expansion and contraction of belts toward the equator and the pole have in fact occurred, as Willett believes, it would be axiomatic that glacial recession following the ice age would be earlier at low, and later at high, latitudes. Moreover, the Hypsithermal would be longer and more intense at low latitudes than at high.

Chapter IV

REGIONAL VEGETATION

The area under consideration has been referred to phytogeographically as the Northwest-American Province, and it can be categorized broadly into Pacific Coastal and Pacific Subalpine Forests (Cooper 1957, unpublished manuscript). The province lies between ca 36° and 58°N latitude and 121° and 154°W longitude, a shore-line distance close to 2500 mi. Although its vegetation is confined almost entirely to the westernmost mountain slopes and the sea coast, certain forest elements have extended eastward from the Puget Lowland to form a branched extension for some distance northward and southward in the Rocky Mountains (see Figs. 6–9).

The Pacific Coastal Forest, along the ocean front between southwestern Alaska and California, occupies, in the main, a narrow strip of variable width. In Alaska where high mountains run close to the ocean, as about Icy Bay and Lituya Bay, it may be only a few miles broad. On the low-lying islands of the Alexander Archipelago and the adjacent mainland, on the other hand, it forms a relatively wide, although discontinuous, stretch. Moderately narrow in northern British Columbia, in the southern part it again widens. The forest reaches inland to the lower slopes of the Cascade Mountains in Washington and Oregon, but in California it is reduced once more to the narrow ocean border.

The finest development of the Pacific Coastal Forest is in the vicinity of Puget Sound and the Olympic Peninsula, and nearly all the characteristic trees grow together from southern British Columbia to southern Oregon. Cooper (1957) calls this part the center of optimum development. He points out that the most suitable climate prevails here as a result of the favorable combination of temperature and moisture. Along the coast, moisture increases northwesterly and temperature southeasterly; from southern British Columbia to southern Oregon these physical factors provide an environment most favorable for growth.

The Pacific Coastal Forest is actually a complex with three climaxes: western hemlock-western red cedar, hemlock-Sitka spruce, and coast redwood. Western hemlock-western red cedar is coincident with the center of optimum development. A large part, however, has been depredated by man and fire with the result that much of it is at present occupied by a subclimax of Douglas fir. Where relatively dry conditions prevail, as on southeastern Vancouver Island, Douglas fir can achieve climax status. Northwestward in northern British Columbia and Alaska is hemlock-Sitka spruce. The hemlock is largely western hemlock, although mountain hemlock and Alaska yellow cedar, which are associates in the Pacific Subalpine Forest to the south, join it along this segment. In fact, mountain hemlock is established farther westward on the Kenai Peninsula then either western hemlock or cedar. Sitka spruce has migrated farthest westward and is thriving on Afognak Island and northern Kodiak Island and on the opposite Alaska Peninsula. It is in this section of the coast that elements of the Pacific Coastal, Pacific Subalpine, and Interior Spruce-Birch Forests commingle. Coast redwood forest lies essentially south of the Oregon-California

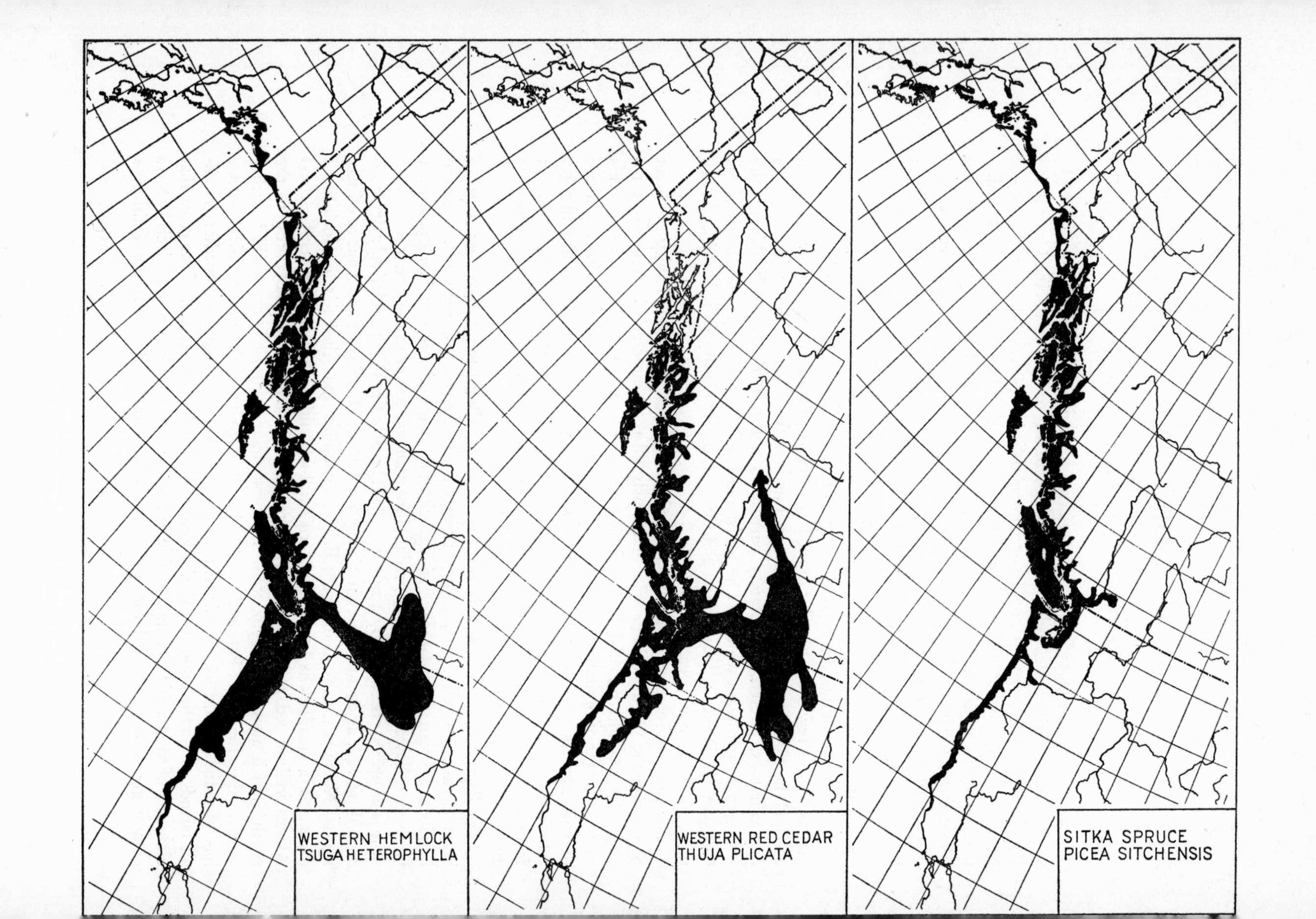
WESTERN HEMLOCK
TSUGA HETEROPHYLLA
WESTERN RED CEDAR
THUJA PLICATA
SITKA SPRUCE
PICEA SITCHENSIS

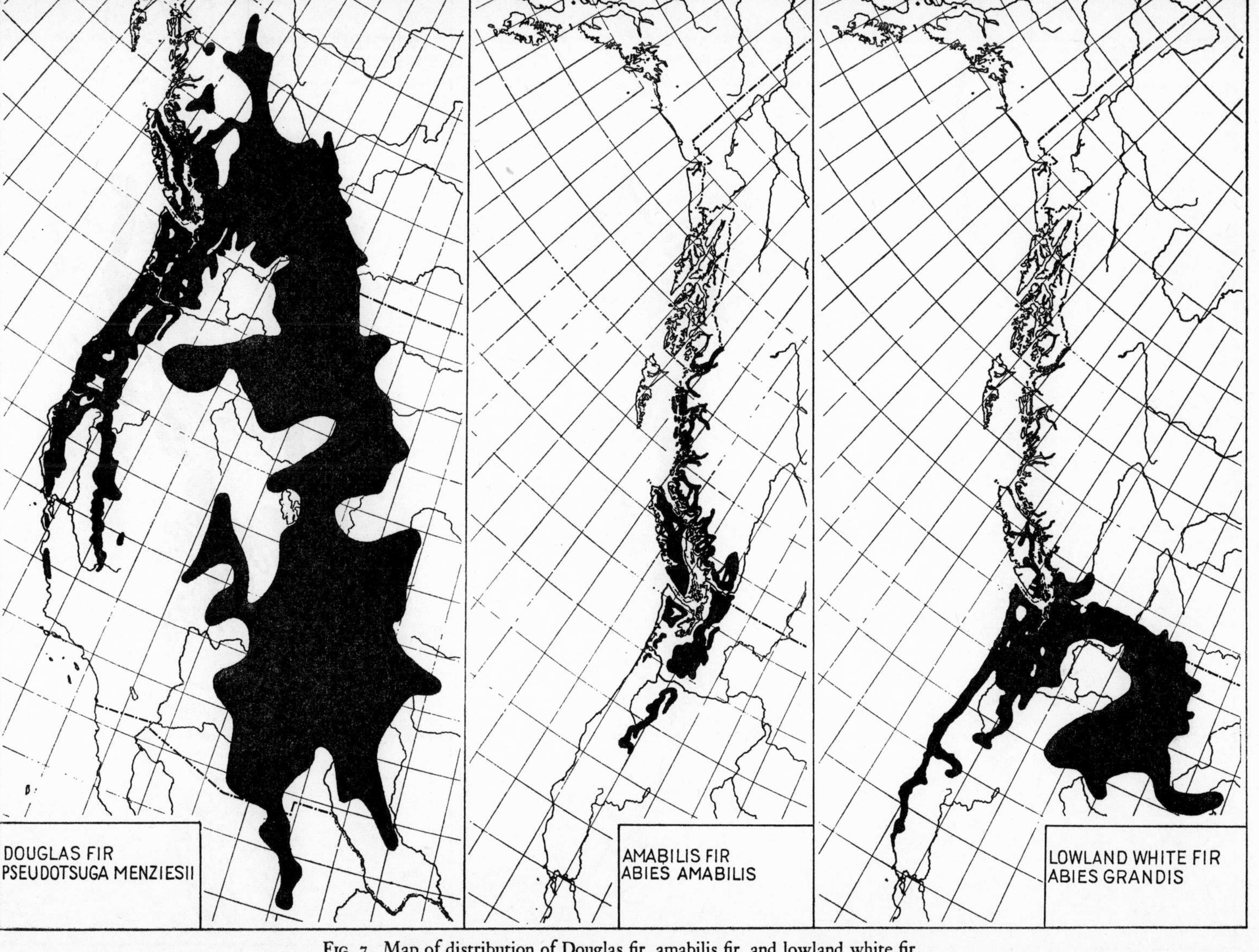

FIG. 7. Map of distribution of Douglas fir, amabilis fir, and lowland white fir.

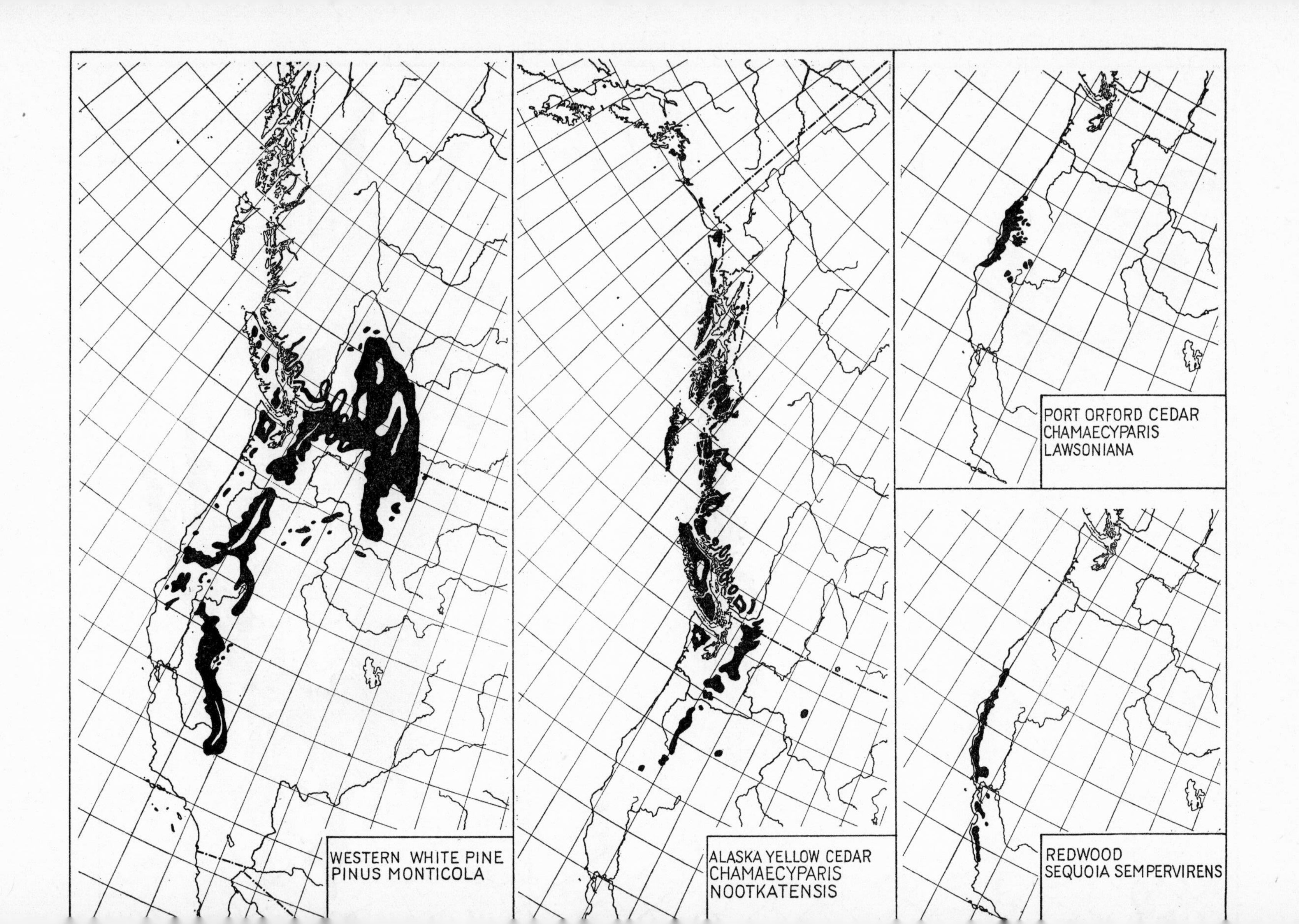
WESTERN WHITE PINE
PINUS MONTICOLA
ALASKA YELLOW CEDAR
CHAMAECYPARIS
NOOTKATENSIS
PORT ORFORD CEDAR
CHAMAECYPARIS
LAWSONIANA
REDWOOD
SEQUOIA SEMPERVIRENS

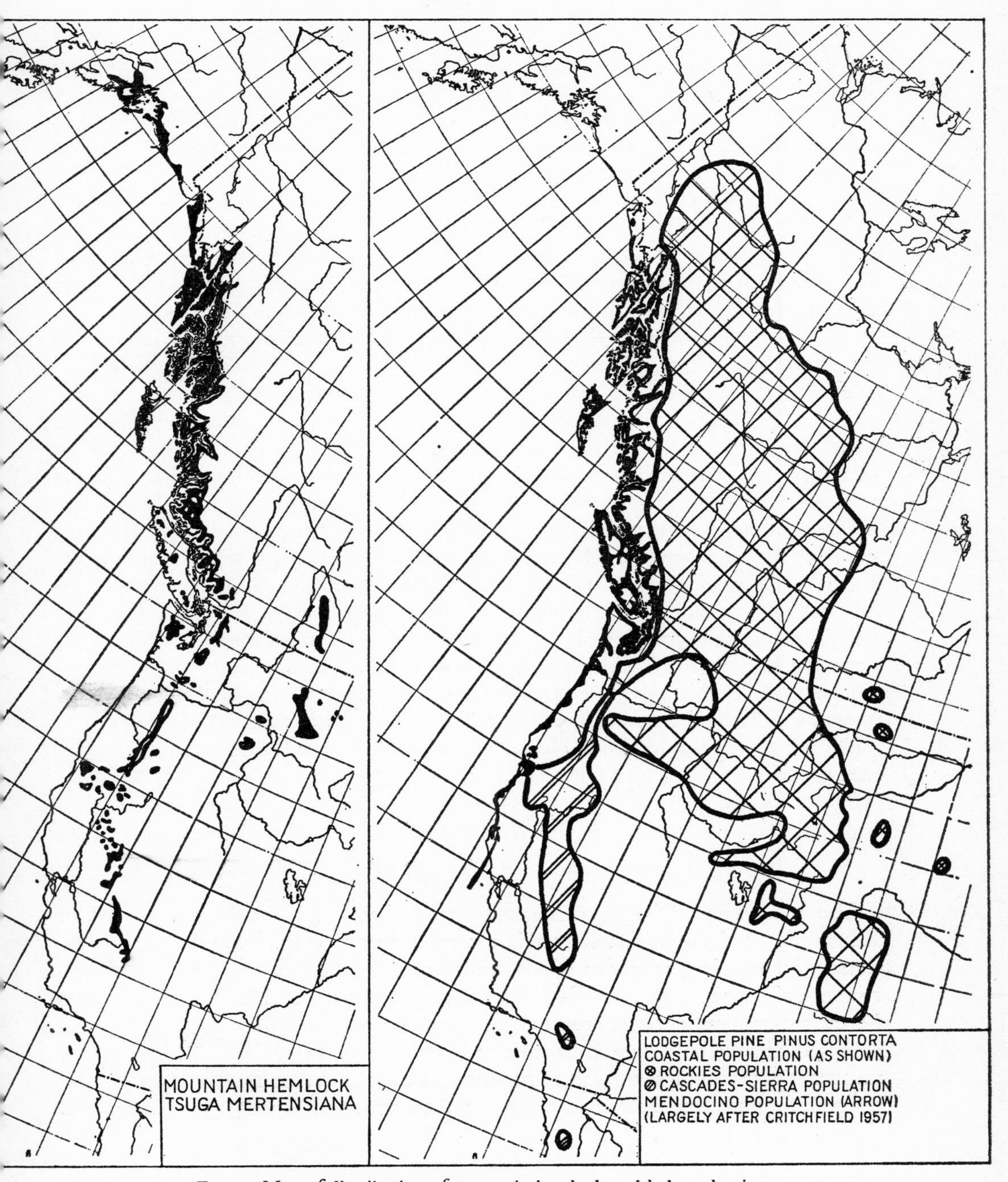

Fig. 9. Map of distribution of mountain hemlock and lodgepole pine.

boundary. It extends to the vicinity of Monterey Bay, with outliers on the seaward slopes of the Santa Lucia Mountains, beyond which are coastal chaparral and sagebrush.

The Pacific Subalpine Forest attains its best development in the Olympics and in the Cascades of Washington and Oregon. This climax is undifferentiated and appears in an altitudinal belt below timber line. Where it stands above the Pacific Coastal Forest, a transition zone is interposed. Northwesterly and southerly, the Subalpine Forest becomes depauperate of conifers and is progressively less distinct. In California it continues along the Sierra Nevada, but its elements have begun to number fewer and fewer, so that in the cross ranges the forest is impoverished, and the last trees are found in Lower California. In northern British Columbia and southeastern Alaska also it has lost representatives. Amabilis fir and Alaska yellow cedar, as well as mountain hemlock, become coastal, although mountain hemlock frequently in association with alpine fir also continues to occupy a subalpine belt. Northwestward from the Alaskan panhandle, mountain hemlock and Alaska yellow cedar become mixed with the low-level, coastal trees. Since the Pacific Subalpine Forest is merely of partial concern here, it will not be discussed in detail, and only the area of the northern Cascades and northwestward will be taken into account.

The Pacific Coastal and Pacific Subalpine Forests represent climatic climaxes covering the largest part of this section of North America. The remaining area above and beyond timber line is occupied by arctic-alpine tundra and will be mentioned only briefly. The classification of these forests as primary units is based on life form, natural geographic grouping arising from developmental relationships, and climatic control (Weaver and Clements 1938, Good 1953). The secondary divisions, resulting from edaphic, physiographic, or other regimens, will be discussed separately as will the successions that have lead to the maturation of the climax associations. This vegetation systematics is elaborated in order to provide at least a qualitative measure of the environment for the purpose of interpreting the pollen profiles.

ALASKA

Southeastern District

The Southeastern District of Alaska is arbitrarily placed between the vicinity of Yakutat Bay and the British Columbia coastal boundary (Fig. 3). Vegetation below timber line consists primarily of the climatic climax Pacific Coastal Forest interspersed with numerous, and often extensive, muskeg areas. The Pacific Subalpine Forest has only meager zonal representation. Zach (1950) considers muskeg a physiographic climax; physiography appears to determine the development of forest or muskeg though both share the same climatic regime. Where the terrain is well drained, forest is established; on the other hand, under conditions of poor drainage, muskeg abounds.

Forest

The highest latitudes reached by a number of southerly ranging plants are in this section of the Alaskan coast. Western red cedar (*Thuja plicata*), amabilis fir (*Abies amabilis*), and western yew (*Taxus brevifolia*) are coniferous examples; white beaked-rush (*Rynchospora alba*), red alder (*Alnus oregona*), big-leaf maple (*Acer macrophyllum*), and salal (*Gaultheria shallon*) may also be cited. Because certain southerly ranging species reach southeastern Alaska, the composition and character of the vegetation in the panhandle changes from southeast to northwest. The western hemlock (*Tsuga heterophylla*)-western red cedar association is reduced in area and where western red cedar reaches the end of its range at ca 57°N (Taylor 1929, Andersen 1953), it is replaced by western hemlock-Sitka spruce (*Picea sitchensis*) (Fig. 6). Taylor (1932) includes Sitka spruce in the western hemlock-western red cedar association of the Southeastern District. It must be pointed out in this connection, however, that the climax status of Sitka spruce in both associations has been challenged (Harold E. Andersen, U. S. Forest Service, personal communication). Andersen is of the opinion that Sitka spruce behaves as an intolerant species in Alaska and believes that western hemlock is the forest climax. Spruce remains as a minor component because it is maintained by blowdowns and other disturbances. The status of western red cedar has also been investigated rather recently, both in Alaska by Gregory (1957) and in British Columbia by Schmidt (1955). These authors find that this species does not exhibit advanced regeneration in well-stocked, old-growth stands. In Alaska seed germinates, but the numerous young seedlings are unable to survive, whereas in British Columbia a paucity of advanced regeneration has been attributed to probable germination failure and seedling mortality. Although of only minor ecological significance, the composition of the prevailing all-aged forest is 73 per cent western hemlock, 23 per cent Sitka spruce, and only 3 per cent western red cedar, with other species forming the remainder (Taylor 1932).

The Pacific Coastal Forest in the Southeastern District ranges from the upper tide level to ca 1500 ft in altitude (Plate VI). At the upper level a transition zone is encountered through which the luxuriance of the trees diminishes, certain species become discontinuous, and the composition and proportion of elements change. Western hemlock is by far the most abundant dominant. Sitka spruce also occupies extensive tracts, although largely at low elevations. The relative profusion of these two trees is apparent from the air—western hemlock stands out with a light-green cast and Sitka spruce appears dark green.

According to Sudworth (1908), western hemlock (Plate VII) grows best on deep, moist, porous soils on low slopes, flats, and stream bottoms, and yet with sufficient moisture, both atmospheric and edaphic, it can grow on poor, thin soils on all exposures. Where soil is poor and low in moisture content, the tree prefers cool, northerly sites. It is very tolerant of shade, especially in the seedling stage, and displays a moderate germination rate, usually requiring a highly organic seed bed (Allen 1902). Western hemlock produces seed every year with large productions at irregular intervals. Taylor (1929) states that Alaskan specimens average 125 ft in height and 2.5 in diameter, and Anderson (1943) describes this species as achieving a height of 200 ft and a diameter of 5.

Sitka spruce attains much greater sizes (Plate VIII). According to Taylor (1929), it reaches a diameter of 8 ft and a height of 160 or more. Sudworth (1908) writes that the tree occurs on damp alluvial and sandy bottoms, along streams, and on moist slopes, but best growth is on moist, deep, and rich soils under humid conditions. Sitka spruce appears to be a species that is variably tolerant, less so than western hemlock and western red cedar (Cary 1922). It drops large quantities of seed every few years, but some seed is produced annually. The germination rate is generally high; for best reproduction and growth, however, mineral soil is necessary (Hoffman 1912). It is of interest to mention the studies by Taylor (1935) on seedling survival of both Sitka spruce and western hemlock. Taylor finds that where small quantities of nitrate nitrogen are present in the soil, the percentage of Sitka spruce seedlings is low, whereas with an increase of this form of nitrogen, the percentage increases up to a point. Where ammoniacal nitrogen accumulates in the soil, oxidation to nitrate nitrogen cannot take place and as a consequence spruce seedlings are infrequent, although western hemlock seedlings, which apparently thrive within certain quantitative limits of ammoniacal nitrogen, are abundant.

Western red cedar, Alaska yellow cedar (*Chamaecyparis nootkatensis*), mountain hemlock (*Tsuga mertensiana*), amabilis fir, and western yew contribute only ca 4 per cent to the Pacific Coastal Forest in southeastern Alaska. Western red cedar is found at low elevations on moist flats, benches, gentle slopes, river bottoms, muskeg areas, and swamps (Sudworth 1908). It is very tolerant although this condition may be variable. Sudworth points out that its tolerance is greatest in southern latitudes, where growth is optimum. Seed production is high but, as mentioned previously, germination and viability appear to vary. Kellogg (1910) mentions a diameter for western red cedar of over 3 ft at Ketchikan, but on the basis of Gregory's (1957) data, trees are at least of 5-ft diameter breast high.

Alaska yellow cedar and mountain hemlock occur from tidewater to timber line. Yellow cedar is usually of moderate size. Northwest of Lituya Bay, however, one specimen, found at ca 350-ft elevation, measured a 6.7-ft diameter breast high with an estimated 125-ft height (Plate IX). The girth of this tree is as great or slightly greater than the largest previously recorded Alaska yellow cedar (American Forestry Association 1955). Alaska yellow cedar has soil requirements much like western red cedar in that it thrives best on moist, rich, deep soil, and it is less tolerant than western red cedar or western hemlock (Sudworth 1908). Mountain hemlock is most abundant near timber line. This species develops favorably on moist, well-drained soils on protected northern exposures. In the low-elevation forest, it usually grows poorly on muskeg. It is very tolerant—more so than its associates with the exception of western hemlock (Sudworth 1908).

Amabilis fir rarely occurs in southeastern Alaska (Fig. 7). Schmidt (1957) states that it reaches 55°N. According to Taylor (1929) it is reported from sea level to ca 1000-ft elevation, growing in the vicinity of Boca de Quadra and Portland Canal on well-drained slopes of canyons, benches, and flats, where the soil consists of moist, sandy loam and shallow, gravelly sand. Amabilis fir is moderately tolerant, being less so than western yew, western red cedar, Alaska yellow cedar, and western hemlock, and is a prolific seed producer (Sudworth 1908). Western yew is established about Annette, Mary, and Gravina Islands and on Prince of Wales Island as far north as 55°N (Taylor 1929). Occurring as a small tree or shrub, it is slow growing, very tolerant, and is found on damp benches and ravines where soil is rich.

The interior of the coastal forest is usually dark, wet, and gloomy. Undergrowth is dense in young stands whereas mature ones exhibit only a thin growth of shrubs, a few herbs, and a thick, spongy ground cover consisting mainly of mosses, with lichens and hepatics. Many of the plants are epiphytic, and it is this characteristic that accounts for a good deal of the gloominess. Common shrubs are *Menziesia ferruginea* and *Vaccinium ovalifolium*, and representative herbs are *Coptis asplenifolia*, *Rubus pedatus*, and *Cornus canadensis*. Mosses include *Rhytidiadelphus loreus* (Hedw.) Warnst., *R. triquetrus* (Hedw.) Warnst., *Hylocomium splendens* (Hedw.) BSG, and *Mnium glabrescens* Kindb. The lower edge of the forest borders on tide flats, river mouths, and along the fiords and bays where the terrain is not too steep. Some trees have become established on steep cliffs, and it is remarkable how they can persist under such adverse conditions. Frequently, a fringe of alder (*Alnus crispa* var. *sinuata* and *A. oregona*) and willow (*Salix alaxensis*, *S. sitchensis*, *et al.*) is found at the outer edge. These and black cottonwood (*Populus trichocarpa*) follow the watercourses and occupy the river bars, flats, and glacial outwash.

Where the forest is immature, shrubs and herbs may constitute a rank undergrowth. Where windfall, avalanching, biotic infestation, logging, or burning have disturbed the climax stands, subseres arise that include many of the species in the youthful forest. Light apparently is the most important factor controlling the composition and density of the plants in the undergrowth. Some young stands, whose canopies are so close together that light is unable to reach the floor, have relatively few tolerant species in the ground cover. Sitka spruce directly behind the beach northwest of Lituya Bay is an example. Here the orchidaceous *Goodyera decipiens* and *Corallorhiza mertensiana* and the liliaceous *Streptopus amplexifolius* and *Maianthemum dilatatum* occur with the foamflower *Tiarella trifoliata* and the fern *Dryopteris linnaeana*, but the ground cover is sparse. Farther back from the beach the canopy is relatively open, with the result that devils club (*Oplopanax horridus*) forms almost a pure shrub layer with some blueberry (*Vaccinium ovalifolium*) and salmonberry (*Rubus spectabilis*).

Salmonberry also frequently forms an almost solitary shrub cover in young coniferous timber. Where drainage is impeded and paludification incipient, skunk cabbage (*Lysichitum americanum*) is often present with devils club. Disturbance that creates openings in the canopy of climax forest results in the development of local subseres. Devils club, salmonberry, blue currant (*Ribes bracteosum*), goats beard (*Aruncus sylvester*), elderberry (*Sambucus racemosa* subsp. *pubens*), cow parsnip (*Heracleum lanatum*), and ferns (*Athyrium filix femina* subsp. *cyclosorum*, *Dryopteris austriaca*, *D. linnaeana*) are some more prominent invaders at low and middle elevations. These readily intrude on slide areas as well; however, since slides run through alpine, subalpine, and lower belts of vegetation, the upper parts of their paths are invaded, albeit slowly, by mountain species such as fireweed (*Epilobium latifolium*), luetkea (*Luetkea pectinata*), heath (*Empetrum nigrum* and *Cassiope mertensiana*), willow (*Salix reticulata*, *S. stolonifera*), and Alaska alder (*Alnus crispa* subsp. *sinuata*).

The prisere near sea level is clearly demonstrated on the outwash, moraines, and till of the regional glaciers (Plate X). It has been thoroughly studied by Cooper (1923, 1924, 1931a, 1937, 1939), Taylor (1932), Lawrence (1950, 1958), Crocker and Major (1955), and Crocker and Dickson (1957), among others. Moss (*Rhacomitrium canescens* Brid. and *R. lanuginosum* [Hedw.] Brid.), fireweed, lupine (*Lupinus nootkatensis*), horsetail (*Equisetum variegatum* subsp. *alaskanum*), and mountain dryad (*Dryas drummondii*) are the most conspicuous plants to become established initially. Less noticeable during this early stage are tiny seedlings of Sitka spruce, western hemlock, mountain hemlock, willow, alder, black cottonwood, and a number of plants generally found at higher elevations such as *Saxifraga oppositifolia* and *Silene acaulis*. Colonization is most likely to occur where wind protection is afforded, as on the down-valley sides of moraines, at the margins of kettle holes, and along active or abandoned outwash channels. On these inorganic, gravelly, and sandy seed beds, spruce and mountain hemlock seedlings are capable of thriving whereas western hemlock seedlings almost always fail to survive. It appears that the absence of ammoniacal nitrogen in the soil favors the survival of spruce at least, but western hemlock, which thrives when this form is available, is unable to maintain itself. Nitrate nitrogen, on the other hand, is supplied by the leguminous lupine and by alder, and the dryad is also suspected of fixing nitrogen. Thus, the absence of an organic soil where ammoniacal nitrogen is likely to accumulate and a supply of nitrates favors spruce development.

Alaska alder, willow (*Salix barclayi*, *S. sitchensis*, and *S. alaxensis*), and black cottonwood grow rapidly into dense thickets (Plate XI). Their growth is more rapid in the beginning, and spruce may be difficult to discern hidden beneath the broadleaf species. In these communities, the roots of alder are commonly parasitized by the broom-rape, *Boschniakia rossica*. Black cottonwood is capable of achieving mature size in the shortest time and for a period dominates the thicket. Sitka spruce grows slowly but steadily, however, and owing to its greater growth potential soon crowds and overtops the cottonwood (Plate XII). Alder is probably the most abundant member. It is also capable of reaching tree proportions, although of smaller size than cottonwood. The intolerance of alder, willow, and cottonwood prevents each from remaining members of the community, with the result that they soon die out and are succeeded by a spruce subclimax. During the time leading up to the formation of spruce forest, usually at least 100 yr, these broadleaf species contribute to the accumulation of humus in the soil. With the succession to spruce occupancy, coniferous litter and duff along with the annual remains of mosses, herbs, and shrubs previously mentioned for this stage add to the organic layer on the floor. The environment thus becomes favorable for the establishment of western hemlock, which begins to appear in the ground cover and also appears later in the understory. Sitka spruce and western and mountain hemlock may exhibit a tendency to layer in young transitional stands and thus reproduce vegetatively (Cooper 1931b). At 300 to 500 yr of age, depending on locality, the subclimax begins to break down and is gradually replaced by western hemlock, which is highly shade tolerant (Harold E. Andersen, personal communication). Accordingly, in the climax forest, where hemlock is as much as 500 yr old, 800 to 1000 yr at least have been necessary for maturation.

The development of soil in relation to the vegetation chronosequence on terrain deglaciated within the last 200 yr or so is significant. Crocker and Major (1955) and

Crocker and Dickson (1957) studied soil on sites of varying ages at Glacier Bay and in front of Mendenhall and Herbert Glaciers near Juneau. These investigators find that with age, soil reaction (pH) under alder decreased rapidly within 35–50 yr and less so subsequently, whereas under other species the rate of decrease was much less. The sharpest and most striking change is in the mineral soil whereas the forest-floor reaction declines very little. Total organic carbon increased throughout the chronosequences and total nitrogen rose through the alder stage, but following the transition to spruce subclimax, this latter element decreased significantly. Dryad is also capable of accumulating considerable nitrogen, although much less effectively than alder. It is obvious from these studies that the environment undergoes considerable alteration even as few as several decades after deglaciation.

Hydrarch succession is evident in kettle pools on terrain recently deglaciated. Plants found in kettles of different ages in front of Mendenhall Glacier illustrate the stages in the succession. A floating stage represented by bur-reed (*Sparganium hyperboreum*) dominates the central part of the pool, and partly submerged plants standing about the margin include *Hippuris vulgaris*, *Eleocharis palustris*, and *Equisetum variegatum* subsp. *alaskanum*. These in turn succeed to tussocks of *Carex hindsii*, *Calamagrostis canadensis* subsp. *langsdorffii*, and cottongrass (*Eriophorum scheuchzeri* and *E. russeolum*) and a varied assemblage consisting of *Menyanthes trifoliata*, *Tofieldia occidentalis*, *Parnassia palustris*, *Platanthera dilatata*, *Mimulus guttatus*, *Pedicularis sudetica*, and *Polygonum bistorta* subsp. *plumosum*. The next older stage is represented by woody plants, including willow, blueberry (*Vaccinium uliginosum*), and Sitka spruce, which will succeed to the spruce subclimax and ultimately climax Pacific Coastal Forest.

Timber line, according to Fernow (1902), lies from ca 2400 ft in the southeast to 1800 in the northwest. At these elevations and for a hundred feet or more below and several hundred above, trees of the Pacific Subalpine Forest are manifest. These are gradually reduced in stature so that eventually *krummholz* colonies that reach to ca 3300 ft in altitude appear (Heusser 1954a). Solitary trees in several instances have been observed to higher elevations. On south-facing slopes along upper Taku Glacier in the zone of arctic-alpine tundra, Sitka spruce was found growing at a maximum of 3900 ft (Heusser 1954b). On northerly slopes, timber line and the uppermost trees do not gain these elevations, and representatives of the Pacific Subalpine Forest prevail to lower levels.

Mountain hemlock is the major dominant of the subalpine forest. It is usually a relatively small tree of 1 ft or less in diameter and 20 to 30 in height. On occasion better specimens are encountered—one was found at ca 2500-ft elevation along a branch of Gilkey Glacier, which drains into Berners Bay on Lynn Canal via the south fork of the Antler River. Measuring 2.4 ft in diameter breast high and 65 ft in height, the tree is growing in a west-facing, open stand of mountain hemlock, where its associates are much smaller in size. The plant cover consists, in addition, of *Sorbus sitchensis*, *Cladothamnus pyroliflorus*, *Vaccinium alaskaensis*, *V. uliginosum*, *Cassiope mertensiana*, *Phyllodoce glanduliflora*, *Empetrum nigrum*, *Luetkea pectinata*, *Cornus canadensis*, *Lycopodium alpinum*, *L. selago*, and *Veratrum eschscholtzii*.

Alpine fir (*Abies lasiocarpa*) is found occasionally in profusion in the subalpine forest, but most often it is absent or only of local occurrence. It has been observed frequently where river valleys and low passes connect with the interior. Because of this, these places have been suspected of constituting migration routes into southeastern Alaska (Heusser 1954a). Fernow (1902) reports the best stands about White Pass, above the head of Lynn Canal. The only observation of this species in the Alexander Archipelago appears to have been made at timber line in the vicinity of Hollis on Prince of Wales Island (Robert A. Gregory, U. S. Forest Service, personal communication). Alpine fir may have a greater range in Alaska, but because of the infrequency of timber-line studies, knowledge of its present extent is probably incomplete. Alaska yellow cedar, according to Taylor (1932), may be more abundant near timber line, although this abundance appears to be southeasterly in the district.

The alpine-subalpine ecotone can be depicted as an interfingering of forest components from below and tundra components from above. In the classic illustration, arboreal species lose their erect stature and become prostrate, finally reaching the elevation of uppermost growth as gnarled, depauperate individuals. Such a progression toward the limit of impoverishment is commonly observed in the mountains of southeastern Alaska. Quite often, however, fair-sized mountain hemlock of the upper forest terminates more or less abruptly, and a zone primarily of Alaska alder digitates upward into the alpine tundra. This condition is interpreted as resulting from the recent rise of the snow line and the subsequent succession on slopes formerly covered by snow so late in the growing season that plant invasion could not take place. Mountain hemlock once stood at higher elevations than at present, but was killed as the snow line became lower accompanied by destructive avalanching.

Along a transect from the edge of such a hemlock forest at ca 1400-ft altitude up into the tundra near Juneau, the alder zone lies between the forest and ca 2400 ft (Plate VI). Its principal associates are *Rubus spectabilis*, *Urtica lyallii*, *Heracleum lanatum*, *Spiraea beauverdiana*, *Veratrum eschscholtzii*, *Aruncus sylvester*, *Dryopteris austriaca*, and *Picea sitchensis*. Where a break in slope occurs, *Calamagrostis canadensis* subsp. *langsdorffii* and *Lysichitum americanum* constitute a wet-meadow community. Alder at this elevation grows downslope owing to the weight of heavy snow and to the fact that snow is on the ground during the early and latter part of the growth season. Above the alder at ca 2500 ft, low shrubs and herbaceous cover occupy the slopes. Shrubs include *Rubus spectabilis*, *Vaccinium caespitosum*, *V. uliginosum*, *Cladothamnus pyroliflorus*, and *Phyllodoce glanduliflora*, and the following herbs are representative: *Carex spectabilis*, *Epilobium latifolium*, *E. angustifolium*, *Lupinus nootkatensis*, *Geranium erianthum*, *Sanguisorba menziesii*, *Fritillaria camschatcensis*, *Artemisia arctica*, *Dryopteris linnaeana*, *Geum calthifolium*, *Valeriana sitchensis*, *Ranunculus cooleyae*, *Aconitum delphinifolium*, *Lloydia serotina*, and *Anemone narcissiflora* subsp. *alaskana*. Above 3000 to 3300 ft, alpine tundra extends over wide areas, bordering the glaciers and ice fields. The following groups constitute the maximum cover and are best represented in this order: heaths; sedges, grasses, and rushes; Compositae; Rosaceae; willows; lycopods and polypods; and saxifrages. Up to ca 5000 ft, heath mats formed largely by *Cassiope mertensiana*, *C. stelleriana*, and *Empetrum nigrum* appear to constitute the highest development of cover. Above 5000 ft, the tundra becomes increasingly xeric, and vascular plants, for the most part *Artemisia arctica*, *Potentilla emarginata* subsp. *nana*, and *Hierochloe alpina*, become sparse. At 7000 ft, only lichens and some mosses are found.

In this sector as in others of Pacific coastal Alaska, heavy precipitation prevents fire from becoming a serious detriment to the vegetation. However, summer, which is the driest season of the year, frequently has stretches of two or three weeks with little or no rainfall. It is during these times that fire may become a hazard, particularly where drier conditions normally prevail, as at and above the head of Lynn Canal and toward the interior along the Stikine River (Graves 1916). Burns in the archipelago usually are local, although extensive ones are known to have occurred in the past. Early during this century, for example, they swept many square miles of timber on the Kasaan Peninsula on Prince of Wales Island. Dead snags commonly seen in the coastal forests are often the result of fire (in addition to infestation, overmaturity, and inadequate aeration of root systems).

Muskeg

Southeastern Alaska is a region par excellence for the formation of muskeg, and its occurrence here deserves a special description. Wherever drainage is hindered by low and gently sloping topography, muskeg is almost certain to be found (Plate XIII). It has formed on flats in river valleys, on benches and former marine terraces, on lake borders, and on low-gradient slopes both on the mainland and on the islands. Exceptionally extensive areas are on southern Kupreanof and northern Mitkof Islands and almost all of Annette Island. Many of the small islands, as, for example, Pleasant Island in Icy Strait, are formed almost entirely of muskeg. The only timber on such islands occurs along the immediate coast; elsewhere muskeg commonly forms between the timbered drainage systems. Aerially, it appears in varying shades of brown. Where it is extensive on low and somewhat hilly ground, the dark-green forest, growing in proximity to the drainage and on the better-drained hills in irregular patches, creates a colorful mosaic.

Muskeg has been studied particularly by Dachnowski-Stokes (1941) and Rigg (1914, 1937), and also by Zach (1950), Lawrence (1958), and Heusser (1952, 1953, 1954c). Dachnowski-Stokes classifies slope, raised, and flat types, which are respectively equivalents, in a broad sense, of soligenous, ombrogenous, and topogenous forms of the European classification. He explains that the term "muskeg" is of Indian (Algonquian) origin and that it refers to natural areas of sphagnum moss, sedge, and open-growth scrub in Alaska and northwestern Canada.

Slope (soligenous) muskeg appears on inclined ground at a low angle of repose. Its formation and development are controlled by the movement of surface water and by climate (Jessen 1949); the source of water percolates through the peat and carries minerals (Drury 1956). It exists under a climate characterized by cool summers, heavy precipitation, and high humidity, having its origin mostly as sedge marsh, and often containing one or more layers of ligneous peat (recurrence surfaces). Slope muskeg exhibits optimum development where the topography is low and hilly. With an increase in slope angle, the peat becomes shallow and the proportion of forest increases. In southeastern Alaska, slope muskeg is the most common of the three types.

Lodgepole pine (*Pinus contorta*) characteristically grows on muskeg and appears as low, open, scrub. Where conditions are favorable on certain sites, the tree reaches fair size and age. One lodgepole on a muskeg near Auke Bay, northwest of Juneau, had a 2-ft diameter breast high, was 55 ft tall, and 275 yr of age (Plate XIV). Lodgepole is almost entirely restricted to muskeg. Cooper (1931c) mentions that it grows in swails and on outwash in Glacier Bay, and it has been observed on poorly drained land in forest, but will be succeeded if drainage becomes better. Its occurrence almost exclusively on muskeg is a result of its shade intolerance. Sudworth (1908) states that the tree has a very low tolerance, especially when young, although it is able to persist in very dense stands for 20 to 30 yr. It fails to compete on the upland and is succeeded by Sitka spruce. Lodgepole pine is otherwise remarkable. Hansen (1947a) enumerates the reasons that enable it to invade in the prisere or subsere as follows: aggressiveness and adaptability, prolific seed production as early as 6 yr, seed remaining viable for extended periods, and an ability to develop on a wide variety of soil conditions. In general, the ecological amplitude of lodgepole is quite broad, although this appears to be brought about by the existence of several geographic variations of the species (Critchfield 1957). The tree occurs northwestward in the coastal forest as far as the Yakutat foreland (Johnson and Sandor 1957) (Fig. 9).

Mountain hemlock, Alaska yellow cedar, and western red cedar may be associated with pine on the muskeg. Western hemlock and Sitka spruce often occur as well but are marginal. Shrubby cover, usually in colonies, consists of *Vaccinium uliginosum*, *Kalmia polifolia*, *Ledum palustre* subsp. *groenlandicum*, *Empetrum nigrum*, and *Juniperus communis* var. *montana*. Typical herbs are *Carex pauciflora*, *Scirpus caespitosus* subsp. *austriacus*, *Eriophorum angustifolium* subsp. *scabriusculum*, *Rynchospora alba*, *Lycopodium annotinum*, *Tofieldia occidentalis*, *Coptis trifolia*, *Drosera rotundifolia*, *Sanguisorba menziesii*, *Cornus canadensis*, *Fauria crista-galli*, and *Rubus chamaemorus*. Mosses are mostly species of sphagnum (*Sphagnum warnstorfianum* du Rietz, *S. palustre* L., *S. papillosum* Lindb., *S. fuscum* [Schimp.] Klinggr., *et al.*).

Raised (ombrogenous) muskeg appears dome shaped or convex in form. It too is controlled by climatic conditions, and the water for plant growth falls directly on the surface as contrasted with a stream or water-table source (Jessen 1949, Drury 1956). Its origin is often soligenous or topogenous deposits of sedge and wood peat. Dachnowski-Stokes (1941) states that this type arises where precipitation is heavy but not as heavy as that where slope muskeg abounds. The peat appears to be better aerated, as evidenced by the relatively better growth of pine and other conifers on raised muskeg compared to one on a slope. Sphagnum moss (*Sphagnum papillosum* Lindb., *S. fuscum* [Schimp.] Klinggr., *et al.*), the main peat contributor at present, is commonly found overlying one or more ligneous layers that represent sufficiently dry intervals when stands of timber were able to occupy the surface. At present surface plants may include *Vaccinium uliginosum*, *V. vitis-idaea* subsp. *minus*, *Andromeda polifolia*, *Kalmia polifolia*, *Ledum palustre* subsp. *groenlandicum*, *Empetrum nigrum*, *Oxycoccus microcarpus*, *Carex pauciflora*, *Scirpus caespitosus* subsp. *austriacus*, *Eriophorum angustifolium* subsp. *scabriusculum*, *Coptis trifolia*, *Drosera rotundifolia*, *Rubus chamaemorus*, *Cornus canadensis*, *Geocaulon lividum*, and *Lysichitum americanum*. Pit ponds, water-filled depressions, frequently appear on the surface of both raised and slope muskeg. They vary in size from small openings devoid of plants on raised muskeg to areas sometimes forming a large part of slope muskeg and containing water lilies (*Nuphar polysepalum*, *Nymphaea tetragona* Georgi subsp. *leibergi* [Morong] Pors.) and pondweed (*Potamogeton alpinus* subsp. *tenuifolius*). Lawrence (1958) discusses their development and cites the work of Turesson (1916), who points out that pit ponds are at least in part the result of shading from the dead leaves of *Lysichitum americanum*.

An additional type that deserves mention in the ombrogenous category is the blanket muskeg or blanket bog (Jessen 1949) that covers the terrain, its surface expression reflecting the subsurface topography. Slope and blanket muskeg commonly form intermediate types, and probably for this reason Dachnowski-Stokes (1941) does not distinguish between them. Blanket muskeg consists of sedgey peat and may contain recurrence horizons. It is quite open, may occur on plateaus and high slopes near timber line, and is most extensive under conditions of a pronounced oceanic climate.

Flat (topogenous) muskeg is found in broad, glaciated river valleys or extensive, partly drained lowlands associated with lakes such as occur in pitted outwash plains. The source of water is the water table, and the peat accumulates in depressions to this level, which more or less controls its development (Dachnowski-Stokes 1941, Jessen 1949, Drury 1956). The surface is horizontal or gently sloping and is not able to spread or build up beyond a certain level. It develops through a succession from aquatic plants to transitional sedge-and-grass communities and, in turn, to the invasion of sphagnum mosses, heaths, and conifers.

In the early stage flat muskeg often exhibits a quaking character about open pools. The vegetation at this time may have a meadow aspect and consist of sphagnum species along with *Menyanthes trifoliata*, *Eriophorum scheuchzeri*, *Lysichitum americanum*, *Iris setosa*, *Platanthera dilatata*, *Sanguisorba sitchensis*, *Caltha palustris* subsp. *asarifolia*, *Potentilla palustris*, *Oxycoccus microcarpus*, *Drosera rotundifolia*, and *Fritillaria camschatcensis*. Subsequently in later stages sphagnum peat accumulates, and heath (*Andromeda polifolia*, *Ledum palustre* subsp. *groenlandicum*, *Vaccinium vitis-idaea* subsp. *minus*), sweet gale (*Myrica gale* var. *tomentosa*), and conifer scrub become representative occupants of the surface.

South-Central District

The South-Central District of Alaska lies between Yakutat Bay and Cook Inlet (Fig. 2). It is for the most part quite narrow and, in reality, is made up of a number of discontinuous segments that result from interruptions by Malaspina Glacier and Icy Bay, Bering Glacier and its drainage, the Copper River mouth, and the glaciers entering Prince William Sound and the Gulf of Alaska from the Kenai Peninsula. The Pacific Coastal Forest is the major unit of vegetation. Muskeg is interspersed throughout, but only in Prince William Sound does it reach areal proportions approaching those of the southeastern panhandle. Owing to the steepness of the coastal border at most places, the forest is generally not found far from the ocean, and consequently, the alpine zone is reached a short distance from sea level.

The Pacific Coastal Forest extends northwestward, comprised of mountain hemlock, Sitka spruce, western hemlock, and Alaska yellow cedar. The latter two trees are the least abundant and become freely intermixed, although Alaska yellow cedar occurs rather infrequently. In actuality, the forest represents a consolidation of trees from the coastal and subalpine units to the southeast. It is interesting to note, however, that from the standpoint of proportion, the trees at the ends of their ranges still show an affinity for the character of the formation of which each is a member. Sitka spruce remains largely coastal, and mountain hemlock thrives mostly back from the coast and at timber line. Sudworth (1908) places timber line from 400- to 1600-ft elevation along the coast eastward from Prince William Sound. In the sound, he states it runs from ca 300 ft at the heads of fiords to over 1450 on headland slopes; on the Kenai Peninsula, he places it generally up to altitudes of between 1200 and 1600. Cooper (1942) finds timber line in Prince William Sound up to 2000 ft outside the confines of the fiords.

The forest about Prince William Sound and on the adjacent southern side of the Kenai Peninsula is representative of this section of the coast. Cooper (1942) provides the most thorough account of the northern fiords and forelands of Prince William Sound. The outer islands, namely Hawkins, Hinchinbrook, Montague, Knight, and several small ones, are described by Heller (1910). Of the four conifers present, Sitka spruce and mountain hemlock are most widespread and abundant. Mountain hemlock appears most frequently along the cold northern border while oceanward where conditions are more equable Sitka spruce is commonly seen. Western hemlock and Alaska yellow cedar are present in a few localities in the eastern part of the sound, but westward they reach the ends of their ranges (Figs. 6, 8).

Western hemlock is not reported beyond the southeastern Kenai Peninsula in the vicinity of Seward (Hultén 1941). The northern and western limit of Alaska yellow cedar appears to be about Port Wells in the northeastern part of the sound (John D. Grove, U. S. Forest Service, personal communication). Mountain hemlock is abundant in the Kenai Mountains from sea level to timber line on Turnagain Arm (Osgood 1901a) and has been observed some miles east of Anchorage (Harold J. Lutz, Yale University, personal communication). Hultén (1941) lists the tree as occurring between Skilak and Tustumena Lakes and cites a report by Capps (1935) stating that hemlock, ostensibly mountain hemlock, was found west of Cook Inlet. These localities probably mark the limit of its range (Fig. 9). In this district Sitka spruce extends all along the Gulf of Alaska side of the Kenai and up to the head of Kachemak Bay; at places on the south side of Turnagain Arm; and on the Aleutian Range side of Cook Inlet between Tuxedni Bay and the vicinity of Iliamna Bay (James W. Scott, U. S. Bureau of Land Management, personal communication). It has also been seen at least as far north as Goat Creek on Knik Arm between Anchorage and Palmer, and Sitka spruce-white spruce (*Picea glauca*) hybrids have been observed in the vicinity of Kenai Lake and from the northern head of Kachemak Bay along the coast as far north as Nikishka (H. J. Lutz and J. W. Scott, personal communications). These hybrids are represented by various intermediate forms, among which are *Picea lutzii* Little and *P. glauca* var. *porsildii* Raup (Little 1953).

The regional trees at maturity near sea level average 1 to 2 ft in diameter and 40 to 50 in height (Cooper 1942). Alaska yellow cedar is reported up to 3 ft in diameter. Sitka spruce grows to the largest sizes, although trees over 3 ft in diameter, with heights as much as 100, are uncommon. Fernow (1902) states that Sitka spruce in Prince William Sound attains a maximum diameter of 5 ft and an ultimate height of 150. Sizes decrease rapidly with an increase of altitude and from protected to exposed sites. Blueberry (*Vaccinium ovalifolium*) grows as the most abundant member of the shrub cover in association with *Menziesia ferruginea*, *Sorbus sitchensis*, *Sambucus racemosa* subsp. *pubens*, and *Oplopanax horridus*. The ericaceous *Cladothamnus pyroliflorus*, which in the southeastern sector grows in the subalpine zone, is also a member of this cover but occurs most often along the muskeg borders. Typical herbs in the community are *Dryopteris linnaeana*, *D. austriaca*, *D. oreopteris*, *Blechnum spicant*, *Lycopodium annotinum*, *Streptopus amplexifolius*, *Listera cordata* var. *nephrophylla*, *Coptis asplenifolia*, *Rubus pedatus*, *Cornus canadensis*, and *Trientalis europaea* subsp. *arctica*. Mosses, *Hylocomium proliferum* (L.) Lindb., *Rhytidiadelphus loreus* (L.) Warnst., and *Sphagnum* spp., *et al.*, dominate the ground cover (Cooper 1942).

A study of the prisere was carried out by Lutz (1930) along a 1100-ft transect extending out from the terminus of Sheriden Glacier, east of Cordova. His observations show that the legume *Lupinus nootkatensis* behaves as an early invader on the outwash, as it does in southeastern Alaska. Lutz points out the importance of this plant in providing soil nitrogen for species in the seral stages that follow. Alaska alder, Sitka spruce, and mountain hemlock succeed almost simultaneously, and tacamahac poplar (*Populus tacamahacca*) appears shortly after these. The number of individuals of all species except alder increases after the arrival of poplar, but subsequently alder is most numerous. Sitka spruce gains dominance in the young conifer forest where it is associated with mountain and some western hemlock. The area about Cordova where Lutz' study was made receives considerable precipitation and is much milder than inner parts of the fiords, such as about Valdez, which are drier, colder, and less oceanic. This difference in climate reflects a change in the composition of the forest and the plants participating in the prisere. Accordingly, successions that take place in the more continental localities terminate with a high proportion of mountain hemlock.

The early prisere in the northern sound consists of a rather heterogeneous assemblage of plants. Cooper (1942) lists 78 entities that had become established in less than 21 yr at three stations near Columbia Glacier. Where avalanching has interrupted succession on forested slopes, seres may not progress beyond an early stage. Alaska alder may occupy avalanche tracks for lengthy periods before replacement by conifers ensues. Seres generally begin with dense growths of fern (*Athyrium filix femina* subsp. *cyclosorum*), particularly on moist slopes, followed by thickets of salmonberry mixed with currant (*Ribes laxiflorum*) and blueberry (*Vaccinium ovaliolium*) (Cooper 1942). A "tall herb community" of *Veratrum eschscholtzii*, *Heracleum lanatum*, and *Senecio triangularis* commonly invades along the streams. On open slopes, willow (*Salix barclayi*, *S. commutata*, and *S. sitchensis*) is often the associate of Alaska alder.

The regional forest is bordered and interspersed by several kinds of treeless vegetation. These are represented by muskeg, heath, alpine-tundra, and strand-dune communities. Ecotones of varying widths exist between these natural units, and several agencies of disturbance have affected the relative extent of each. Because of the expansiveness and floristic character of the treeless vegetation, Cooper (1942) considers the entire complex to be a transition between the unbroken forest climax southeastward and the tundra climax westward.

The types of muskeg present in southeastern Alaska are also found in the South-Central District. The size of the area each occupies, however, is quite different in the two districts. Large tracts of blanket muskeg and the blanket-slope intermediate variety are, for example, much more prevalent at or near sea level along the south-central coast; on the other hand, raised muskeg appears to be rare. Rigg (1914), Dachnowski-Stokes (1941), Cooper (1942), and Heusser (1955a) report on the character of muskeg in this district.

The blanket form was observed about Katalla and Martin Lake, near Alaganik, and in the sound on Bligh Island, on the forelands between Tatitlek and Cordova, on eastern Hinchinbrook Island, and on northern and northwestern Montague Island. It was not seen on the Kenai Peninsula. At many of these places it is indistinguishable from the blanket-slope transition type. Plants on the surface were noted as largely *Scirpus caespitosus* subsp. *austriacus* and *Carex pauciflora* with *Cornus canadensis*, *Geum calthifolium*, *Empetrum nigrum*, *Andromeda polifolia*, *Oxycoccus microcarpus*, and *Drosera rotundifolia*. Hollows in the muskeg are occupied by pools, which appear to support few aquatics. The shrubby *Myrica gale* var. *tomentosa* has locally invaded some of the surfaces.

Slope muskeg is scattered throughout the district near sea level. It is not extensive and pit ponds interrupt the surfaces. Low mountain hemlock and spruce grow marginally, and they sometimes grow on the muskeg in small colonies. Cyperaceous and ericaceous species are the most common members of the surface cover. The following are also typical: *Gentiana douglasiana*, *Pedicularis parviflora*, *Rubus chamaemorus*, *Fauria crista-galli*, *Tofieldia occidentalis*, and *Pinguicula villosa*. Cooper (1942) found *Carex nigricans* on muskeg ("Carex bog") in northern Prince William Sound. In the Southeastern District this species is largely alpine. Slope muskeg on the Kenai is the habitat for two noteworthy plants not observed in the sound: *Betula nana* subsp. *exilis* and *Pedicularis labradorica*.

Flat muskeg is found in the Katalla, Martin, and Copper River valleys, often in early stages of development. In the region of the Kenai Lowland later stages occur. Heath (*Empetrum nigrum* and *Ledum palustre* subsp. *decumbens*), bog birch (*Betula nana* subsp. *exilis*), and sphagnum (*Sphagnum fuscum* [Schimp.] Klinggr., *S. balticum* Russ., *et al.*) constitute the principal cover on the Kenai. Black spruce (*Picea mariana*), averaging between 10 and 15 ft tall and appearing scrubby, is the major arboreal species.

Treeless areas called "Empetrum heath" by Cooper (1942) are recognized by him as occupying glaciated surfaces in northern Prince William Sound where relatively cold, dry conditions prevail. This plant cover forms a mat, no more than a foot in thickness, which is made up of the dead and living parts of first, *Empetrum nigrum*, and second, *Cassiope stelleriana*. Other notable heaths contributing are *Phyllodoce glanduliflora*, *Vaccinium caespitosum*, and *V. uliginosum*. The club mosses *Lycopodium selago*, *L. alpinum*, and *L. sabinaefolium* var. *sitchense* and the rosaceous *Luetkea pectinata*, among others, are additional. It is suspected that this type represents a transition from the relatively cold and wet muskeg to the colder and drier alpine tundra.

Alpine tundra extends over a large part of the district between timber line and the snow line or existing glacier areas. Heller (1910) states that on the outer islands of the sound, the heaths, *Phyllodoce glanduliflora* and *Cassiope stelleriana*, are the most characteristic species of the zone with additional species including *Luetkea pectinata*, *Lupinus nootkatensis*, *Valeriana sitchensis*, and *Sedum rosea* subsp. *integrifolium*. These plants are representative of the eastern sector. Northwesterly in the mountains above Girdwood on Turnagain Arm, I listed about 30 different species of alpine plants, among which are *Cassiope stelleriana*, *Empetrum nigrum*, *Loiseleuria procumbens*, *Luetkea pectinata*, *Lycopodium selago*, *L. alpinum*, *Hierochloe alpina*, *Lloydia serotina*, *Sibbaldia procumbens*, *Campanula lasiocarpa*, *Silene acaulis*, and *Epilobium latifolium*.

Strand-dune communities are scattered at various places on the ocean front. They are continuous for many miles along the beach west of Icy Cape and recur toward Katalla and on the dunes at the mouth of the Copper River. Stretches at the southern end of Montague Island on the outer part of Prince William Sound also support this vegetation. On parts of the coast from Icy Bay to Yakutat Bay and particularly southeastward to Icy Cape in the Southeastern District, strand and dune communities are well established. They have been studied by Cooper (1936), and their natural groupings are given by Thomas (1957) for Middleton Island in the Gulf of Alaska. Thomas lists the common species as *Elymus arenarius* subsp. *mollis*, *Honckenya peploides* subsp. *major*, *Mertensia maritima*, and *Senecio pseudo-arnica;* less frequent are *Salix barclayi*, *Rumex fenestratus*, *Moehringia lateriflora*, *Barbarea orthoceras*, *Arabis hirsuta* subsp. *eschscholtziana*, *Fragaria chiloensis*, *Lathyrus maritimus*, *Angelica lucida*, *Heracleum maximum* Bartr., and *Taraxacum vulgare* (Lam.) Schrank. Although absent from Middleton Island, *Carex macrocephala* subsp. *anthericoides* and *Glehnia littoralis* subsp. *leiocarpa* are found occurring sporadically on the mainland in addition to the above. Along the mainland directly behind the strand, the forest often is stunted, wind sheared, and sand blasted and so thick that it is impossible to penetrate without a machete. Farther back, however, the understory is open and the trees grow relatively tall. Forest that begins directly above the high-tide mark has this appearance. Its edge is open if the beach is rather broad, and usually has young Alaska alder and Sitka spruce growing with *Lathyrus maritimus* and *Lupinus nootkatensis*.

The Interior Forest in the South-Central District reaches across the Kenai Lowland and up into the low passes of the Kenai Mountains. White spruce and Kenai birch (*Betula kenaica*) are the climax dominants. Quaking aspen (*Populus tremuloides*) is associated with the above in successional communities or may occur in pure stands.

Aspen commonly is indicative of recent fire, and following destruction by fire, its regeneration is largely by root suckers (Lutz 1953). Fires are fairly frequent over the Kenai Lowland and one notable burn occurred in 1947. North of Kachemak Bay, where the only pollen studies were made in the lowland, white spruce occurs north of the Anchor River and Sitka spruce to the south, although hybrids of the two are intermixed on both sides of the river (J. W. Scott, personal communication). Kenai birch becomes important toward the head of Cook Inlet. Much of the forest is in groves, small colonies, and individual trees, amongst low shrubs and herbs, typical of which are Alaska alder, *Calamagrostis canadensis* subsp. *langsdorffii*, *Heracleum lanatum*, *Lupinus nootkatensis*, *Geranium erianthum*, *Veratrum eschscholtzii*, and *Epilobium angustifolium* (Plate XIV). Only this brief description of the Interior Forest is warranted in view of the limited pollen studies made along its southernmost margin.

Southwestern District

Kodiak, Afognak, and Shuyak Islands, and the adjacent members of this archipelago, as well as the mainland coast along Shelikof Strait, are considered under the heading Southwestern District (Fig. 2). They are areas where Sitka spruce has invaded and is at the limit of its range. (Fig. 6). Sitka spruce is the only conifer of the Pacific Coastal Forest to advance this far southwestward. Beyond its limit the vegetation is essentially treeless except for small occasional groves of tacamahac poplar and black cottonwood; Kenai birch is locally a small tree, and Alaska alder may be semi-arboreal.

Spruce is fairly prevalent on Afognak and Shuyak (Plate XVI), but on Kodiak it forms closed stands only toward the northeastern end of the island whereas southwestward along the gulf and along Shelikof Strait, its numbers are fewer (Plate XVII). It has been observed in colonies to a maximum elevation of 1300 ft on Kodiak. Griggs (1914, 1934) states that spruce extends as far as Ugak Island on the south and Uganik Island on the north. More recent observations (H. E. Andersen, personal communication) disclose that colonies of spruce have become established at Uyak Bay on the north coast, ca 30 mi in advance of the Uganik Island locality reported by Griggs. On the mainland Griggs (1934) notes this species as far west as Cape Kubugakli, which lies opposite Karluk on Kodiak. Other mainland stations are at the northern entrance to Kashvik Bay, on the unnamed cape dividing upper Kuliak Bay, and on Kukak Bay; in addition, dead trees killed by the 1912 volcanic eruption were seen at Amalik Bay, southwest of Kuliak Bay.

The distribution of tacamahac poplar on Kodiak is mapped by Capps (1937) as far as Uyak Bay to the north, and to the southwest as far as the upper arms of Alitak Bay and to Olga Bay. He states that it attains a diameter of 3 ft and more. Black cottonwood, according to Hultén (1943), has been collected as far as Alitak Bay. Kenai birch is reported to reach Uyak Bay on the northern coast and Two Headed Island off southeastern Kodiak (Griggs 1914). Alaska alder appears in patches on the lower slopes throughout the islands. Tacamahac poplar, Kenai birch, and Alaska alder grow on the mainland in the vicinity of Kukak Bay, Katmai Bay, and elsewhere.

The oldest spruce forest on Kodiak possesses trees over 4 ft in diameter (Griggs

1934) and more than 75 in height. Young spruce trees are about 1 ft in diameter and 30 to 40 tall (Plate XVIII). The low branches of the young trees are scrubby and often dead or dying, whereas those of the old are stubby and have been dead for many years. They are partly covered and even sometimes completely ensheathed by mosses, the most common of which are *Hylocomium splendens* (Hedw.) BSG and *Rhytidiadelphus triquetrus* (Hedw.) Warnst. These species are frequent in the ground cover. Some dead trees are standing, and fallen timber is scattered on the floor. The shrub cover is chiefly *Vaccinium ovalifolium*, and the herbs include *Rubus pedatus* and the ferns *Athyrium filix femina* subsp. *cyclosorum*, *Dryopteris austriaca*, *D. phegopteris*, and *D. linnaeana*. In young stands where considerable light passes through the crowns, *Rubus spectabilis* is more often than not the major shrub, growing in association with *Oplopanax horridus*, *Viburnum edule*, and *Sambucus racemosa* subsp. *pubens*. In stands of tacamahac poplar, black cottonwood, and willow, spruce has established itself in the understory and in time will, no doubt, achieve supremacy.

Griggs (1914, 1934) discusses the forest-tundra ecotone on Kodiak Island. He notes dead trees and fallen timber in the oldest forest. Many of the trees appeared tall and slender and had evidently developed under closed conditions. Older specimens, however, still had their low branches almost intact, indicating that they grew up in the open. At ca 3 mi from the edge of the forest, these old members of the first generation were found to be as much as 319 yr in age. Griggs concludes from this that the margin had advanced at a rate of ca 1 mi per century. At the margin and in the forest-tundra ecotone, timber was observed to be healthy and growing with a normal excurrent form, although with considerably broad bases. In the ecotone, trees appear singly or in groves in varying numbers. Griggs found them to be less than 100 yr in age and producing abundant, viable seed. He found as many as 100 or more seedlings per square foot on previously unoccupied volcanic ash. From these data and from Bowman's (1934) discovery of spruce pollen in only the upper levels of Kodiak peat, Griggs reaches the conclusion that Sitka spruce on the island attained its present position quite recently, and the advance was "thus shown to be a long-term secular migration . . . rather than a phase of a cyclic oscillation back and forth."

The coastal tundra is a complex of communities whose ecological relationships are little known. Alaska alder can be found almost anywhere on the lower slopes. All the ferns previously mentioned as occurring with spruce associate here with alder, as do a number of additional species: *Rubus spectabilis*, *Veratrum eschscholtzii*, *Heracleum lanatum*, and *Boschniakia rossica*. Some areas exhibit a shrubby cover of *Spiraea beauverdiana* and *Rosa nutkana*. Meadows are often dominated by *Calamagrostis canadensis* subsp. *langsdorffii*, but this grass may be only occasional and the cover characterized instead by *Epilobium angustifolium*, *E. latifolium*, *Geranium erianthum*, *Sanguisorba sitchensis*, *Fritillaria camschatcensis*, *Valeriana sitchensis*, *Rubus stellatus*, and *Castilleja unalaschcensis*. Near the coast the umbellifers *Ligusticum hultenii*, *Conioselinum benthami*, *Angelica genuflexa*, and *A. lucida* gain importance. Flat muskeg abounds over the broad floors of the glaciated valleys—the valley of Karluk River below Karluk Lake is a good example. The muskeg is broken by small lakes and innumerable pit ponds and from the air appears tussocky in places. Slope muskeg is common on many of the sluggishly drained hillsides and benches. The cover, formed to a large extent by heath (*Empetrum nigrum*, *Ledum palustre* subsp. *decumbens*, *Vaccinium uliginosum*, and *V. vitis-idaea* subsp. *minus*), also includes *Cornus suecica*, *Rubus chamaemorus*, *Betula nana* subsp. *exilis*, and *Trientalis europaea* subsp. *arctica*. The species *Sphagnum girgensohnii* Russ. is typical of the mosses growing on this muskeg. It seems apparent from the description of Aleutian Island plant communities (Hultén 1937a) that the communities on the upland of Kodiak Island are but little altered as they continue southwestward.

Griggs (1918, 1922) shows that ca 1 ft of ash fell in the vicinity of Kodiak village during the eruption of Mt. Katmai and its neighbors in 1912. Southwestward from Kodiak the amount decreased greatly; Karluk, for example, received only 0.02 ft of ash. Vhere the ash was heaviest at the northern end of Kodiak Island, the vegetation was disturbed and many plants perished. Recovery, however, was much more rapid than had been expected. During the second and third years following the eruption, plants were able to grow up through the ash and appear with greater vigor than before. The grass *Calamagrostis canadensis* subsp. *langsdorffii* was able to recover exceptionally well; at some places it sent shoots up through a 20-in ash layer. The horsetail *Equisetum arvense* was observed to come through as much as a 36-in layer and appears to have spread more rapidly than any of its associates. Griggs (1922) points out that vigor following the ashfall was caused by the reduction in the degree of competition between species.

In the forest, several years elapsed before seedlings were established, but during the latter part of 1915, they began to appear and included most of the floral representatives. Mosses reoccupied the forest floor quite rapidly because their spores were able to invade the cracks that developed in the ash subsequent to the heavy rainfall following the eruption. It seems remarkable that many of the plants were able to sustain burial for three or more years. In 1956, near Kodiak village, I observed a 2-in-thick layer of turf accumulated since the ashfall. To the casual observer at the present time, the evidence of the Katmai eruption is not readily apparent on Kodiak Island, and it is indeed difficult to believe it took place as recently as 1912.

BRITISH COLUMBIA

The vegetation of northern coastal British Columbia, as indicated previously, differs very little from that of southeastern Alaska. The differences, stated briefly, involve (1) luxuriance, (2) units and composition, (3) zonal demarcation, and (4) autecology of the component species. Looked upon broadly, these differences are gradational as the "center of optimum development" is reached.

The Queen Charlotte Islands characterize the northern coastal district (Figs. 3, 4). The Pacific Coastal Forest, dominated by western hemlock, Sitka spruce, and western red cedar, is well developed in the vicinity of the coastal areas and up to an altitude of ca 1000 ft. Under a cool and moist climate with a long growing season, the forest is conspicuously luxuriant. Trees grow to large sizes, particularly on well-drained ground, with trunks and branches covered with thick colonies of moss. Western hemlock is most abundant at low elevations. It is not the largest tree, however, and specimens probably do not measure over 3 to 4 ft diameter breast high and 130 to 150 in height. Sitka spruce is the largest, and frequently attains sizes of 6 to 8 ft in diameter with heights from 100 to 200 (Plate XIX). One specimen reported in the *New York Times* of 17 August 1956 was 16 ft in diameter and 250 ft tall at ca 1000 yr of age. The Sitka spruce of maximum size, according to the American Forestry Association (1956), measures a 16.5-ft diameter breast high and a 180-ft height. Spruce on the Queen Charlottes is of the finest quality growing in the British Columbia coastal district, and western hemlock is also superior to that found in the southern part (Whitford and Craig 1918). Western red cedar is least abundant compared to the two preceding trees. It grows to large sizes, but generally it is 3 to 8 ft in diameter and from 125 to 175 high. No Douglas fir (*Pseudotsuga menziesii* [Mirb.] Franco, as reviewed by Krajina [1956] and replacing the invalid *Pseudotsuga taxifolia* [Poir.] Britton) nor true fir (*Abies*) is known on the Queen Charlottes. Sudworth (1908) records the presence of amabilis fir, but this report has not since been confirmed (British Columbia Provincial Museum 1921).

The forest floor is commonly pocketed and raised into mounds where huge trees have been toppled during storms. It is covered with rotting trunks and other arboreal debris along with a considerable accumulation of partly decomposed vegetable material. This layer, consisting of living moss and decaying organic matter, may be as much as 2 to 3 ft in thickness. Trees of relatively poor growth are present under such conditions, and the vegetation may be classified as a forest-muskeg transition. The undergrowth in these transitional stands is often formed almost exclusively by an extremely thick entanglement of salal. Since the stands are relatively open, lodgepole pine, which is not present in the climax forest because it is unable to compete, thrives successfully. Undergrowth under climax conditions, however, is comparatively sparse, being composed by the heaths *Vaccinium ovalifolium*, *V. parvifolium*, and *Menziesia ferruginea*. Openings in the climax forest, formed by the space vacated by toppled trees, permit the invasion of devils club, salmonberry, and blue currant.

Fringe areas near tidewater and streams are occupied by red alder, willow (*Salix scouleriana*), western crab apple (*Malus fusca*), and wild currant (*Ribes bracteosum* and *R. laxiflorum*), among other species. Alder under optimum conditions attains relatively large sizes of over 1 ft in diameter. A strand vegetation thrives along stretches of the islands. In the neighborhood of Sandspit on Moresby Island and along the eastern and northeastern coasts ending at Rose Point on Graham Island, this vegetation flourishes, consisting of such plants as *Elymus arenarius* subsp. *mollis*, *Honckenya peploides* subsp. *major*, *Lathyrus maritimus*, *Atriplex gmelini*, *Salicornia herbacea*, and *Plantago maritima* subsp. *juncoides*.

Between ca 1000- and 2000-ft elevation, according to Osgood (1901b), the forest composition changes gradually, while above 2000 the transition becomes abrupt. Western red cedar is no longer found, and western hemlock and Sitka spruce are few. The Pacific Subalpine Forest of mountain hemlock and Alaska yellow cedar is manifest in this upper zone, which varies with slope exposure and the elevation of timber line. MacKenzie (1916) places the upper tree limit over 1300 ft above sea level whereas Osgood (1901b) states that it reaches to ca 2500. Although mountain hemlock and Alaska yellow cedar are the dominants of the subalpine zone, Alaska alder is important on these slopes, and a few examples of depauperate western hemlock, Sitka spruce, and lodgepole pine grow on the high ridges. Sudworth (1908) records that mountain hemlock and Alaska yellow cedar extend to 5000 ft in altitude, but this is obviously an error since no peaks on the islands are higher than ca 4000. The highest elevation at which trees are growing is believed to be between 3000 and 3500 ft. Osgood (1901b) estimates that alpine vegetation lies above 2500 ft, but this elevation is, of course, variable. He writes that four principal mountain areas are occupied by alpine plant cover: southwestern Graham Island, Louise Island, and Moresby Island opposite Louise Island and opposite Lyell Island. The following are among the typical alpine plants recorded by Osgood: *Cassiope stelleriana*, *C. mertensiana*, *Phyllodoce glanduliflora*, *Vaccinium uliginosum*, *V. caespitosum*, *Loiseleuria procumbens*, *Luetkea pectinata*, *Pedicularis lanata*, and *P. ornithorhyncha*.

The remainder of the vegetation on the Queen Charlotte Islands is for the most part muskeg. Slope, raised, and flat muskeg have been observed and studied here (Heusser 1955b). Flat muskeg appears to be the most prevalent and is largely on Graham Island, northeast of the Queen Charlotte Ranges, and on parts of the Skidegate Plateau. In fact, most of the area occupied by muskeg on the Queen Charlottes is on Graham Island. The southern islands of the archipelago are generally too steep and too well drained to permit its development.

Raised muskeg appears to be more prevalent here than in southeastern Alaska, whereas slope muskeg is about as common. The slope type is associated with the hilly country of the northern lowland of Graham Island but is found in general where low slopes abound. Both slope and raised muskeg seem to be distributed widely. Trees, by and large, are low and sparse on the muskeg surfaces, although at former times they appear to have covered many of them fairly densely, as indicated by timber remains underlying the surfaces. Flat muskeg east of Masset Inlet supports sizeable trees at the margins, but repeated burning has devastated much of this cover. At the present time the formation of peat is favored by the cool and moist marine climate that extends through a long growing season, and at the same time, represses the activity of decay organisms. The plant cover on the muskeg appears to be quite similar to that on southeastern Alaskan muskeg. Common members are: *Sphagnum* spp., *Scirpus caespitosus* subsp. *austriacus*, *Carex pauciflora*, *Empetrum nigrum*, *Ledum palustre* subsp. *groenlandicum*, *Kalmia polifolia*, *Andromeda polifolia*, *Gaultheria shallon*, *Oxycoccus microcarpus*, *Vaccinium uliginosum*, *V. vitis-idaea* subsp. *minus*, *Rubus chamaemorus*, *Cornus canadensis*, *Gentiana douglasiana*, *Pinguicula vulgaris*, *Trientalis europaea* subsp. *arctica*, *Drosera rotundifolia*, and *Juniperus communis* var. *montana*. Lodgepole pine, western red cedar, mountain hemlock, and Alaska yellow cedar are typical, although the latter two do not grow on the low-elevation muskeg, and red cedar is seldom found on that at high levels. It is estimated that muskeg does not occur at more than 1500 ft above sea level.

The vegetation of the northern mainland coast and adjacent islands is described in a general manner by McCabe and Cowan (1945). The outermost islands, such as Banks, Aristazabal, and Calvert, are marked by a narrow, peripheral stand of trees, consisting largely of Sitka spruce, behind which are extensive barrens containing innumerable lakes and muskeg and much exposed rock. Where the forest is relatively open along the shore, salal often grows into dense, impenetrable thickets. The majority of the inner slopes of these islands are timbered. The outer slopes of the islands adjacent to the mainland are also heavily timbered, but only in part, for the ridges of the hills and the lowlands between constitute open ground. Along the mountainous "inside" fiords, the forest shows greater continuity because of better drainage, but steep, naked slopes of granitic rock are occupied by few trees.

Lodgepole pine appears on rocky exposures and wet muskeg and on such sites develops scrubby form. At places of better drainage, lodgepole was observed with diameters of 3 ft at the butt. Western red cedar mixed with western hemlock is prevalent on the heavily wooded slopes of the outer hills. At high elevations, red cedar becomes associated with Alaska yellow cedar to some extent. Stands of larger, and more numerous, specimens of Sitka spruce are found mostly at the stream deltas, and Sitka spruce and amabilis fir associate on the low slopes of southern exposures. At these elevations western yew may also be found, both occasionally and frequently. Douglas fir ceases to be coastal along northern Vancouver Island. Farther northwest, it prevails at the heads of fiords, as near Bella Coola. According to Schmidt (1957), this species occurs near tidewater as far as the vicinity of Kemano at 53°30′N (Fig. 7). McCabe and Cowan (1945) state that fires are occasional toward the heads of inlets and rather infrequent on the islands. It is possible that Douglas fir may owe its presence to this factor. Burned areas were observed, nevertheless, on northern Aristazabal Island and on southeastern Princess Royal Island.

Little is known about subalpine and alpine vegetation in the northern part of the British Columbia Coast Mountains. Schmidt (1957) states that at Kemano, ca 75 mi south of the Skeena River, the upper altitudinal limit of western red cedar is at 2500 ft; of Douglas fir, 2700; of western hemlock, 3000; of amabilis fir, 4350; and of alpine fir, 4800. Observations by McAvoy (1929, 1931) in the Bella Coola area, less than 100 mi southward, disclose that timber line is at ca 4500-ft altitude, formed largely by alpine fir and low juniper (*Juniperus communis* var. *montana*) with some whitebark pine (*Pinus albicaulis* Engelm.). She describes successions in the alpine zone that proceed to an ultimate cover of heath dominated by *Phyllodoce empetriformis*.

Brink (1959) published a survey of the subalpine-alpine ecotone in Garibaldi Park in the southern Coast Mountains. The lower subalpine forest is found between 3500 and 5000 ft and consists principally of amabilis fir, mountain hemlock, and Alaska yellow cedar. Between 5000 and 6300 ft, vegetation is a mosaic of heath, sedge meadow, forb meadow, and trees. Heath (*Phyllodoce empetriformis*, *P. glanduliflora*, *Cassiope mertensiana*, and *C. tetragona*) is predominant. Trees in groves reach to 6000 ft, and a *krummholz* between 6000 and 7300 is formed largely of alpine fir; only occasionally do mountain hemlock, whitebark pine, and juniper intermix.

Vancouver Island vegetation characterizes the southern coastal district. Magnificent forests still occupy parts of the island, but fire and logging have destroyed many of the stands. This is particularly true over much of the southeastern half, inland from the Strait of Georgia and the Strait of Juan de Fuca. This part of the island is much drier than the northern and western coasts where fires have been less extensive and less frequent. According to Schmidt (1957), who has mapped the area of timber burned 300 to 400 yr ago, extensive fires occurred 130, 210, 300, 350, 400, 550, 620, 750, 860, 930, and between 1100 and 1200 yr ago. He points out that even-aged forests are found where fires occurred within the past 500 yr; uneven-aged ones are present where burns have not taken place for longer periods or at all. Fires are ignited by man but also by severe ligntning storms. A recent storm during July 1941, for example, ignited 240 forest fires.

Climate, fire, and, to some extent, soil are largely responsible for the distribution and number of species. Schmidt states that direct climatic control is most pronounced at the upper altitudinal limits of trees where lower temperatures (recurrent frosts) and shorter growing seasons are probably the limiting factors. As a direct control, temperature appears to be much more influential than precipitation. This is indicated by the fact that nearly all the tree species in the coastal district grow under wide ranges of annual precipitation. Composition, on the other hand, can vary with the amount of seasonal precipitation. Even-aged Douglas fir predominates where less than 5 in of precipitation fall during June, July, and August; where precipitation is greater than 12 in during these months, western red cedar, western hemlock, Sitka spruce, and amabilis fir prevail. It should be made clear, however, that it is not the amount of precipitation that directly affects this distribution. Precipitation only affects forest composition indirectly through its control of fire, which directly controls distribution. Soil conditions exert only a small influence on the presence or absence of tree species.

The Pacific Coastal Forest, which reaches ca 4000-ft elevation on Vancouver Island, is composed of the western hemlock-western red cedar climax and the Douglas fir subclimax and climax. As pointed out above, the relatively moist areas of northern and Pacific coastal Vancouver Island support western hemlock, western red cedar, Sitka spruce, and amabilis fir. Douglas fir in subclimax stands (Plate XX) is present in these areas only by virtue of its ability to develop after fires. The tree is particularly prevalent over the southeastern part of the island, where summer months are dry and annual precipitation is low. Hansen (1950a) considers it a climax species in this area because conditions are unfavorable for competition by western hemlock, even in the absence of fire.

Forest succession following fire in the western hemlock-western red cedar area of Vancouver Island is strikingly portrayed by Schmidt (1957). He compares the percentage stand composition by numbers of trees in groups of large trees, intermediate trees, and advance regeneration at intervals of 100, 300, 400, 600, 800, and 1100 to 1200 yr since a major fire. The basis for his study is formed by 142 temporary plots. Initially, Douglas fir "seeds in" directly from local trees that have survived the fire whereas western hemlock, western red cedar, and amabilis fir, being thin barked and easily killed by burning, supply seed from unburned areas. Western hemlock and western red cedar, which are adapted for long-distance seed dispersal, become established fairly early. Amabilis fir, however, does not have this ability and even after 300 yr, it represents less than 10 per cent of the advance regeneration. Between 700 and 800 yr are usually necessary before this species becomes an important associate of the large trees.

After 100 yr have elapsed, Douglas fir comprises over 70 per cent of the large trees whereas intermediate representatives tally about 25 and no advance regeneration is present. Advance regeneration at this time is over 80 per cent western hemlock, and this species forms over 60 per cent of the intermediate trees. Western red cedar in the three groups is only ca 10 per cent or less (Plate XXI). As succession progresses the relationships change and after 1100 to 1200 yr, they are quite different than they were at the 100-yr stage. Of the large trees, cedar and hemlock have ascended to ranks of over 30 per cent each and amabilis fir to over 10; Douglas fir has descended to ca 10. The intermediate trees are over 50 per cent amabilis fir and ca 40 hemlock; cedar comprises only a few per cent of the total and Douglas fir is absent. Of the advance regeneration, amabilis fir forms almost 70 per cent, hemlock ca 30, and red cedar only a few per cent. This minor amount of cedar regeneration is striking for a climax species. However, Schmidt (1955) states that although western red cedar does not regenerate from seed to any extent in mature stands, vegetative reproduction by adventitious roots is relatively common. Compared to western hemlock and amabilis fir, cedar has a lower mortality rate once established beyond the seedling stage. These facts insure its perpetuation in the climax forest. The high proportion of amabilis fir in the climax is much the same as on the southwestern slopes of the Olympic Mountains in Washington (Hanzlik 1932).

The size and great age of mature Douglas fir is indicated by a section cut from one mature specimen at Schoen Lake in the Nimpkish drainage area of northern Vancouver Island. This section, from the butt of the tree exhibited in the Parliament Building at Victoria, measures almost 9 ft in diameter. The tree stood 230 ft tall and was 1092 yr of age when it was cut down. Western red cedar may exceed this diameter by many feet but is usually much lower in stature. Western hemlock is frequently found near 4 ft in diameter and about 200 in height. Amabilis fir at maturity is comparable in size. On the west-central coast of Vancouver Island, Schmidt (1957) measured a mature amabilis fir over 5 ft in diameter breast high, 207 ft in height, and 420 yr old.

Several additional conifers occur at low elevations: Alaska yellow cedar, Sitka spruce, lowland white fir (*Abies grandis* Lindl.), western white pine (*Pinus monticola* Dougl.), and lodgepole pine. Alaska yellow cedar may be found close to sea level about the northern end of Vancouver Island (Hope Island at ca 100-ft elevation), but southward it becomes a part of the subalpine forest. Sitka spruce is found mainly along the western coast of the island and at the northern end. Sudworth (1908) notes that it reaches ca 1000 ft above sea level near the mouth of the Strait of Juan de Fuca. Lowland white fir, by contrast, extends along the Strait of Georgia, up the major valleys into the interior of the island, and over to the upper inlets of the west coast (Schmidt 1957) (Fig. 7). It rarely goes above 1000-ft altitude and is almost exclusively restricted to alluvial soil, where it grows in association with black cottonwood and red alder. Schmidt records diameters between 3 and 4 ft and heights over 200 at maturity. The largest tree on Vanocuver Island measures over 5 ft in diameter breast high and a height of 240 ft at 280 yr of age. Lowland white fir, which grows very rapidly and in 50 yr can attain a height of 140 ft, is somewhat more tolerant of shade than Douglas fir and about the same as Sitka spruce but is the least tolerant of the regional true firs, and in dense coniferous forest is unable to compete successfully. Western white pine is distributed over much of Vancouver Island in the mountains and on the opposite mainland, where it reaches to over 2200-ft elevation above the head of Bute Inlet (Sudworth 1908) (Fig. 8). So far as I am aware, white pine does not reach farther northwestward along the coast than the mountains southeast of Quatsino Sound. According to Hansen (1947a), it is a member of the subclimax and persists largely because of fire. Lodgepole pine and western white pine are not particularly abundant on the island. Lodgepole continues to grow near the ocean on rocky bluffs and on wet, poorly drained sites.

Several broadleaf trees not encountered heretofore are mentioned since they are southerly ranging species that do not grow farther northward than Vancouver Island. These include Oregon ash (*Fraxinus oregana* Nutt.), cascara (*Rhamnus purshiana* DC.), western dogwood (*Cornus nuttallii* Aud.), Oregon oak (*Quercus garryana* Dougl.), and madrono (*Arbutus menziesii* Pursh). Ash, cascara, and dogwood occur along streams and alluvial bottoms of southeastern Vancouver Island, whereas oak and madrono occupy dry knolls and bluffs. Madrono ranges northwestward along the Strait of Georgia as far as Seymour Narrows (Sudworth 1908). Hansen (1950a) states that Oregon oak forms small pure stands near Victoria and ranges as far north as Courtenay on the eastern side of the island, reaching its best development and greatest numbers on glacial outwash south of Olympia and in the Willamette Valley of Oregon. The distribution of oak and madrono coincides generally with the relatively dry southeastern area of rain shadow on Vancouver Island.

The dominants of the Pacific Coastal Forest, western hemlock and western red cedar, reach their maximum upper altitudinal limits on central Vancouver Island at, respectively, 4400 and 4000 ft (Schmidt 1957). Douglas fir grows as high as 4100-ft elevation. At ca 4000 ft toward the north end of the island and perhaps 200 to 300 higher toward the south, the Pacific Subalpine Forest is encountered (Plate XXII). Amabilis fir, Alaska yellow cedar, mountain hemlock, and alpine fir are the principal members. Amabilis fir and alpine fir reach their upper limit of growth at over 5000 ft above sea level (Schmidt 1957). Amabilis fir extends altitudinally higher than yellow cedar but not as high as mountain hemlock and alpine fir, which are the timber-line species in the east-central part of the island. In the Coast Mountains whitebark pine is a timber-line tree but does not appear to be present westward.

Alpine fir, according to Schmidt, descends to a lower altitudinal limit of 2300 ft but is not often found below 3000. Below ca 4000 ft it associates with Douglas fir, western hemlock, western red cedar, western white pine, and lodgepole pine. Although growing with typical *krummholz* form at timber line, at lower elevations alpine fir grows to fair size. The maximum recorded on Vancouver Island is somewhat over 2 ft in diameter breast high, has a height of 76 ft, and has attained an age of 140 yr. Mountain hemlock occurs at 3000- to 5500-ft elevation (Sudworth 1908).

Muskeg of any noteworthy extent is found only on northern Vancouver Island where both flat and slope types, covered with a scrub of lodgepole pine, are present. Near the mouth of the Fraser River, on Lulu Island particularly, flat muskeg is less extensive. Hansen (1940) lists the chief cover plants as *Ledum palustre* subsp. *groenlandicum*, *Kalmia polifolia*, *Andromeda polifolia*, *Gaultheria shallon*, *Vaccinium uliginosum*, *Oxycoccus microcarpus*, *Drosera rotundifolia*, *Rubus chamaemorus*, *Carex* spp., *Spiraea douglasii* Hook., *Pteridium aquilinum* subsp. *lanuginosum*, and *Sphagnum* spp. Topogenous muskeg is fairly common on the lowland bordering the Strait of Georgia and is relatively extensive in the lake country westward and northwestward of Campbell River. Rigg (1922) describes one area near Victoria in which lodgepole pine is dominant and the undergrowth consists of *Ledum palustre* subsp. *groenlandicum* and salal. The muskeg or bog literature for this part of the coast and southward is written chiefly by Rigg, Hansen, Dachnowski-Stokes, and Osvald. Their major papers are cited in the bibliography.

Since the term "muskeg" has been applied only in a regional sense to Alaska and northwestern Canada, it is perhaps best to dispense with it in reference to points farther south along the coast of Washington, Oregon, and California. Sites to the south possess many of the characteristics of muskeg, namely moss, sedge, and scrubby cover, but in addition support southerly ranging plants that register a sharp contrast with muskeg of Alaska and Canada. Because a distinction seems in order, the remainder of the muskeg-like sites will be referred to as topogenous bogs.

WASHINGTON

The Washington area of concern includes the Olympic Peninsula, the Coast Range, the Puget Sound Lowland, and, to a minor degree, the northern Cascades (Fig. 5). The Pacific Coastal Forest is generally below 3000-ft altitude, and its development is unmatched in magnificence, particularly on the western side of the Olympic Peninsula. Fire and logging have destroyed considerable stands, but in the Olympic National Park the natural cover remains essentially undisturbed. The Pacific Subalpine Forest above ca 3000-ft elevation has also been preserved in the Olympic National Park and in Mt. Rainier National Park as well.

The grandeur of Pacific Coastal Forest on the western Olympic Peninsula is perhaps best illustrated by the sizes of the trees. Their record measurements are unchallenged by others of the same species growing elsewhere in North America (American Forestry Association 1955, 1956). Diameter breast high and height are for western red cedar, 21 ft by 130; western hemlock, 8.7 by 125; Douglas fir, 17 by 221; Sitka spruce, 16.5 by 180; amabilis fir, 6 by 186; Alaska yellow cedar, 6.7 by 175; and red alder, 2.8 by 98. The finest stands are on well-drained bottomlands and slopes at low elevations (Plate XXIII).

In the extensive survey of the botany of the Olympic Peninsula made by Jones (1936), the Pacific Coastal Forest is subdivided into western hemlock-western red cedar and Sitka spruce-western hemlock climaxes and a Douglas fir subclimax. Piper (1906) recognizes these general subdivisions but does not develop them in detail.

Sitka spruce-western hemlock exists behind the immediate beach, sea cliffs, sand dunes, and salt marshes to ca 1000-ft elevation (Jones 1936). Sitka spruce is dominant, occurring with western hemlock and some western red cedar. Sitka spruce may compose the stand entirely, but minor numbers of Douglas fir and lodgepole pine may be present. Facing the ocean, spruce has been stripped of most of its branches by the mechanical effect of sand abrasion and by the desiccating effect of wind and salt spray (Plate XXIV). Much of the timber along the ocean front consists of dead snags that are upright or leaning amongst the other trees, having been wind thrown completely or broken off at their butts. In active dune areas, spruce often is buried by sand to considerable depths, so that the broken and ragged tops are all that protrude. Salal is the principal shrub near the edge of the strand, while farther back it occurs largely with red alder, willow (*Salix hookeriana* Barr., *S. lasiandra* Benth.), and salmonberry. Where swamps are prevalent in the southwestern part of the peninsula, the trees and shrubs are commonly associated with skunk cabbage. Along streams, the woody shrubs include devils club, vine maple (*Acer circinatum* Pursh), salmonberry, salal, and blueberry (*Vaccinium ovalifolium* and *V. parvifolium*).

Many of the strand plants range to Alaska, but most of them do not grow farther northward than Vancouver Island (Cooper 1936). Typical sand-dune species along the west coast are *Elymus arenarius* subsp. *mollis*, *Ammophila arenaria* (L.) Link, *Poa macrantha* Vas., *Abronia acutalata* Standl., *A. latifolia* Esch., *Fragaria chiloensis*, *Convolvulus soldanella* L., *Franseria chamissonis* Less., and var. *bipinnatisecta* Less. Jones (1936) states that tidal flats are particularly well developed at the mouths of the Dosewallips and Duckabush Rivers along Hood Canal on the eastern peninsula. Salt grass, *Distichlis spicata* (L.) Greene, and woody glasswort, *Salicornia pacifica* Standl., are codominants on these flats.

Behind the immediate coast, occupied by Sitka spruce and western hemlock, the western hemlock-western red cedar climax prevails on the undisturbed terrain to elevations up to 1500 and 2000 ft. Western hemlock is dominant in the association with Douglas fir, lowland white fir, western white pine, and western yew being minor associates. Douglas fir is more common on the eastern and southern Olympic Peninsula. The climax is quite similar to that in the Puget Lowland as described by Hansen (1947a and b). Jones (1936) writes that "the general character of the climax forest is dense, sombre, and mossy, consisting often of nearly pure stands of straight slender hemlocks." Except along streams and in moist copses, the undergrowth is sparse.

Typical shrubs are blueberry (*Vaccinium parvifolium* and *V. ovatum* Pursh), *Menziesia ferruginea*, devils club, salal, *Pachystima myrsinites* (Pursh) Raf., *Rosa gymnocarpa* Nutt., and *Ribes bracteosum*. The thick mosses that directly cover the floor, but also grow luxuriantly on the trees and some of the shrubs, are principally *Eurhynchium oreganum* Jaeg. & Sauerb., *Rhytidiadelphus loreus* (Hedw.) Warnst., *R. triquetrus* (Hedw.) Warnst., and *Hylocomium splendens* (Hedw.) BSG. The flora, in general, is composed of comparatively few species, but these are widely distributed.

The greater part of the forest below an altitude of ca 2000 ft is Douglas fir subclimax. Its status under the more moist climatic conditions of the peninsula appears to be the same as in the relatively moist sections of Vancouver Island. The successional nature of Douglas fir has been studied by Hofmann (1920), Jones (1936),

Isaac (1940), and Munger (1940), among others, who agree that largely as a result of fire, Douglas fir is temporary under humid conditions and will be replaced by the climax conifers. Hofmann attributes its ability to succeed after fire chiefly to (1) heavy seed crops prior to burning, (2) caching of seed by rodents, and (3) ability of seed to remain viable and survive intense fire.

Following fire, according to Jones (1936), the pioneers are *Epilobium angustifolium*, *Pteridium aquilinum* subsp. *lanuginosum*, *Anaphalis margaritacea*, and *Senecio sylvaticus* L., along with several mosses. Later, the following invade: *Rubus macropetalus* Dougl., *R. parviflorus*, *Salix scouleriana*, red alder, vine and big-leaf maples, *Ribes sanguineum* Pursh, *Cornus nuttallii* Aud., salal, *Holodiscus discolor* (Pursh) Maxim., *Vaccinium parvifolium*, *Rosa gymnocarpa* Nutt., *Symphoricarpus albus* (L.) Blake, and *Arctostaphylos uva-ursi*. According to Piper (1906), red alder and willow become conspicuous in the subsequent stage and dominate the community until superseded by Douglas fir. Munger (1940) states that Douglas fir can dominate the broadleafs within a decade. After 100 yr a prominent understory of tolerant conifers develops in the young Douglas fir. By the time 200 yr have passed, insects, disease, and physical damage cause the density of Douglas fir to decline. When the forest is 300 yr of age, the tolerant conifers become part of the major stand, and at 400 to 500 yr, the Douglas fir reaches senility. Hereafter its disappearance is rapid at the expense of the climax dominants, western hemlock and western red cedar. During a late stage in the succession, Munger (1940) measured 590-yr-old Douglas firs on the Wynoochee River in the southern Olympics from 5 to over 8 ft in diameter and 250 to 275 ft tall.

The major shrubs of the Douglas fir subclimax are salal, *Berberis nervosa* Pursh, *Vaccinium parvifolium*, and *Salix scouleriana;* abundant ferns are *Pteridium aquilinum* subsp. *lanuginosum*, *Polystichum munitum*, and *Blechnum spicant*. On the bottomlands, western red cedar, Douglas fir, western hemlock, lowland white fir, western yew, and Sitka spruce grow in association with red alder, big-leaf maple, and black cottonwood.

Topogenous bogs are found at many places on the Olympic Peninsula. They appear in various stages of succession, particularly about Ozette Lake, near the Hoh and Raft Rivers, north of Grays Harbor, in the vicinity of Admiralty Inlet, and along Hood Canal. The relatively early stages are characterized by *Sphagnum* spp., *Carex livida*, *Drosera rotundifolia*, *Sanguisorba microcephala* Presl, *Gentiana sceptrum* Griseb., *Kalmia polifolia*, *Ledum palustre* subsp. *groenlandicum*, and *Spiraea douglasii* Hook. Later, western red cedar, western hemlock, and lodgepole pine invade.

Jones (1936) describes a zone characterized by western hemlock, amabilis fir, and western white pine lying between ca 1500- and 3000-ft altitude. Western red cedar is scarce, except bordering the lower streams, and Douglas fir is found infrequently. It seems that this zone represents a transition between the Pacific Coastal Forest and the Pacific Subalpine Forest. Hanzlik (1932) indicates that amabilis fir appears to be climax on the southern and western slopes of the Olympic Mountains in this general altitudinal belt. He describes a western hemlock understory in successional Douglas fir after 300 to 400 yr. The hemlocks measure 3 to 4 ft in diameter with ages of 200 to 250 yr. About this time amabilis fir becomes established. Later, when Douglas fir is 500 to 600 yr of age, the old trees are scattered and few in number. Western hemlock at this stage also begins to decline, since it is relatively short lived. Finally, amabilis fir reaches supremacy as an uneven-aged climax stand.

Stages of succession preceding Hanzlik's (1932) 300- to 400-yr-old Douglas fir forest may be represented on the moraines and outwash of Blue and Hoh Glaciers occupying the slopes of the Mt. Olympus massif. These deposits between ca 2700 and 3000 ft in altitude were laid down progressively after recession of the glaciers started about the beginning of the 1800's (Heusser 1957a). Initial vascular invaders observed are *Epilobium latifolium*, *E. luteum*, *Mimulus guttatus*, *M. lewisii*, and *Anaphalis margaritacea*. Alaska alder and willow subsequently develop into thickets. Conifers invade early but are not readily apparent until they begin to overtop the thickets. On the terminal moraine of Blue Glacier, the forest is ca 125 yr old, made up of western white pine, Douglas fir, amabilis fir, western and mountain hemlocks, and a few black cottonwoods that are fast becoming senile. Amabilis fir was the only coniferous reproduction observed. The remaining ground cover of seed plants was sparse and consisted of *Pyrola bracteata* Hook. and *Vaccinium membranaceum* Dougl. Bryophytes are conspicuous on the boulders, however, and from specimens kindly identified by Dr. Elva Lawton of Hunter College, New York, include *Rhytidiopis robusta* (Hook.) Broth., *Rhytidiadelphus loreus* (Hedw.) Warnst., *Rhacomitrium brevipes* Kindb., *Mnium glabrescens* Kindb., and *Ptilidium californicum* (Aust.) Underw. & Cook.

The Pacific Subalpine Forest is manifest between ca 3500- and 5000-ft elevation (Jones 1936). The climax constituents are mountain hemlock, Alaska yellow cedar, alpine fir, and amabilis fir. Bordering Blue Glacier at 4500-ft elevation, I measured the largest, and apparently the oldest trees, to be mountain hemlocks at 2-ft diameter and at least 700 yr old. At 5000 ft, a grove of *krummholz* trees at timber line was observed on an old pre-1250 A. D. lateral moraine of Blue Glacier. The trees, which have as much as a 10-in diameter near the ground and are 8 ft tall, are alpine fir, mountain hemlock, and Alaska yellow cedar. The finest trees are firs 450 yr old. They are bearing cones, although no reproduction was noted beneath them; indeed, ground cover is sparse. Bordering the edge of the grove, heaths are predominant: *Cassiope mertensiana*, *Phyllodoce empetriformis*, *Vaccinium deliciosum* Piper, and *Empetrum nigrum*. In addition, *Rubus pedatus* and *Lycopodium sabinaefolium* var. *sitchense* are associated, and nearby the following were observed: *Polystichum lonchitis*, *Juniperus communis* var. *montana*, *Sedum divergens* Wats., *Sorbus occidentalis* (Wats.) Greene, and *Douglasia laevigata* Gray.

Succession on the moraines in the subalpine-alpine ecotone takes place initially in protected locations. Plants participating are *Trisetum spicatum*, *Carex phaeocephala*, *C. pyrenaica*, *C. spectabilis*, *Juncus drummondii*, *Luzula piperi* (Coville) Jones, *Saxifraga tolmiei*, *Spiraea hendersoni*, *Luetkea pectinata*, *Phyllodoce glanduliflora*, *Phacelia sericea* (Graham) Gray, *Penstemon menziesii* Hook., *Haplopappus lyallii* Gray, *Senecio fremonti* T. & G., and *Antennaria media* Greene. It was of interest to note low, wind-sheared, and snow-blasted conifers, one each of western white pine and Sitka spruce, established at 5000-ft elevation beyond the aforementioned grove of *krummholz* trees. On moraines in the subalpine zone, willow and Alaska alder may be the early woody pioneers. Observations indicate that mountain hemlock, alpine fir, and Alaska yellow cedar, as well, will invade almost directly following glacier recession. After ca 40 years, in protected places, alpine fir may be 23 yr of age and have a 14-in height while mountain hemlock may be 36 yr old at this size.

A considerable part of the subalpine zone is occupied by lush meadows, where the slopes are gradually inclined and the ground is moist throughout the growing season. Among other plants, *Deschampsia atropurpurea* (Wahlenb.) Scheele, *Carex nigricans*, *Erythronium montanum* Wats., *Veratrum eschscholtzii*, *Leptarrhena pyrolifolia*, *Dodecatheon jeffreyi* Van Houtte, and *Valeriana sitchensis* are found.

Eastward in the northern Cascades, the Pacific Subalpine Forest lies above ca 1500-ft elevation and extends to ca 7000 (Hansen 1947a). Its lower altitudinal border is weakly defined and is transitional with the Pacific Coastal Forest, which in the Puget Lowland is represented by the Douglas fir subclimax. The forest at low elevations is rather distinct from that in the vicinity of the upper altitudinal limit. Moreover, at ca 5000 ft the trees of the upper and lower elevations become more or less freely intermixed in a transitional zone. Probably the least-disturbed area exemplifying the subalpine forest is found in Mt. Rainier National Park. Taylor (1922) summarizes its general character on this volcanic peak, and Piper (1906) briefly describes the forest in the Cascades.

The characteristic trees at low and middle elevations are almost the same as those that occur in the Olympic Mountains. The major exception is noble fir (*Abies procera* Rehd.), which is found in the Cascades but is absent from the Olympics. Sudworth (1908) reports it from the Olympics, but Jones (1936) states that its presence has never been confirmed. Western red cedar is comparatively rare in the low altitudes, as are Engelmann spruce (*Picea engelmanni* [Parry] Engelm.) and western larch (*Larix occidentalis* Nutt.), which grow mainly confined to the eastern slopes. Neither Engelmann spruce nor larch grows in the Olympics. In the Cascades, dense, nearly pure stands of lodgepole pine often stretch out over large areas. On the Olympic Peninsula, lodgepole is relegated, almost without exception, to the low, swampy ground near the ocean.

At the high elevations and at timber line, whitebark pine is the only addition to the upper-altitudinal conifers in the Olympics. Like noble fir and Engelmann spruce, whitebark pine has also been reported from the Olympics, but specimens have never substantiated the reports. According to Piper (1906) this species reaches higher elevations than any other tree in Washington. It has been found as high as 7600 ft, although its occurrence at this altitude is quite rare. Piper places the limit of the subalpine forest at 7500 ft.

Elements of the Pacific Coastal Forest, for example, western hemlock and western red cedar, grow along the western slope of the Cascades to southern Oregon. Those of the Pacific Subalpine Forest also range as far, and notably three, mountain hemlock, western white pine, and whitebark pine, occur in the Sierra Nevada in California. Elements of the Northwest-American Province also are present along a defile that extends eastward from the vicinity of the lower Fraser River valley to the main part of the Rocky Mountains. Daubenmire (1943) terms this a "climatic peninsula" and explains that the well-developed northerly storm track, coinciding with the "peninsula," produces a climate almost identical to that on the west slope of the northern Cascade Mountains. Daubenmire (1943) refers to the work of Butters (1914) in stating that one-eighth of the Selkirk Mountains flora is derived from the Pacific distribution locus. Western red cedar, western hemlock, lowland white fir, western yew, western white pine, and western dogwood (*Cornus nuttallii* Aud.) are the more noteworthy Pacific Coastal Forest species that range into the Rocky Mountains (Figs. 6–8). Those in the Subalpine Forest include mountain hemlock, alpine fir, whitebark pine, and to some extent, Alaska yellow cedar (Figs. 8, 9).

OREGON

The region encompassed by western drainage in the Coast Range and by the Pacific slopes of the Klamath Mountains is pertinent in Oregon (Fig.5). Fire and logging have ravaged the greater part, although forest of exceptional beauty, but of limited extent, remains. One particular area, that of the Tillamook Burn in the northern Coast Range, has been decimated by fire repeatedly (Neiland 1958). In 1933, a tremendous fire destroyed 244,706 acres of forest, and in 1939 and 1945 most of the area was burned again. Because of these holocausts, the climax communities are greatly reduced in size, largely occurring either as small enclaves in the burned or logged timber or in tracts purposely set aside and protected as preserves.

Douglas fir is probably both the most abundant and the most widespread tree in the Coast Range. It owes its presence to a considerable degree to fire, but as Munger (1940) points out, over a large part of the Coast Range where low summer humidity and high summer temperature prevail, western hemlock, western red cedar, and the true firs cannot thrive. In the absence of competition from these trees, Douglas fir achieves climax status. Where Douglas fir grows with the above competitors, it does so because of fire and cannot proceed beyond the subclimax stage. Munger states that western hemlock and Sitka spruce are predominant in youthful as well as aged forest along a northerly strip that tapers off and ends about halfway down the coast. Douglas fir plays little or no part in succession here. In the drier parts of west-central and southwestern Oregon, Douglas fir is unlikely to be replaced by western hemlock. Under these conditions, the intolerant Douglas fir perpetuates itself through the establishment of young trees in the spaces opened as the old fir dies. Munger goes on to state that Douglas fir might predominate in a climax of uneven-aged trees or might even occur mixed with both tolerant and intolerant conifers. The recent studies of Neiland (1958) and Merkle (1951) bear out the conclusions reached by Munger regarding the successional status of Douglas fir.

Working in the Tillamook Burn, which receives more precipitation, both annually and during the April–September period, than any other part of Oregon (Wells 1941), Neiland (1958) finds that the unburned forest between 2500- and 3000-ft elevation represents a successional stage to western hemlock climax. Noble fir is rare below 2900 ft in altitude, but its importance increases up to 3400, where it becomes predominant. She observed western red cedar only rarely and concludes from this and other observations that it "seems uncommon in most parts of the northern Oregon

Coast Range forests." Western yew is the only understory tree and increases in proportions below 2500-ft elevation. Shrubs in the upland are chiefly vine maple and the heaths *Vaccinium membranaceum* and *V. parvifolium*.

Merkle's (1951) study area was Mary's Peak, ca 70 mi southward from the Tillamook Burn. Precipitation probably varies between 40 and 70 in annually compared with 100 to over 120 at the Burn (Wells 1941). On the relatively cool and moist north slope, Merkle finds western hemlock predominant from 2500- to 3400-ft elevation. Specimens grade from seedlings and small trees to large trees 2 ft in diameter breast high and 80 or more tall. Above 3400-ft elevation, noble fir dominates, falling into age classes from seedlings to trees 4 ft in diameter breast high and 150 or greater in height. Noble fir is almost pure between 3600- and 3800-ft altitude just below the summit. Below 2500 ft, this species is very sparse. Western red cedar is represented only by small trees and is infrequent. Douglas fir is mostly in the large-tree class, with specimens up to 5-ft diameter breast high and over 150 tall. Reproduction below 3600-ft elevation is almost entirely western hemlock. Merkle concludes from these data that the cycle from Douglas fir subclimax to western hemlock climax does take place on the north slope of Mary's Peak.

On the warmer and drier south and southeast slopes, by contrast, Douglas fir is apparently climax below 3400-ft elevation, except in the ravines and valleys. Dense stands, with individuals 2 to 3 ft in diameter breast high and 125 and over in height, are fairly even aged, and Douglas fir reproduction occurs where there are openings. Noble fir becomes associated mostly higher up on the east slope. A thick ground cover up to near 3200-ft elevation consists of salal and Oregon grape (*Berberis nervosa* Pursh). On the north slope ground cover is sparse. It is principally wood sorrel (*Oxalis oregana* Nutt.); salal and Oregon grape are nearly absent.

A general description of the region is presented by Peck (1925, 1941) and Bailey (1936) and in a number of papers by Hansen (1941a, 1943a, 1944, 1947a). Using a phytogeographic provincial base, Peck subdivides the region north of the Coquille River into the Coast Mountain Area and Northern Coast Area; south of this river, he distinguishes the Southern Coast Area and the Southern Coast Mountain and Siskiyou Area.

North of the Coquille River, the descriptive remarks and studies of the dynamic relationships of the vegetation components presented by Neiland (1958) and Merkle (1951) generally suffice for the Coast Range. In short, the coniferous forest is composed of Douglas fir, western hemlock, western red cedar, Sitka spruce, western yew, lowland white fir, noble fir (at high elevations), and amabilis fir and western white pine (both northern Coast Range). Red alder and big-leaf maple are the most abundant deciduous types. Ferns (*Pteridium aquilinum* subsp. *lanuginosum*, *Blechnum spicant*, and *Polystichum munitum*) and various mosses often form the conspicuous herbaceous ground cover. Additional common species are: *Selaginella oregana* D. C. Eaton, *Erythronium revolutum* Smith, *Montia flagellaris* (Bong.) Robins., *Tiarella trifoliata*, *T. unifoliata*, *Holodiscus discolor* (Pursh) Maxim., *Rubus spectabilis*, *Oxalis oregana* Nutt., *Vaccinium parvifolium*, *Cladothamnus pyroliflorus*, and *Sambucus racemosa* subsp. *pubens*.

The northern coast, usually no more than several miles broad, is a continuation of the Washington coastal strip. It is characterized by sand dunes, beaches, tidal marshes, lakes, swamps, and sphagnum bogs. The forest behind the immediate zone of dunes and beaches is designated Sitka spruce-western hemlock climax (Hansen 1947a). It is a southern segment of the spruce-hemlock climax in Washington (Jones 1936) and contains, in addition to the dominants, some western red cedar and lowland white fir. Douglas fir and lodgepole pine are also profusely scattered in the forest, but both are successional predecessors of the climax. At some places along the coast, for example, between the mouth of the Siletz River and Boiler Bay, lodgepole grows with good form in practically pure stands. Dense shrub thickets in the understory are formed principally by *Myrica californica* Cham., *Rubus spectabilis*, *Vaccinium ovatum* Pursh, *Gaultheria shallon*, and *Rhododendron californicum* Hook. Toward the ocean side, where blowing sand is a powerful abrasive, lodgepole and Sitka spruce become increasingly sheared until they form thickets only several feet in height. Between the thickets, *Gaultheria shallon* and *Vaccinium ovatum* Pursh create a dense and often impenetrable evergreen scrub.

The coastal lakes exhibit hydroseres, which conventionally begin with the aquatics *Myriophyllum spicatum*, *Potamogeton natans*, and *Nuphar polysepalum*. At the edge of the water, the semiaquatics *Typha latifolia*, *Scirpus validus*, and *Spiraea douglasii* Hook. appear. Farther back, species from the upland are established, lodgepole pine usually being the pioneer conifer to invade. Where bogs occur the major plant constituents are sphagnum moss, sedge, heath (*Ledum columbianum* Piper, *Vaccinium uliginosum*, *V. ovatum* Pursh, *Gaultheria shallon*, and *Oxycoccus microcarpus*), skunk cabbage, western wax myrtle (*Myrica californica* Cham.), pitcher plant (*Chrysamphora californica* [Torr.] Greene), *Spiraea douglasii* Hook., and *Drosera rotundifolia*. In later stages, lodgepole pine, western red cedar, western hemlock, and Sitka spruce invade and grow into small stands, of which the first two named are often the most abundant members.

Between the edge of the forest and the strand line, plants possessing a high salt tolerance thrive on the dunes and beaches and in the tidal marshes. Grasses (*Calamagrostis nutkaensis*, *Elymus arenarius* subsp. *mollis*, *Ammophila arenaria* [L.] Link, and *Poa macrantha* Vas.), sedges (*Carex macrocephala* subsp. *anthericoides*), and rushes (*Juncus lescurii* Boland and *J. falcatus* E. Mey.) are typical inhabitants along with the following nongrass or nongrasslike representatives: *Polygonum paronychia* C. & S., *Atriplex gmelini*, *Abronia latifolia* Esch., *Honckenya peploides*, *Potentilla anserina*, *Lupinus littoralis* Dougl., *Lathyrus littoralis* (Nutt.) Endl., *L. maritimus*, *Conioselinum benthami*, *Glehnia littoralis* subsp. *leiocarpa*, *Convolvulus soldanella* L., *Plantago maritima* subsp. *juncoides*, *Franseria chamissonis* var. *bipinnatisecta* Less., *Tanacetum camphoratum* DC., and *Cotula coronopifolia*. In the tidal marshes located about the river mouths are the characteristic *Triglochin maritimum*, *Distichlis spicata* (L.) Greene, *Puccinellia pumila*, *Scirpus americanus*, *Salicornia pacifica* Standl., *Glaux maritima*, and *Grindelia stricta* DC., among others.

The vicinity of the strand is seldom static. Storms moving northward along the coast or inland are almost constantly reworking the beach and dune sand. Where deflation basins or "blow-outs" are created, the plant communities are destroyed, or where moving dunes encroach on stabilized areas, the plant cover becomes interred by the shifting sand (Plate XXV). High winds carry appreciable quantities of salt spray, which can prove detrimental to species not adapted to high levels of salinity in the environment. High winds create high tides, which have the same detrimental effect on salt-intolerant freshwater communities. Because of the variable occurrence and severity of coastal storms, various stages of succession are apparent in the vegetation.

The sand-dune succession begins with stabilization of the dune by the more halophytic species mentioned above, followed in turn by the development of thickets made up largely of *Gaultheria shallon* and *Vaccinium ovatum* Pursh. These are invaded by lodgepole pine, which is later supplanted by Sitka spruce. Subsequently, as edaphic conditions are modified by the increase of organic matter, western hemlock becomes part of the community. The succession terminates with the Sitka spruce-western hemlock climax. It is apparent from the remains of former tree cover found buried in the dunes that forests have frequently been overwhelmed by sand in the past. Such evidence is widespread on the Oregon coast (Cooper 1958b) and indicates that dune stabilization is indeed only temporary.

Along the southern coast below the mouth of the Coquille River, lodgepole pine, Sitka spruce, and salal no longer dominate the areas behind the beach. Instead, the vegetation becomes less coniferous, being composed of small trees and tall shrubs represented by *Ceanothus thyrsiflorus* Esch., *Garrya elliptica* Dougl., *Rhododendron occidentale* (T. & G.) Gray, and *Ribes menziesii* Pursh. Above the beach on the slopes facing the ocean, the assemblage changes in the absence of tree cover, and *Zygadenus fremonti* Torr., *Eriogonum latifolium* Smith, *Mesembryanthemum chilense* Molina, *Sidalcea malvaeflora* var. *californica* (Gray) Jeps., *Plantago subnuda* Pilgr., *Agoseris hirsuta* Greene, and *Helenium bolanderi* Gray occur here. Of probable phytogeographical significance are the disjunctive colonies of *Empetrum nigrum*. They were observed growing in sandy soil on bluffs north of Cape Blanco, where *Vaccinium uliginosum*, its associate on coastal Alaskan muskeg, and *Ledum columbianum* Piper were established nearby. On the beach, the principal plants include *Triglochin striata* Ruiz & Pav., *Ammophila arenaria* (L.) Link, *Oenothera cheiranthifolia* Hornem., *Phacelia argentea* Nels. & Macbr., *Cryptantha leiocarpa* (F. & M.) Greene, and *Corethrogyne californica* DC.

The forest of the southern Coast Range and Klamath Mountains on the Pacific slope contains two trees endemic to southwestern Oregon and northwestern California: Port Orford cedar (*Chamaecyparis lawsoniana* Parl.) and weeping spruce (*Picea breweriana* Wats.). Port Orford cedar ranges in scattered stands from the coastal dunes and seaward slopes to elevations near 3000 ft (Sudworth 1908, Baker 1945) (Fig. 8). It grows principally with Douglas fir as a successional community, and were it protected from fire, Port Orford cedar would predominate in climax stands. Other associates are lowland white fir, Sitka spruce, western hemlock, western red cedar, western white pine, and tan oak (*Lithocarpus densiflora* [H. & A.] Rehd.). The cedar grows to considerable size, and a specimen of 8.7-ft diameter breast high and 200-ft height is reported (American Forestry Association 1955). Weeping spruce thrives on the high slopes of the Siskiyou Mountains between elevations of 4000 and 5000 ft or more (Sudworth 1908). Little is known about the tree and its occurrence. Associates include mountain hemlock, western white pine, and, to some extent, Douglas fir.

A large proportion of the slopes from sea level to middle elevation is covered with broadleaf, evergreen trees and shrubs. Oak (*Quercus chrysolepis* Liebm. and *Q. vaccinifolia* Kell.), other fagaceous species (*Lithocarpus densiflora* [H. & A.] Rehd., var. *echinoides* [R. Br.] Jeps., *Castanopsis chrysophylla* [Dougl.] DC., and var. *minor* Jeps.), California laurel (*Umbellularia californica* Nutt.), dwarf ceanothus (*Ceanothus pumilus* Greene), box-leaved garrya (*Garrya buxifolia* Gray), and madrono are the chief cover constituents. This vegetation represents an extension of the broad-sclerophyll climax, well developed in California (Cooper 1922).

CALIFORNIA

The characteristic trees of the Pacific Coastal Forest that range northward in British Columbia and Alaska attain their southernmost limits in California (Figs. 5, 6–9). Western hemlock, according to Jepson (1925), extends southward to the Gualala River in Sonoma County; western red cedar grows as far as Humboldt County, and Sudworth (1908) places the end of its range just eastward of Cape Mendocino and south of Ferndale. Sitka spruce reaches Mendocino County, growing along the lower streams no farther down the coast than Caspar; lowland white fir ranges to Sonoma County north of Fort Ross (Sudworth 1908). Lodgepole pine, which is of considerable phytogeographical importance, although not a member of the forest in a climax sense, thrives as far as the neighborhood of Point Arena (McMillan 1956).

These dominants of the climax associations of the Pacific Coastal Forest at high latitudes are generally minor associates of the forest where they occur in California. In fact, they fail to gain recognition in the vegetation classification of Munz and Keck (1949), although they are mentioned in the classification by Clark (1937). In northern California, certain trees of the coastal forest assume some importance. Sitka spruce particularly is often the major or the only tree facing the strand as, for example, along the ocean side of Lake Earl near Crescent City. A good stand of lowland white fir mixed with redwood (*Sequoia sempervirens* [Lamb.] Endl.), Douglas fir, and western hemlock was observed near Mendocino City, and McMillan (1956) frequently notes lowland white fir and western hemlock facing the ocean between Fort Bragg and Albion.

The major climax-forest associations of the California Coast Range are the redwood and the broad-sclerophyll or mixed evergreen. In addition, scattered areas of closed-cone pine forest are to be found at relatively low elevations near the coast, and in the northern Coast Range at high elevations, of much less importance in relation to this study, are the yellow pine and red fir forests. Nonforest climax associations are strictly coastal and consist of strand and salt-marsh communities and a northern coastal scrub (Munz and Keck 1949). The redwood climax may be considered the only association member of the Pacific Coastal Forest complex in California (Cooper 1957).

Redwood is distributed on the ocean side of the Coast Range from the lower Chetco River in southwestern Oregon to the Santa Lucia Mountains as far south as

Punta Gorda, Monterey County (Sudworth 1908) (Fig. 8). Its extent inland generally reaches 2500-ft elevation, but in the Santa Lucia Mountains, it gains an altitude of 3000. The areal limit of redwood within its range is dependent upon frequent coverage by summer fog. Cooper (1917) finds that it does not grow in areas without summer fog, even if the precipitation is as great as, or greater than, in fog-covered areas. For optimum development heavy winter precipitation and abundant summer fog are essential. Moreover, Byers (1953) shows that summer fog may blanket the redwood area but only rarely infiltrates the groves, which are altitudinally lower than the fog layer. Consequently, "fog drip" is not an effective factor, although for Douglas fir and other trees on the slopes at high elevations up to ca 3000 ft, it is apparently important. Byers points out that the occurrence of redwood, which requires a high ratio of water supply to water loss (Cooper 1917), is dependent upon summer fog because the amount of evapotranspiration is reduced by the decrease in sunshine and the reduction of daytime temperatures.

The main redwood tracts are situated north of the Navarro River in Humboldt County (Baker 1945). They occupy the ridges and slopes, largely in association with Douglas fir, which may comprise more than half of the forest. On the river flats, however, redwood develops into practically pure stands, and the finest specimens grow in such places. South of the Navarro River, it occurs to a greater extent locally where favorable sites prevail. In the Santa Cruz Mountains, between San Francisco and Monterey Bays, redwood forest becomes temporarily more extensive whereas southward in the canyons of the Santa Lucia Mountains, only outliers are found. Here the ranges of both redwood and Douglas fir terminate.

The principal associate of redwood is Douglas fir while others less important include tan oak, lowland white fir, western hemlock, western red cedar, and madrono (Sudworth 1908). Douglas fir and tan oak commingle on upper slopes whereas at low elevations in the valleys, western hemlock, and to a small degree western red cedar, make up much of the remainder where ranges overlap. In northern California Sitka spruce, Port Orford cedar, western hemlock, and lowland white fir are distributed with redwood on the river flats. Western yew, California nutmeg (*Torreya californica* Torr.), California laurel, western wax myrtle, cascara, red alder, and California rhododendron (*Rhododendron californicum* Hook.) occur more generally over the range of redwood. The forest is more or less open with a shrub layer consisting of huckleberry (*Vaccinium ovatum* Pursh), salal, thimbleberry, and Oregon grape, among other shrubs that grow in transitional stands. Typical plants near the ground, mainly according to Jepson (1925), include *Polystichum munitum*, *Hierochloe occidentalis* Buckl., *Scoliopus bigelovii* Torr., *Clintonia andrewsiana* Torr., *Maianthemum dilatatum*, *Trillium ovatum* Pursh, *Asarum caudatum* Lindl., *Vancouveria parviflora* Greene, *Achlys triphylla* (Sm.) DC., *Saxifraga mertensiana* Bong., *Whipplea modesta* Torr., *Oxalis oregana* Nutt., *Viola sempervirens* Greene, and *Mimulus dentatus* Nutt.

Redwood is the tallest known living tree. On the North Dyerville Flats, east of Cape Mendocino, accurate measurements indicate a maximum height of 364 ft. The greatest diameter measured is 21 ft at 6 high for a tree 300 tall (American Forestry Association 1956). Sudworth (1908) writes concerning the autecological character of redwood that older specimens are fairly tolerant of shade, but for seedlings considerable light is required for survival. Sprouts, which commonly form clones about the parent tree, are, on the other hand, highly tolerant. Redwood produces seed in moderate amounts, but only a small proportion is viable, and the amount of reproduction by this means is comparatively minor. Reproduction is most frequently by means of stump sprouts from both old and young trees. Following cutting, the stand reverts to a broad-sclerophyll subclimax, consisting typically of tan oak, coast live oak (*Quercus agrifolia* Nee), and madrono, with sprout clones distributed in the subsere. During fire, the older trees that have quite thick bark can survive, but young trees and seedlings rarely remain alive following even a light ground burn (Fritz 1931).

Along the inner margin of the redwood forest at high elevations and on the upper slopes of the hills within the forest, mixed-evergreen or broad-sclerophyll forest extends up to 2500-ft altitude (Munz and Keck 1949). Dense stands of trees 100 ft or more in height are characteristic, and tan oak and Douglas fir are the important members (Clark 1937). This forest is prevalent east of the redwood in Mendocino and Sonoma Counties whereas in Humboldt and Del Norte Counties to the north, redwood gains importance and tends to displace the mixed-evergreen trees. The remaining more prominent members are madrono, California laurel, big-leaf maple, chinquapin (*Castanopsis chrysophylla* [Dougl.] DC.), canyon oak (*Quercus chrysolepis* Liebm.), California black oak (*Q. kelloggii* Newb.), coast live oak, Oregon oak, valley oak (*Q. lobata* Nee), buckeye (*Aesculus californica* [Spach] Nutt.), and red alder. Shrubs include salmonberry, ceanothus (*Ceanothus thyrsiflorus* Esch.), and western azalea (*Rhododendron occidentale* Gray). Cooper (1922) differentiates several communities in the broad-sclerophyll forest: tan oak-oak-madrono, coast live oak-madrono, coast live oak, tan oak, coast live oak-valley oak, canyon oak-California black oak, and canyon oak.

Closed-cone pine forest is scattered from near sea level to 1200-ft elevation from Mendocino County south to Santa Barbara County (Munz and Keck 1949). According to McMillan (1956), it is identified to a large extent by the edaphic restriction of its components, which grow on serpentine or highly acid soil. McMillan notes that Bishop pine (*Pinus muricata* Don), Bolander pine (*P. bolanderi* Parl., closely allied to lodgepole), and cypress (*Cupressus pygmaea* Sarg.) are the representatives of the forest in Mendocino County. In the Santa Cruz Mountains, knobcone pine (*P. attenuata* Lemm.) and ponderosa pine (*P. ponderosa* Dougl.) are associated with another cypress (*C. abramsiana* Wolf). Farther south on the Monterey Peninsula, Bishop pine and Monterey pine (*P. radiata* Don) are found along with two additional species of cypress (*C. goveniana* Gord. and *C. macrocarpa* Hartw.). Dwarfing is characteristic of *P. bolanderi* Parl., *P. attenuata* Lemm., *C. pygmaea* Sarg., *C. abramsiana* Wolf, and *C. goveniana* Gord., although on the deeper soil bordering the "pygmy conifer" areas, the trees exhibit better growth. Representative shrubs are manzanita (*Arctostaphylos nummularia* Gray and *A. columbiana* Piper), huckleberry (*Vaccinium ovatum* Pursh), salal, California rhododendron, western wax myrtle, chinquapin (*Castanopsis chrysophylla* var. *minor* [Benth.] DC.), tan oak (*Lithocarpus densiflorus* var. *echinoides* [R. Br.] Abrams), and ceanothus (*Ceanothus gloriosus* var.

exaltatus Howell). Herbaceous species in Mendocino County more commonly include *Xerophyllum tenax* (Pursh) Nutt.; *Gentiana oregana* Engelm. and *Whipplea modesta* Torr. are on drier sites and *Gentiana sceptrum* Griseb. on sites relatively moist; and *Castilleja affinis* H. & A., *Lilium maritimum* Kell., *Habenaria maritima* Greene, and *Spiranthes romanzoffiana* are associated with the shrubby manzanita (*Arctostaphylos nummularia* Gray). Bogs are distributed throughout the forest, and their plant cover is described by Rigg (1933), Dachnowski-Stokes (1936), and McMillan (1956). Sphagnum is usually abundant under a shrub cover of Labrador tea (*Ledum glandulosum* Nutt.), western wax myrtle, and salal and with the herbaceous plants, *Hypericum anagalloides* C. & S., *Drosera rotundifolia*, *Veratrum fimbriatum* Gray, and *Helenium bolanderi* Gray.

A northern coastal scrub, often with extensive grassland, lies between the strand and the redwood (Munz and Keck 1949). It occupies a discontinuous and narrow coastal strip from southern Oregon to Point Sur in Monterey County at elevations generally under 500 ft. The plants of the scrub are seldom more than 6 ft in height and consist of a varied assemblage of *Baccharis pilularis* DC., *Mimulus aurantiacus* Curt., *Castilleja latifolia* H. & A., *Rubus vitifolius* C. & S., *Lupinus variicolor* Steud., *Heracleum lanatum*, *Eriophyllum staechadifolium* Lag., *Gaultheria shallon*, *Anaphalis margaritacea*, *Artemisia vulgaris* var. *litoralis* Suksd., and *Erigeron glaucus* Ker. In the sections of grassland, *Danthonia californica* Boland., *Deschampsia holciformis* Presl, *Calamagrostis nutkaensis*, *Holcus lanatus* L., and other species prevail between the areas of scrub.

In the northern Coast Range at high elevations, yellow pine and red fir forests are of limited extent and deserve no more than brief mention. These attain their maximum development in the southern Cascades and Sierra Nevada. The yellow pine occurs between 3000- and 6000-ft elevation and dominates the stands in association with sugar pine (*Pinus lambertiana* Dougl.), incense cedar (*Libocedrus decurrens* Torr.), white fir (*Abies concolor* Lindl. & Gord.), Douglas fir, and several others. The red fir (*Abies magnifica* Murr.) ranges above 6000 ft, where its principal associates are the interior form of lodgepole pine (*Pinus contorta* var. *murrayana* Eugelm.), western white pine, and Jeffrey pine (*Pinus jeffreyi* Murr.).

Finally, coastal strand and salt-marsh communities are scattered all along the ocean shore (Munz and Keck 1949). Many of the strand and dune plants previously mentioned for southwestern Oregon are also established in California, where they commingle with species that do not grow beyond the northern boundary of the state. These confined plants, including *Eriogonum parvifolium* Sm., *Lupinus chamissonis* Esch., and *Haplopappus ericoides* (Less.) H. & A., are the dominants of the dune-shrub community (Cooper 1936). Other noteworthy dune plants are *Artemisia pycnocephala* DC., *Abronia umbellata* Lamb., *Poa douglasii* Nees, and *Convolvulus soldanella* L. In the salt marshes about the bays and inlets the common *Distichlis spicata* (L.) Greene and *Triglochin maritimum* are associated with *Frankenia grandifolia* C. & S., *Limonium californicum* Hel., and other saline plants. Where freshwater marshes occur behind the coast, bulrush (*Scirpus olneyi* Gray, *S. validus*, *S. acutus* Muhl.), cattail (*Typha latifolia*), and sedge (*Carex obnupta* Bailey) are common.

Chapter V

LATE-PLEISTOCENE PALYNOLOGY

HISTORICAL REVIEW

Palynology embraces all studies dealing with pollen and spores. The term, proposed by Hyde and Williams (1944), is based on the Greek *paluno*, to strew or sprinkle, and is akin to *palē* or fine meal. The intention of Hyde and Williams in suggesting a new word was to avoid the ambiguity and inadequacy of the term pollen analysis. Palynology has met with general acceptance by those concerned with the subject and seems well established in the literature. Nevertheless, because of the broad meaning implied when the word stands alone, and unless such is intended, it is necessary to use a qualifier or to express the term in a specific sense. From the microfossil standpoint, where pollen and spores have stratigraphic and environmental significance as in this study, palynology may be considered a subdivision of micropaleontology. Recent aspects of the field are summarized and discussed by Faegri (1956).

Pollen and spores in Pleistocene deposits were first recognized by Früh in Switzerland and the observations published in 1885 (Erdtman 1943), although pollen in pre-Quaternary deposits had been observed previously by Göppert as early as 1836 (Faegri and Iversen 1950). In 1896 the German Weber, a peat stratigrapher, carried out quantitative as well as qualitative pollen studies. Not until after the turn of the century, however, had the significance of pollen stratigraphy begun to be realized. Lagerheim, a Swedish botanist, recognized the usefulness of pollen in determining the sequence and rate of plant immigration, as well as the relative frequency of the migrant species. Lagerheim, it is generally agreed, was the first person to appreciate potentialities in pollen analysis, but it was his student, von Post, who elaborated the modern aspects of the technique. Von Post was able by means of pollen analysis to interpret not only vegetation changes but also past climates and other environmental factors. His thesis including several pollen diagrams was made public during a lecture at Oslo in 1916 (von Post 1918).

The innovation of pollen analysis immediately attracted the attention of Pleistocene students. Papers began to appear outside of Sweden, largely from Europe at first, but later from widely scattered places. Jessen (1920) in Denmark, Auer (1921) in Finland, and Firbas (1923) in Austria are some of the early contributors. Subsequent widespread application is shown by the work of Erdtman and Hultén (1924) in Kamchatka, Auer (1933a) in Tierra del Fuego, and Cranwell and von Post (1936) in New Zealand. Undoubtedly, the leading contributor to Pleistocene pollen stratigraphy, pollen morphology, and the bibliography of pollen literature is Erdtman. His serial publications, *Literature on Pollen Statistics* begun in 1927, *Grana Palynologica* from 1948, and *Grana Palynologica, Nova Series* from 1954, along with his texts (Erdtman 1943, 1952, 1957) have become standard reference works. Other notable sources of information have been published by Godwin (1934), Wodehouse (1935),

Bertsch (1942), Wilson (1944), and Faegri and Iversen (1950). The Muséum National d'Histoire Naturelle in Paris launched the publication of the periodicals *Palynologie* in 1956 and *Pollen et Spores* in 1959.

The introduction of pollen analysis to the study of North American deposits followed less than a decade after the appearance of von Post's publication. In 1927 Auer (1927, 1930, 1933b) presented his findings from southeastern Canada while at the same time Fuller (1927) introduced the technique to American literature. A year later Draper (1928, 1929) published the first United States diagrams. In rapid succession, papers appeared by Lewis and Cocke (1929), Sears (1930a and b), Bowman (1931), Voss (1931), Houdek (1933), and Potzger (1932). During subsequent years, interest in palynology is demonstrated by the studies of Hansen (1937), Wilson (1938), Artist (1939), Deevey (1939, 1951), Cain (1939, 1944a), Benninghoff (1942), Buell (1945), Frey (1951, 1953), S. T. Andersen (1954), Leopold (1956), Davis (1958), and Ogden (1959).

The papers cited deal almost entirely with the East and Middle West. Pioneer work in the Far West was begun in the Puget Sound area of Washington by Hansen (1938), who since has published numerous papers dealing with the Pacific Northwest and western Canada (Hansen 1947a and b, 1948, 1949a and b, 1950b, 1952, 1955, *et al.*). Other papers on western Canada, but outside the region of this study, are by Erdtman (1931), Iversen (Porsild 1938), and Heusser (1956). Eastern Canadian diagrams, subsequent to those by Auer and Bowman, are represented principally in the publications of Wenner (1947), Johnson (1949), Potzger (1953), Potzger and Courtemanche (1956), Grayson (1956), and Livingstone and Livingstone (1958). Noteworthy pollen studies of southern North America are those by Deevey (1944) and Clisby and Sears (1955, 1956).

Previous investigations in the Pacific coastal region of this study are chiefly by Hansen. In fact, those in Washington and Oregon are exclusively by him (Hansen 1938, 1941a, b, and c, 1943a and b, 1944, 1947a and b). The only pollen diagrams of California prior to this study, so far as I am aware, are of Searles Lake (Roosma 1958). Those for coastal British Columbia are by Osvald (1936), Hansen (1940, 1950a), and Heusser (1955b).

A review of Alaskan work has been written recently (Heusser 1957b). Bowman (1934) presented the first pollen analyses in his paper on Kodiak Island. Samples were gathered by Griggs (1934) who used Bowman's findings to corroborate his own conclusions concerning the advance of the Sitka spruce forest on Kodiak. In 1946 Knox analyzed pollen in soil collected by Judson (1946) on Adak in the Aleutian Islands. Additional pollen studies in the Aleutians were made by Anderson from samples collected by Bank on Tanaga and Unalaska Islands (Anderson and Bank 1952). Postglacial forests of interior Alaska are reconstructed by Hansen (1953) and by Benninghoff (personal communication) and those of south-central and southeastern Alaska by Heusser (1952, 1953, 1954c, 1955a). The most recent contribution to the literature is by Livingstone (1955a, 1957), who discusses the late-Pleistocene history of northern Alaskan tundra on both sides of the Brooks Range.

PRINCIPLES AND PROCEDURES

Research in late-Pleistocene palynology and related fields has set down certain basic facts while at the same time pertinent procedures have been refined. A *modus operandi* has been derived and this forms a foundation for interpreting past vegetation and accompanying environments.

Most pollen in the air, during and after the flowering period, comes from anemophilous or wind-pollinated species. Pollen from entomophilous or insect-pollinated plants is often found but probably never amounts to more than a few per cent of the total annual production of airborne pollen. Sporulating species, particularly ferns and fern allies, may contribute large quantities of spores. Wind currents scatter pollen and spores, occasionally for vast distances but usually not many miles or tens of miles from their points of origin. Innumerable grains reach the female stigmas, undergo germination, and fertilization ultimately results, but countless more do not reach this end. Those that do not often perish by decomposition, but many become preserved in some receptive medium.

Oceans, lakes, bogs, and muskegs are representative preserving sites. Pollen and spores that fall on their surfaces eventually become a part of the sediments contributed, in addition, by windborne and waterborne, microscopic and macroscopic animals, plants, and inert detritus. As sediments accrue or progressively displace the water body, pollen and spores will, barring catastrophic disturbance of vegetation, continue to become incorporated annually in the accumulating sediments. Most are remarkably decay resistant, even more so in sediments where oxidation is low. Thus, pollen sedimentation may begin with the inception of the site and continue without interruption to the present.

Just as the air at flowering time is dominated by species whose grains are characteristically airborne, sediments from local sites should theoretically contain the same pollen dominants. It has been shown, however, that, owing to peculiar circumstances of pollen sedimentation and preservation, this relationship does not exist. It is necessary to make adjustments in order to assess the proportion of species in the natural vegetation represented by the pollen record. Variations in vegetation composition are usually reflected by the pollen proportions, but before an interpretation is made, certain considerations are necessary. These variations may be manifold and of variable dimension and can be shown to be attributable to alterations of the environment, particularly of climatic factors.

Samples are removed at close intervals between the bottom and most recent sediments, including these levels as well. Sampling is carried out by increments usually of 0.5 m, using a sampler whose chamber can be opened and closed by turning a handle while the instrument is inserted in the deposit. Shafts are coupled to the sampler as deeper parts of the peat section are removed.

Laboratory treatment varies with the nature of the sediments (Faegri and Iversen 1950). Nonsiliceous material can be boiled with stained potassium hydroxide (KOH) solution, strained, centrifuged, and mounted. If pollen is not plentiful, acetolysis (employing acetic anhydride and sulphuric acid) concentrates the pollen by removing cellulose and hemicellulose but not lignin. Lignin is removed by chlorination using sodium chlorate and hydrochloric and acetic acids. Siliceous sediments are removed by hydrofluoric acid or by the differential-flotation method of Frey (1955). This latter technique utilizes a bromoform-acetone mixture, the specific gravity of which has been adjusted to float off the microfossils. The pollen content of each sample is accordingly separated and examined under the microscope. The fossil grains can be identified to family and genus and sometimes to species so that their proportion is readily calculated from counts. Constancy of morphological characters generally enables identifications to be made with considerable certainty.

After the percentage of different pollen and spores has been determined from all levels in the section, a profile for each entity is constructed that depicts its stratigraphic characteristics. Percentages may be based only on counts of total tree pollen where forest history is the main objective. Studies that wish to show the past relationship between forest and treeless vegetation, such as forest-tundra or forest-prairie, will let the total pollen form the basis for calculating percentage. Other methods endeavor to represent site and nonsite pollen separately. This separation is not always feasible because some plants grow at and beyond the site and contribute to the record. Strictly aquatic pollen can be calculated as an individual group, although this is often unnecessary since this type is usually not numerous.

Interpretation of the profiles is made after the successional and environmental relationships of the plants composing the vegetation are understood. Since in late-Pleistocene studies many sections are from sites that rest on glaciated terrain or on related proglacial deposits, all have a common origin but are not necessarily of the same age. Those from sites near the margin of the ice sheet or glacier will be older than those progressively nearer the source of glaciation. Radiocarbon dating has fixed the ages of many sections, and for some, complete chronologies have been made that date the major environmental changes.

SOURCES OF ERROR

Pollen profiles derived from a peat section are the basis for the reconstruction of the environments prevailing during the length of time the sediments were deposited. In order to correctly interpret the profiles, in terms primarily of the vegetation and secondarily the environments, certain inherent errors and inconsistencies must be recognized and taken into account. Many of them are minor and of little consequence, others can be guarded against, while still others are major, cannot easily be overcome, but may be dealt with through reasoning and botanical experience. Sources of error fall into four categories: methods, vegetation representation, sedimentation, and interpretation.

Methods

The errors associated with field work and laboratory treatment are obviously those made by the investigator. With care and deft handling of the techniques involved, however, errors can practically be eliminated. Preparation and forethought, as with any research requiring field work, are important prerequisites.

Sampling must be done with patience and skill, both of which are often difficult to maintain under adverse circumstances. Careful records must be kept while sampling in order to make certain that no increments are repeated or omitted. The sampler must be as clean as field conditions permit, and one must guard against the mixing of upper sediments with those underlying. The choice of sampler is important in this regard and the models designed, for example, by Hiller (Erdtman 1943), Livingstone (1955b), Vallentyne (1955), Potzger (1955), Brown (1956), and Rowley and Dahl (1956) have distinct advantages. Sampling during the height of flowering should be avoided since pollen may be introduced into sections otherwise lacking the type pollen. If this is not possible, it is done preferably during rainy or highly humid periods, when the air is relatively pollen free.

Every effort should be made to obtain the deepest possible section at each site, since truncated sections can only provide incomplete profiles (Potzger 1956). Sounding each site at several places preliminary to sampling is practiced for best results. Sampling intervals closely spaced 1 dm or less apart are bound to include most, if not all, of the vegetation succession. Intervals of 1 ft or 0.5 m are not adequate. Rate of sedimentation should be considered—this is usually indicated by the type and depth of peat. Where it has been slow it may be necessary to sample at less than 1-dm intervals. It is generally not possible, however, to determine where close sampling is desirable unless microscopic inspection of the peat is done in the field or complete cores are taken. Under most field circumstances it is inconvenient to use a microscope. The investigator, therefore, should make it a practice to consistently sample at 1-dm or even 5-cm intervals, or even, preferably, obtain a continuous section by using individual liners inside the chamber of the instrument while collecting each increment.

A thoughtful discussion and résumé of the statistically important errors relating to the employment of certain laboratory methods are given by Deevey and Potzger (1951). As these authors point out, "The usual practice of counting about 150 pollen grains at each level is defensible so long as it is realized that small differences between frequencies at adjacent levels have no statistical significance. When major shifts of vegetation are recorded by successive pollen spectra, as when a pine zone overlies a spruce-fir zone, the pollen worker does not need to be a statistician to observe and interpret the difference: when such shifts are repeatedly found in pollen profiles obtained from widely separated localities, there can be no question as to their validity. Small differences within fairly homogeneous pollen zones, however, cannot be considered to be real without statistical proof. . . . Where the differences in pollen percentages are small, we doubt that reliable results can be obtained unless at least 500 grains are counted at each level."

In the laboratory careful technique is mandatory. Perhaps the best way to avoid errors is to follow a consistent treatment for all samples, if possible. Some samples, because of their nature, will require special handling. But since some treatments differentially destroy certain pollen, a single procedure that affects adversely only few if any of the pollen is most desirable for uniform and comparable results. Where special chemical or physical treatment of the sediments is necessary, any changes in the pollen profiles where samples have been so treated must be judiciously interpreted.

Cleanliness will reduce the possibility of contamination. Even so, laboratory work should not be carried out during flowering of local vegetation. Where distilled water is unavailable, tap water is used but is a possible source of contaminants. Accordingly, tap water should be inspected from time to time. Contamination usually can be detected under the microscope since fresh pollen often retains its protoplasmic content after KOH treatment and stains poorly.

Several other errors may be introduced during laboratory preparation and counting. It has been demonstrated that pressure on the cover glass when the material to be examined is being mounted will cause sorting of the grains. Also, insufficient mounting medium can cause the pollen to be obscured by associated nonpolliniferous material. Both inconsistencies can be overcome, however, if the investigator consciously makes an effort toward uniformity of all mounts.

The remaining sources of error to be mentioned in this section arise during identification. Broken grains commonly result from the chemical and mechanical treatment. The number of fragmentary grains is usually a function of type and duration of treatment and kind of pollen. Usually conifer pollen, possessing bladders and consisting of relatively large grains, tends to fragment. Often the investigator can mentally piece these together during the course of counting if the fragments can be identified. For example, if one species each of pine, spruce, and mountain hemlock is the only coniferous representation in the sample, it is usually possible to identify pieces of bladders and cells by the coarseness of reticulations, size, and intensity of staining. On the other hand, where several species of pine or spruce are present, the identification of their broken grains is generally impossible. Intact pollen grains and spores as well are often impossible to identify below the family or genus level even with the use of the size-frequency method. Since the ecological character of the species representing these microfossils can cover a wide range of conditions, the significance of the pollen and spores may be difficult to assess. For accurate results care should be taken with all identifications. Only after the investigator has made his determination with confidence should it be recorded.

Vegetation Representation

The composition and changes of the dominant anemophilous vegetation of an area are depicted by the fluctuations of local pollen profiles. Entomophilous plants, however, are often underrepresented or even unrepresented in the profiles. This discrepancy between vegetation and the pollen record is one of several serious shortcomings recognized in the method. Considerable attention has been given to underrepresentation and overrepresentation, and the important factors bearing on the matter must be evaluated so that compensation can be made.

Underrepresented, in general, are those plants characterized by entomophily, although anemophilous species with a comparatively low pollen production may also fall in the category. This generality may not apply to some entomophiles growing at the sampling site. Examples are members of the Araceae and Ericaceae, whose pollen can occur in excessive amounts in the peat. Overrepresented are certain anemophiles. Notorious in this group are some species belonging to the Pinaceae and Betulaceae. Lodgepole pine in western North America is strongly overrepresented by its pollen in sediments.

The disparity between the pollen record of a species and its actual representation in the vegetation stems mostly from the mode of pollination, the productivity, how well the grain is adapted for dispersal, and the atmospheric conditions during anthesis. Plants that produce large amounts of pollen not equipped for dispersal may suffer poor representation. Conversely, those that are poor producers but whose pollen is easily airborne may be misrepresented as well. Production will also vary within the species population. Open-grown trees, for example, exhibit greater pollen productivity than those in dense stands. Moreover, trees aggressively extending their ranges appear to yield comparatively more pollen. This is illustrated by the individuals or small enclaves of Sitka spruce established in the forest-tundra ecotone of Kodiak Island.

Wind and water transport play noteworthy roles in bringing about misrepresentation. Vegetation upwind from the sampling site can often be overemphasized in the pollen record, and the magnitude of any disturbances altering the composition of the vegetation can easily be misinterpreted. In similar fashion peat sections gathered in proximity to the ocean will contain a greater proportion of pollen from vegetation growing oceanward on account of the wind blowing inland off the water. Site location is often apparent in the pollen profiles, particularly when sites are from different elevations. In a pollen-content study of moss polsters on the mat of a Quebec bog, made in connection with a vegetation survey, Potzger and his associates (1956) find that the forest of the first 30 m encircling the bog was not reflected.

Type of site also must be recognized when profiles are being compared and studied. Lakes fed by streams that travel considerable distances are liable to contamination via water transport of pollen from plants growing many miles away. Allochtonous pollen of this sort is less problematic when it is derived from areas under the same climatic regime. At low-elevation sites near mountains where several zones of vegetation and climate may occur, the introduction of allochtonous pollen presents much confusion. Obviously such locations should be avoided. In any case, the presence of pollen from plants distantly removed from the vegetation immediately influencing the pollen "rain" at the sampling site is sometimes encountered.

The effect of differential flotation and deposition studied by several European workers is reported by Erdtman (1943) and Faegri and Iversen (1950). American studies have been carried out recently by J. S. Hopkins (1950). It is generally concluded that angiosperm tree pollen falling on water bodies settles out rapidly compared to the winged coniferous kind. The conspicuous *Seeblüten* floating on lakes and ponds in spring has been shown to consist almost entirely of conifer representatives. Wind will carry this pollen to leeward shores where overrepresentation in associated sediments is bound to result.

Other causes of misrepresentation include differential preservation, redeposition, vegetative reproduction, and pseudofluctuation. Often the pollen of some species composing a large proportion of the vegetation is unable to resist even short-term decomposition. Consequently the absence or poor preservation of this pollen in sediments is a serious source of error. North American families typifying this group are the Taxaceae, Taxodiaceae, Cupressaceae, and the genus *Populus* of the Salicaceae. Pollen normally resistant to decay may not withstand prolonged oxidation. It is for this reason that pollen from plants flowering early in high latitudes may not become incorporated in peat because lakes are yet frozen or slowly waning snow covers receptive surfaces.

Redeposition involves the sedimentation of pollen eroded from other contemporary deposits or deposits that are older such as those of the interglacials or even previous intervals. The reworked microfossils, if present, occur predominantly at the bases of sections, although their occurrence throughout is not improbable and depends *inter alia* on whether the site is influenced by feeding streams or dust storms. Lakes in unglaciated mountainous regions where the country rock is igneous should not be subject to redeposition.

Where plants reproduce vegetatively, as in boreal or mountainous regions, their presence is not likely to be deduced from local peat deposits unless the plant is a peat former or a part of the plant is fortuitously transported to the sampling site. Thus, nonrepresentation in the pollen profiles does not rule out the presence of a species.

Pseudofluctuations appear in pollen profiles and are created by a change in a certain species, which in turn causes a false increase or decrease in the number of other species remaining. For example, if a pure stand of a species is destroyed by fire or disease the other species components of the vegetation will appear to increase in the pollen record, although in actuality their numbers may have remained static.

Sedimentation

Errors can arise as a result of natural alterations at the sampling site brought about by climatic or physiographic changes or combinations of these. Local plant successions that result may cause the pollen spectra from the region as a whole to become masked. If these changes are frequent and haphazard they may render a peat section useless. On the other hand, if they are climatically controlled, careful interpretation may place them in harmony with the broader areal climatic history and thereby supply a source of corroborative evidence.

Surface levels of lakes and ponds are subject to fluctuations commonly brought about by the vicissitude of climate. Under cool, humid conditions, they can be relatively high whereas under the influence of a dry climate, lowering can occur. In extreme cases, the water body may even cease to exist. Fluctuations are registered over intervals of varying duration and magnitude depending upon the prevailing precipitation-evaporation relationship. Thus, some may be daily and large (playas), some may be monthly, seasonal, and relatively small (many temperate lakes), while others, measured over hundreds and thousands of years, may be very large (pluvial lakes). The growth of muskeg through peat accumulation is also subject to climatic change. Under cool, moist climate, the growth of important peat formers is optimum and prolonged desiccation can effectively reduce peat production.

Peat types vary with the influence of different climates because of the succession of plants contributing to the sediments. Hydrophytes growing on the bottoms and margins of lakes, for example, may be replaced by mesophytes if the water level lowers for any prolonged period. Muskeg, generally with sedges and mosses as peat formers, may be invaded by heath and even trees of the upland forest if conditions are favorable. These invaders contribute pollen, shed their deciduous parts, finally die, and may be replaced by successive generations of woody plants with the result that the sedge- and moss-type peat becomes overlain by the ligneous type. With a climatic shift favorable to the regrowth of sedges and mosses but unsuitable for woody plants, the ligneous peat will appear as a stratum interbedded in the section. These so-called "recurrence surfaces" have been studied extensively in Europe, particularly by Granlund (1932) but also by Godwin (1954) and others.

Because pollen sedimentation taking place in deep lakes is largely from the dominant regional anemophiles and is less influenced by pollen derived from site-associated plants, which succeed as a result of surface lowering or a hydrosere, pollen stratigraphy from these sediments is less complicated for the study of climatic history. Bog, shallow-lake, and muskeg pollen profiles exhibit greater complexity and are not so easy to interpret because of local influences. They can be studied profitably, however, and can provide much valuable information, particularly in conjunction with the peat stratigraphy.

Physiographic instability can produce discontinuities during sedimentation and can upset the stratigraphy. Discontinuity is serious where erosion of the sediments has occurred and a disconformity or hiatus has been effected. On the other hand, for example, where volcanic ash interrupts organic sedimentation for a time, little error seems likely to be introduced. Faulting, vulcanism, avalanching, marine transgression and regression, and frost action are some of the physiographic phenomena to be considered. These examples of instability are usually apparent in the field or from aerial photographs and geological maps. Unless the investigator is concerned with a special problem, areas involving instability should be avoided. In regions where permafrost prevails and frost action may alter muskeg stratigraphy, lakes should be utilized for studies of climatic history, since no frozen layers appear to prevail in their sediments (Livingstone 1955a).

Interpretation

In order to explain the meaning of the pollen record at a site, the investigator should analyze all the factors and recognizable errors that are involved. When these have been studied carefully, systematically, and logically, an interpretation can be synthesized. Certain errors, as already pointed out, are difficult or impossible to evaluate and can be compounded by unsound interpretation.

Experience and intimate botanical knowledge are, therefore, necessary for any authoritative treatment of data. Besides these, the site type selected and the number of regional sites often can rule out the probability that certain errors are involved in the results. Unless a solitary site is the only one available, sections from several suitable localities should be taken for comparative study. The pollen and peat record from a single site may result in much misinterpretation.

Chapter VI

RESEARCH METHODS

FIELD WORK

The selection of suitable sites is without doubt the most critical aspect of any late-Pleistocene palynology. Any extra time and effort necessary to find a suitable site is well spent, especially when the many hours of laboratory work required to produce the pollen profiles are considered. Although the objective of this study was to collect the oldest sections from a broad distribution of sites, the time and distance factors precluded to some extent the attainment of this goal. Some localities that seemed certain to contain excellent records had to be neglected, since reaching them would have involved excessive time, labor, and cost. On several occasions, however, where it appeared fruitless to search longer, extra effort proved rewarding.

Most sites were located by aerial reconnaissance. Boats were utilized in a few instances but only when a site was known from a map or aerial photograph or from written or oral accounts. Without this information, boats are ineffective because the dense forest along the shores obscures much of the terrain. In locating a site from the air, several precautions had to be taken: (1) a nearby landing area had to be available, from which aircraft on floats could fly out when the tide changed; (2) time required after landing to reach the locality and to sample and return to the aircraft had to be taken into account; (3) low-elevation sites where late-Pleistocene marine transgression would cause sections to be truncated had to be avoided, unless a study of this factor was intended; and (4) areas disturbed by fire, man, or local physiographic instability also had to be avoided, if possible.

The first task at a deposit was to locate its deepest point. One person was responsible for this while the other, if assistance was not required, collected representatives of the plant cover and took notes on the local and surrounding vegetation as well as the nature of the deposit. Sampling was done at depth using a Hiller-type borer with 0.5-m chamber and light-weight alloy shafts and couplings designed by Lichtwardt (1952). Surface and near-surface samples, which usually could not be picked up by the instrument, were collected separately from the walls of pits cut in the peat. During the procedure, one person always handled the borer while the other labeled corks for the vials and saw that the correctly numbered cork went on each vial. All samples were from 0.1-m intervals over the entire length of the section from the surface into the inorganic basement; all were taken with the Hiller except those from Alaganik 1, where road construction had exposed a complete section. The final step was the collection of samples for radiocarbon dating. These were pooled separately from the particular horizon and were placed in polyethylene bags, which were tightly rolled and labeled. The usual precautions against contamination were taken; namely, removing samples only from the undisturbed part of the core in the chamber and cleaning the chamber before taking each increment of the section. Samples for pollen study were treated with alcohol preservative shortly after collection.

LABORATORY TREATMENT

Preparation

Preparation of samples for microscopic study was uniform throughout, and the potassium hydroxide (KOH) method of deflocculation was employed. The concentration of KOH varied somewhat with the degree of humification of the samples. A 5 per cent solution was used for the highly humified peats whereas deflocculation of nonhumified or poorly humified material could be effected with a 3 per cent solution. An effort was made to treat an equal volume of each sample. Sediments of equal volume may differ markedly in weight and may contain different numbers of pollen and spores because of variable moisture content and inorganic fraction, which reflect conditions at the time of deposition. Nevertheless, the treatment of equal volumes tends to maintain a degree of consistency and provides some basis for interpreting changes in microfossil density.

Samples were first examined macroscopically and the characteristics of the sediments recorded, such as plant composition, degree of humification, charred horizons, presence of volcanic ash or other inorganic material, fresh or marine environment, odor, and color. They were next suspended in ca 200 ml of water contained in 400-ml beakers and the necessary amount of KOH added to make whatever per-cent solution was desired. Several drops of aqueous gentian violet dye were added to stain the microfossils. The mixture was boiled for ca 10 minutes with vigorous stirring, and while still hot, was strained through a fine wire mesh and washed. The liquid was then left to stand for several minutes to allow any coarse-grained sediment to settle. Samples that were from the bases of sections and contained mostly inorganic colloidal and larger-size particles were allowed to stand 5 to 10 minutes. Subsequently, centrifuging for ca 5 minutes brought down the fine suspension, which included most of the pollen and spores present in the sample. The sediment in the centrifuge tube was then thoroughly mixed with several milliliters of hot glycerin-gelatin mounting medium and placed in a beaker of hot water for ca 5 minutes. This latter treatment allows the microfossils to absorb the medium. Two drops of the liquid were placed on a clean, labeled microscope slide and mounted under a 7/8-in-square cover glass.

Throughout the preparation, every effort was made to maintain cleanliness and to treat the material consistently. Pollen and spores are numerous in most of the peats of this study, and consequently no special treatment beyond that described was necessary for their concentration. One disadvantage of KOH treatment is that the associated cellulose, hemicellulose, and lignin are not dissolved as in acetolysis chlorination. Mounting in sufficient medium, however, can generally overcome any obscuration caused by undissolved plant remains.

Identification, Counting, and Graphic Presentation

Microfossils were identified and counted using a calibrated Leitz Ortholux binocular microscope equipped with a mechanical stage. A magnification of 135 was ample for routine work whereas difficult microfossils required 560 or oil immersion at 1250. One of the aids used to identify the different pollen and spore types encountered was a set of ca 250 reference slides. These specimens had been prepared by the same method used to treat the peat samples. When unknown grains were observed, known species from the reference collection were compared under a companion calibrated Spencer binocular microscope. Additional aids to identification were the keys and descriptions of Vilson (1934), Wodehouse (1935), Erdtman (1943), Faegri and Iversen (1950), and Hansen (1947a), whose size-frequency curves for west coast species of pine, spruce, and fir were the basis for a number of determinations.

The basic sum of pollen and spores was between 150 and 200 in ca 80 per cent of the slides and included unknowns but excluded *Sphagnum*. That for the remaining slides was mostly 100 but in some cases was less. No basic sum was less than 50. The number of *Sphagnum* grains generally increased the total microfossil count by several hundred. It was because of this overrepresentation that a separate profile for *Sphagnum* was prepared based on its proportion of the total count.

The per-cent representation of non-*Sphagnum* spores and pollen in the basic sum is the foundation for the remaining profiles. Thus, local and regional plants, consisting of trees, shrubs, and herbs of gymnosperms, angiosperms, ferns, and fern allies, are represented. Although this manner of portraying the vegetation may be subject to criticism, it was chosen after much deliberation. Obviously, if the object is to portray regional changes, local plants may distort the broad transformations of vegetation, as in the case of *Sphagnum*. However, many groups (for example, Cyperaceae, Ericaceae, *Myrica*, and *Betula*) are found both locally and regionally, and although in some places local overrepresentation can be recognized and taken into account, it is most often impossible to determine the source of pollen. On the one hand, in a study such as this that covers a wide geographical range, some plant groups are regionally and/or locally important at one place but not at another. On the other hand, local plants (for example, aquatics) may be so few that including them in the basic sum generally causes no serious alterations. Moreover, some (for example, *Lysichitum*) bear considerable stratigraphic significance and should not be excluded. For these reasons and for uniformity as a means for comparison, and because the purely forest aspect of the vegetation had been previously studied over much of the region, it was decided to include all pollen and spores (*sans Sphagnum*) in the basic sum and to interpret both site and nonsite vegetation changes from the standpoint of regional trends.

The pollen profiles depict ca 70 pollen and spores representing orders, families, genera, or species. The sections from southwestern and south-central Alaska show, in addition, arboreal pollen (AP) and nonarboreal pollen (NAP) profiles. Some inaperturate conifer grains (*Taxus*, *Libocedrus*, *Thuja*, *Chamaecyparis*, and *Juniperus*) were ignored and not included in the basic sum. The reason for disregarding these entities is that they appear only in surface peat and not at depth. This condition is considered to be the result of their sporoderm fragility and nonresistance to decay. Their inclusion would only alter the profiles and, accordingly, it was decided they be omitted.

Notes Relevant to the Identification of Certain Spores and Pollen Grains

Descriptive information concerning the identification of many of the spores and pollen grains encountered in the sediments has already been published; it is unnecessary to repeat the data here. However, some have received little or no attention, and the inclusion of pertinent notes regarding these seems warranted.

Below are brief descriptions of noteworthy pollen and spores and of the methods bearing on their identification. All measurements indicated were made on modern material following KOH treatment and mounting in glycerin gelatin.

Polypodiaceae. No spores of the Filicineae were observed other than those of this family. When identification was begun, an attempt was made to separate *Athyrium*, *Cystopteris*, *Dryopteris*, and *Polypodium*, but it soon became apparent that the exosporia, critical for correct identification, were commonly absent. Because of this condition, it was decided to group all polypodiaceous spores, both monolete and trilete, as a single profile in each diagram. Most spores are probably derived from the generally abundant species of *Athyrium* and *Dryopteris*.

Lycopodium. Wilson's (1934) key to the species of *Lycopodium* in the United States and Canada was found to be applicable to North Pacific North America. *Lycopodium selago*, *L. inundatum*, *L. annotinum*, and *L. clavatum* were separated. Of these only *L. clavatum* is subject to possible confusion, particularly with *L. alpinum*. The former spore measures 38.4–40 mu across and the latter 35.2–39.4.

Pinus. Over a large part of the study region, *P. contorta* is the only species of pine to be found. Where *P. monticola* Dougl. overlaps its range, the size-frequency curves of Hansen (1947a) are used to distinguish the two species. In California where *P. contorta*, *P. bolanderi* Parl., and *P. muricata* Don grow in proximity, size-frequency curves were prepared as a possible means of separation (Fig. 10). Whereas *P. muricata* Don is readily identified, the other two species remain inseparable by this method. Since *P. contorta* is generally infrequent and restricted to shore bluffs in this section of its range and *P. bolanderi* Parl. is locally abundant on bog sites, it is likely that most pollen in the size range of these two species is derived from *P. bolanderi* Parl.

Picea. On the Cook Inlet side of the Kenai Peninsula, above Kachemak Bay, *P. sitchensis*, *P. glauca*, and *P. mariana* are found growing together in association with hybrids of the first two. One of these hybrids, *P. lutzii*, has been described by Little (1953). An attempt to separate the species by means of size frequency showed that *P. mariana* was the only one that could be determined (Fig. 11). Regrettably, no pollen of *P. lutzii* was available for comparison. It is probable that its curve is closely related to the curves for *P. sitchensis* and *P. glauca*. Elsewhere along the coast, *P. sitchensis* appears to be the only spruce pollen contained in the peat deposits.

Tsuga. The two species of hemlock, *T. heterophylla* and *T. mertensiana*, observed in the peat are the only representatives of this genus on the northwest coast. Their pollen is easily identified: *T. heterophylla* has a verrucate exine and possesses no bladders; *T. mertensiana*, by contrast, has a granulate exine and finely reticulated bladders. The former ranges in size between 64–80 mu in diameter, and the latter ranges 63–82 mu in over-all length.

Pseudotsuga. Douglas fir, *P. menziesii* (Mirb.) Franco, has a large spheroidal grain,

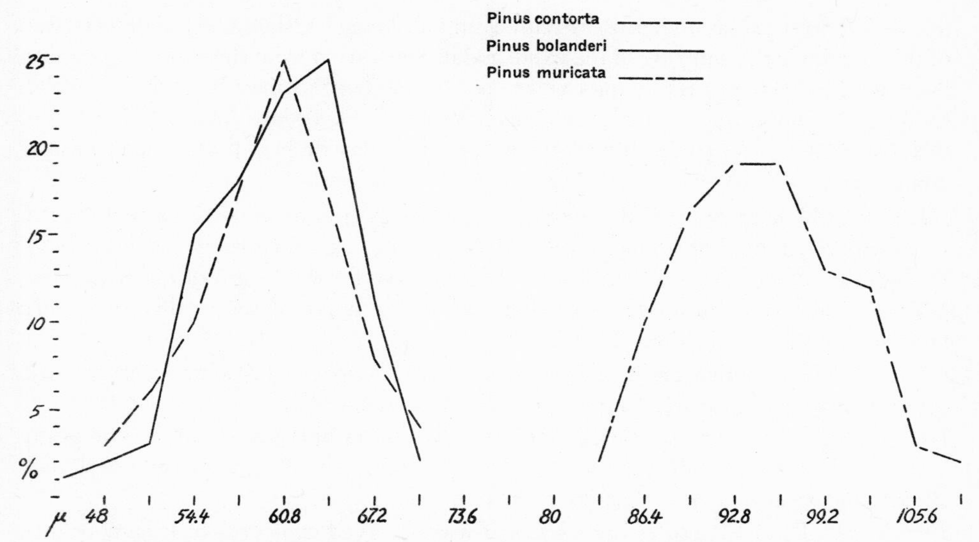

Fig. 10. Size-frequency distribution curves for modern pollen of lodgepole pine (*Pinus contorta*), Bolander pine (*P. bolanderi* Parl.), and Bishop pine (*P. muricata* Don). Curves are based on measurements of the over-all lengths of 100 grains of each of the three species.

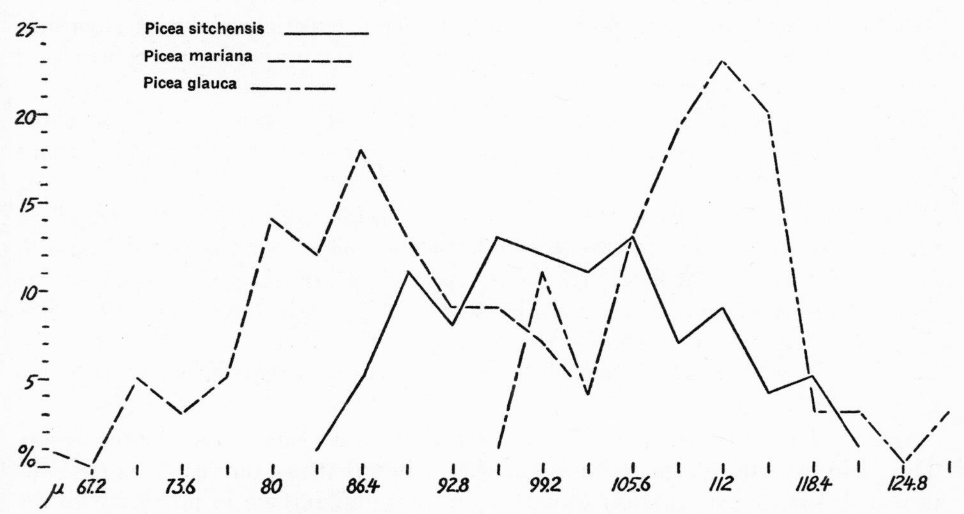

Fig. 11. Size-frequency distribution curves for modern pollen of Sitka spruce (*Picea sitchensis*), black spruce (*P. mariana*), and white spruce (*P. glauca*). Curves are based on measurements of the over-all lengths of 100 grains of each of the three species.

measuring 70–112 mu in diameter, with a smooth exine. A significant characteristic of this species is the splitting of the exine and its separation from the rest of the grain. Since split exines, grains lacking exines, and crushed grains may be included in the total pollen sum, the species may be overrepresented. This source of error is not considered great in this study, however, because Douglas fir was never found in any abundance.

Abies. As Hansen (1947a) demonstrates, species of true fir in northwestern North America are almost impossible to tell apart. One species, *A. lasiocarpa*, is possible to distinguish in most cases, as the size-frequency curve for the length of the cell of the grain is different from curves for other species. In a few cases in this study, *A. lasiocarpa* was determined on this basis.

Cupressus. The pollen grain of *C. pygmaea* Sarg. is spheroidal with an essentially smooth exine and measures 22.4–32.0 mu in diameter.

Lysichitum. A solitary species, *L. americanum*, occurs in the study area. The grain is monocolpate, reticulate with the exception of the general region of the germinal colpus, and measures 19.2–22.4 by 28.8–36.8 mu.

Fritillaria. The pollen of *F. camschatcensis* was observed on occasion. It is monocolpate with coarse reticulations on the proximal surface in the equatorial region and with finer reticulations in the polar areas as well as on the distal surface about the germinal colpus. It measures 28.8–57.6 by 51.2–70.4 mu.

Myrica. Two species, *M. gale* var. *tomentosa* and *M. californica* Cham., occur along this coast. According to Peck (1941), the first grows from northern Lincoln County, Oregon, northward to Alaska and the second from Washington to California. Thus, *Myrica* can probably be referred to species, except where the ranges of the two overlap. Vhere *Myrica* grows in the same general area as *Betula*, and both genera are found in the regional peat deposits, some difficulty is experienced during identification. Wodehouse's (1935) distinguishing character of germ-pore patterns was used to separate the two genera.

Betula. No attempt was made to separate the species of this genus. In Alaska where *B. kenaica*, *B. nana* subsp. *exilis*, and a hybrid of these grow together, separation seems particularly doubtful.

Alnus. In southwestern and south-central Alaska, most of the pollen in the *Alnus* profiles is probably that of *A. crispa* subsp. *sinuata*, which is very common. Some *A. incana* and some intermediate forms of *A. crispa* and subsp. *sinuata* also occur in this region. In southeastern Alaska and southward to California, either *A. crispa* subsp. *sinuata* or *A. oregona*, or both, would seem to comprise most of the alder in the profiles. No separation of the members of this genus present in the study area was accomplished.

Nuphar. The representative species, *N. polysepalum*, is found throughout the region. The grain is monocolpate and covered with spines that measure ca 6.0 mu on the proximal surface but diminish to ca 3.2 on the distal surface in proximity to the colpus. Grains measure 44.8–51.2 by 25.6–35.2 mu.

Sanguisorba. This group in Alaska and British Columbia pollen profiles appears to be represented by *S. menziesii*. The species thrives on muskeg and only occasionally is another species, *S. sitchensis*, present. A third Alaskan representative, *S. officinalis*, grows outside the area of study. In Washington and Oregon, the species in the profiles is probably *S. microcephala* Presl. *S. menziesii* pollen is a stephanocolporate type (Iversen and Troels-Smith 1950) with rather thick exine and six furrows, lacking apparent ornamentation, and measuring 23.7–29.8 by 23.4–25.6 mu.

Geranium. The pollen of this genus, rarely encountered in the profiles, is *G. erianthum*. It is spheroidal, tricolpate with clavate sculpturing and thick exine (ca 6.5 mu), and 76.8–86.4 mu in diameter.

Ericales. The family Ericaceae, with numerous genera and species, and *Empetrum nigrum* make up the order in this part of North Pacific North America. At least 15 different species grow on the sampling sites, and no effort was made to identify any of the members of this notoriously difficult group. Iversen (personal communication, 7 December 1956) believes it is possible to distinguish between *Empetrum* and the Ericaceae on the basis of the sculpturing. He states that under oil immersion in the region around the furrows the small warts in *Empetrum* consist of one granule while the warts in the Ericaceae consist of several fused granules.

Myriophyllum. Pollen of this genus, observed in samples from Oregon and California sections, may be confused with that of *Alnus*. The grains of *Myriophyllum* exhibit narrower germinal apertures, less distinctive aspides, and no arci according to Wodehouse (1935).

Oplopanax. Although *O. horridus* is very common throughout most of this coastal district, its pollen was only rarely observed in the peat samples. The grain is quite distinct, being tricolpate with reticulate sculpturing and with the exine thickened at the colpi. It measures 29.4–43.2 mu along the major axis.

Swertia. On a single occasion, *S. perennis* pollen was counted. The plant is not common in the region. Its pollen is tricolporate and coarsely granular textured, measuring 23–34 mu in size.

Polemonium. Solitary grains of this genus have been noted occurring at various levels in peat sections at widely scattered locations on the coast. At least nine species grow in the region. *P. pulcherrimum* appears to be the most widely distributed representative. The grain of this species is periporate with a striate-rugulate texture (Faegri and Iversen 1950) and is 38.4–56.0 mu in diameter.

Compositae. Following Faegri and Iversen (1950), this family is divided into the Liguliflorae and Tubuliflorae. In the pollen profiles, neither is usually present in more than a few numbers, although the Tubuliflorae were generally encountered more often than the Liguliflorae.

Microfossils Other Than Spores and Pollen Grains

Innumerable supplementary microfossils occur in the deposits. Record was kept of many of them in the course of counting the pollen and spores, although no data other than presence were recorded. Albeit desirable, it was beyond the limits of this study to undertake a statistical investigation of all microfossils. The ones noted could not all be identified, even in the crude manner in which identification was handled. Many specialists would be required to carry out the task completely.

No stratigraphic value could be ascribed with assurance to these microfossils on the basis of presence alone. Many are found largely or only in the upper parts of the sections. This fact may be stratigraphically significant, although it may also be attributed to nonpreservation in the deeper sediments. In the case of the rhizopods, which are particularly characteristic of sphagnum-moss peat, tests of these animals are more numerous and diverse in the upper parts of the sections, where sphagnum remains are abundant. A careful systematic study would be necessary in order to evaluate the stratigraphic importance of these and other nonpalynological microfossils.

One of the more interesting groups noted consists of the rhizopods. Some of these were tentatively identified using Hoogenraad (1935). Tests found at the surface and through to the lower levels of the sections were from *Amphitrema flavum* (Archer) Penard, *A. wrightianum* Archer, *Arcella arctocrea* Leidy, *Assulina muscorum* Greeff, *Bullinulla indica* Penard, *Hyalosphenia papilio* Leidy, and *Trigonopyxis arcula* (Leidy) Penard. Most frequently encountered were *Assulina muscorum* and *Amphitrema flavum*, in that order. *Assulina seminulum* Leidy and *Hyalosphenia elegans* Leidy were not found to such depths as those preceding, but were frequently noted. Observed almost exclusively in the upper levels, also rather frequently, were *Centropyxis aculeata* Stein, *Heleopera rosea* Penard, and *Nebella collaris* Leidy. Tests of *Heleopera picta* Leidy were seen on two occasions in surface samples from sites in southeastern Alaska. Only three species, *Assulina muscorum*, *A. seminulum*, and *Nebella collaris*, were found to range from Kodiak Island to California. Two, *Arcella arctocrea* and *Centropyxis aculeata*, were found to range from Kodiak to Oregon and three, *Amphitrema flavum*, *Hyalosphenia elegans*, and *Trigonopyxis arcula*, from Kodiak to Washington. Three species, *Amphitrema wrightianum*, *Bullinulla indica*, and *Heleopera rosea*, were found from the Kenai Peninsula to Washington, but none was seen in Kodiak samples. Comparatively limited in its range is *Hyalosphenia papilio*, which extends from Kodiak to Kuiu Island in southeastern Alaska.

Besides rhizopods, additional animal microfossils recorded include sponge spicules, rotifers and rotifer eggs, water fleas, and insects. Among the plant microfossils, the algae, particularly diatoms (Bacillariophyceae) and members of the greens (Chlorophyceae), are noteworthy. *Pediastrum* is commonly seen, and the desmids, *Closterium*, *Cosmarium*, *Euastrum*, and *Staurastrum*, occur with variable frequency. Additional identifiable plant material consists of trichomes (usually from *Nuphar polysepalum*), fern sporangia and annuli, and structures resembling ascomata of *Microthyrium*, which are described by Godwin and Andrew (1951).

RADIOCARBON DATES OF PEATS FROM NORTH PACIFIC NORTH AMERICA

In the course of obtaining peat sections in 1956, 17 samples were collected for radiocarbon dating. Age determinations were made by Isotopes Incorporated, Westwood, New Jersey, in 1958 through a grant provided by the National Science Foundation (Heusser 1958, 1959). The ages supplemented those determined by Lamont Geological Observatory for seven samples collected in 1950 and 1955 (Kulp *et al.* 1952, Broecker and Kulp 1957, Olson and Broecker 1959). The chronology for the environmental events derived from the pollen and peat stratigraphy of the sections is founded mostly on these 24 dated samples. Supplemental chronological data have been obtained from certain age determinations of material from this coast reported by Lamont Geological Observatory (Kulp *et al.* 1951, Broecker *et al.* 1956), the U. S. Geological Survey (Suess 1954; Rubin and Suess 1955, 1956; Rubin and Alexander 1958), and Yale Geochronometric Laboratory (Preston *et al.* 1955, Barendsen *et al.* 1957).

Samples range from near Karluk on Kodiak Island, Alaska, to the vicinity of Port Orford, Oregon. All were taken with the Hiller sampler except Alaganik 1 and Lemon Creek (L-106B), which were taken directly from exposed sections. The collection was planned to date the Late-glacial, Postglacial, and Hypsithermal along the coast and to fix chronologically the late-Pleistocene events of glaciation, vulcanism, and changes in land–sea-level relations. The largest proportion of samples is from the Alaskan "Tertiary Province," which lies between the Copper River mouth and Icy Point. These were taken with the object of dating the prominent series of marine terraces that occur along this part of the Alaskan coast.

The method used by Isotopes Incorporated for dating the samples is essentially that described by Broecker, Kulp, and Tucek (1956). In short, sufficient sample, estimated on the basis of carbon content, was burned and the CO_2 evolved was processed to remove impurities. Radon, one of these, was removed by converting purified CO_2 to $CaCO_3$ by reaction with CaO at 750°C. The CO_2 was reevolved and stored or counted. Proportional counting of CO_2 was carried out at two atmospheres pressure, and each sample was counted at least twice. Accuracy of the radiocarbon determination is believed to be correct to within 3 per cent or less. Counting error contributes ca 2 per cent while other errors, such as measurement of pressure and temperature, amount to less than 1 per cent.

The following ages and relevant information for samples are presented in geographical sequence from the southwest Alaskan Pacific to Oregon. Lamont Geological Observatory ages and data are included, and any changes in sample comments over those previously presented (Kulp *et al.* 1952, Broecker and Kulp 1957, Olson and Broecker 1959, Heusser 1959) are the result of more recent findings. Samples dated by Isotopes Incorporated are designated I(AGS); Lamont dates are the L-106B and L-297 series.

Sample No.	Site and Description	Age (yr) B.P.
I(AGS)-1.	Karluk, Alaska	3470 ± 180

Moss peat from the base of a 1.1-m section of muskeg located on a bench just east of Karluk on the south side of the lagoon at the mouth of Karluk River; sample elevation ca 100 ft (57°34′N, 154°28′W). Pollen profiles reveal that the formation of the muskeg resulted from a change to cooler, more humid climate; the proportion of heath, fern, and sphagnum moss increases upward in the section whereas alder and grass decrease (Fig. 13). *Comment:* sample age and succeeding climatic trend show a relationship to southeastern Alaska on the basis of Lamont dating (L-106B, 3500±250; Kulp *et al.* 1952) and peat and pollen studies (Heusser 1953).

I(AGS)-2 Kodiak 3, Alaska 8870±300

Basal-sedge peat from a 2.2-m section in a muskeg situated near Spruce Cape, 2.5 mi northeast of Kodiak village, Kodiak Island; sample from an elevation of ca 100 ft (57°49′N, 152°21′W). A cool, moist, early-postglacial environment is indicated by a pollen record dominated by fern, sedge, and umbellifer (Fig. 14). Three noteworthy volcanic-ash strata lie above in the section, the uppermost, near-surface stratum representing the 1912 eruption of Mt. Katmai in the Aleutian Range. *Comment:* age approximates the boundary between the Late-glacial and Postglacial and may be compared with dates (this date list) from Afognak, Perry Island, and Bering Lake.

I(AGS)-3. Afognak, Alaska 9350±320

Sedge peat from the bottom of a 2.5-m section in a muskeg just northwest of Afognak village, Afognak Island; sample from ca 15-ft elevation (58°01′N, 152°46′W). Pollen in the sample is quite similar to that from Kodiak, although a greater proportion of sedge suggests the close of the Late-glacial and an environment that was cooler and drier (Fig. 14). Three volcanic-ash horizons, stratigraphically correlated with those at Kodiak, overlie the sampled level. Sample age and peat and pollen stratigraphy of the section show that nearby marine waters have not transgressed the site since peat sedimentation began.

I(AGS)-4. Perry Island, Alaska 9440±350

Bottom limnic peat from a depth of 4.0 m in a bog muskeg just east of the larger of the two bays on the southern shore of Perry Island, northwestern Prince William Sound; sample elevation ca 35 ft (60°41′N, 147°54′W). Relatively cool and dry conditions were present at the time, interpreted as the close of the Late-glacial, as shown by the proportion of willow and birch in the pollen assemblage, the balance of which consists largely of fern, sedge, and alder (Fig. 19).

I(AGS)-5. Alaganik 1, Alaska 10,390±350

Sedge peat forming the base of a 2.0-m section exposed by construction of the Copper River Highway at Milepost 19 from Cordova; sample elevation ca 15 ft (60°27′N, 145°17′W). Late-glacial pollen in the sample consists of willow, heath, and sedge and is representative of a relatively dry, cold climate (Fig. 20). In view of the age of the sample, peat and pollen stratigraphy of the section, and nearness of the site to sea level, the nearby coast has been quite stable for at least the past 10,000 yr. *Comment:* sample age is the earliest Late-glacial for this part of the gulf coast. This may be a consequence of early peat deposition from plants that invaded from the driftless area near Alaganik (Tarr and Martin 1914).

I(AGS)-6. Upper Katalla, Alaska 7650±330

Sedge and moss peat underlying a slope muskeg at a depth of 2.3 m, situated 0.5 mi north of Katalla village; sample from an elevation of ca 180 ft (60°12′N, 144°32′W). High proportion of alder pollen in the sample with higher percentages in horizons overlying in the section is interpreted as representative of pre-hypsithermal time (Fig. 21). *Comment:* marine terraces or indications of elevated former strand lines are present at Katalla at less than 100-ft elevation, although regionally they may be present up to 200 or more (D. J. Miller, U. S. Geological Survey, personal communication). Age, pollen spectrum, and elevation of the sample compared with ages, pollen spectra, and elevations of samples from Lower Katalla, Martin Lake, and Bering Lake (this date list) suggest that Upper Katalla sample rests upon a former marine site and its age dates marine regression from the surface.

I(AGS)-7. Lower Katalla, Alaska 3770±200

Silty limnic peat from base of a 1.9-m section in muskeg located 0.3 mi north of Katalla village; sample elevation ca 40 ft (60°12′N, 144°32′W). Site interpreted to have been previously occupied by marine waters (D. J. Miller, personal communication). Superposition of Lower Katalla pollen profiles upon those from Upper Katalla section reveals inception of the deposit during the Late Hypsithermal or early part of the Late Postglacial (Fig. 21). *Comment:* rate of marine regression is figured at ca 3.6 ft/century between 180- and 40-ft elevations in the Katalla district on the basis of Upper Katalla (this date list) and Lower Katalla sample ages.

I(AGS)-8. Martin Lake, Alaska 6810±375

Silty sedge peat at the base of a muskeg, 1.3 m deep, on a peninsula on the west side of Martin Lake, ca 11 mi north of Katalla; sample from ca 100-ft elevation (60°21′N, 144°34′W). Alder is the predominant pollen in the sample, which is of hypsithermal age (Fig. 21). Sample age is interpreted as approximately dating marine regression from the site. *Comment:* taking into account the Upper and Lower Katalla ages (this date list) and the age of the Martin Lake sample, the rate of regression appears as follows in this district: ca 80 ft in 840 yr since ca 7650 B. P. or a rate of 9.5 ft/century; ca 60 ft between 6810–3770 B. P. or 2 ft/century; and ca 40 ft in the last 3770 yr or 1.1 ft/century.

I(AGS)-9. Bering Lake, Alaska 9510±475

Sedge peat underlying a muskeg 3.3 m deep, situated ca 0.5 mi from the northwestern shore and ca 10 mi northeast of Katalla; sample elevation ca 180 ft (60°19′N, 144°20′W). Early peat deposition at this site, as indicated by the age and proportion of willow pollen in the dated sample, is the latter part of the Late-glacial, although climate does not appear to have been as cold or as dry during late-glacial time as at other localities in this list (Fig. 21). The upper limit of marine transgression in the vicinity of this sample site is unknown.

I(AGS)-10. Munday Creek, Alaska 10,820±420

Basal sedge peat from a depth of 7.1 m in a muskeg just west of Munday Creek, ca 1 mi from the beach and ca 10 mi northeast of Icy Cape; sample from an elevation of ca 230 ft (60°01′N, 141°57′W). This peat, according to D. J. Miller (personal communication), rests on a terrace, the uppermost of several definitely determined as marine in this district. Pollen in the sample is Late-glacial and consists predominantly of sedge with smaller amounts of other types characteristic of late-glacial deposits, such as heath, willow, and umbellifer (Fig. 22). These facts provide an approximate regression rate of over 2 ft/century from the late-glacial to the present sea level. *Comment:* rate from a lower terrace at ca 40 ft has been ca 3.8 ft/century as indicated by a U.S. Geological Survey date (W-369, 1050±160; Rubin and Alexander 1958). Sample age and pollen content may be compared with Lamont dates and comments for North Pacific coastal samples (L-297C, 10,850±800; L-297D, 10,300±400; Broecker and Kulp 1957) and for Alaganik 1 site (this date list). Postglacial time ensued at this site ca 10,000 B. P.

I(AGS)-11. Grand Plateau Glacier, Alaska 1210±200

Lowermost sedge peat at a 2.0-m depth in a muskeg ca 3 mi southeast of the glacier, ca 5 mi northwest of the mouth of Sea Otter Creek, and ca 0.5 mi from the beach; sample elevation ca 30 ft (58°57′N, 138°00′W). Site appears to have been a lagoon that became fresh as a result of rising land, falling sea level, or both. Regression rate for sea level from this stand to the present one is ca 2.5 ft/century. *Comment:* sample age and elevation show a close relationship to U. S. Geological Survey sample from Munday Creek at ca 40-ft elevation (W-369, 1050±160; Rubin and Alexander 1958).

I(AGS)-12. Upper Northwest Lituya Bay, Alaska 8140±390

Bottom ligneous peat from a depth of 3.1 m in a muskeg resting on the upper of a pair of marine terraces located ca 7.5 mi northwest of Lituya Bay and ca 1.5 mi from the beach; sample elevation ca 300 ft (58°43′N, 137°45′W). Fern spores predominate the plant microfossils in the sample, which dates from the latter part of the Early Postglacial or the early part of the Hypsithermal (Fig. 23). Rate of regression of the ocean from this position to its present stand has been ca 3.7 ft/century.

I(AGS)-13. Lower Northwest Lituya Bay, Alaska 6890±350

Basal ligneous peat sampled from a depth of 2.2 m in a muskeg ca 0.25 mi southwest of Upper Northwest Lituya Bay site; sample elevation ca 110 ft (58°43′N, 137°45′W). Pollen stratigraphy of the peat section indicates the sample dates from hypsithermal time (Fig. 23). Regression rate from this stand of the ocean is ca 1.6 ft/century. *Comment:* on the basis of this age and that of the sample from Upper Northwest Lituya Bay (this date list), the relative position of land and sea level changed ca 190 ft in 1250 yr or ca 15.2 ft/century.

I(AGS)-14. Southeast Lituya Bay, Alaska 2790±250

Sedge peat from the bottom of a muskeg at a depth of 1.0 m; site lies ca 3 mi southeast of the mouth of Lituya Bay, 1.5 mi northwest of Steelhead Creek, and 0.25 mi from the ocean; sample from an elevation of ca 100 ft (58°36′N, 137°34′W). Muskeg rests on what appears to be the highest of three marine terraces above the present ocean stand. High proportion of sphagnum spores, abundance of pollen of arboreal conifers in the overlying section, and sample age suggest contemporaneity with the Late Postglacial (Fig. 23). Regression rate between this and the present stand of the ocean is ca 3.6 ft/century. *Comment:* regression rate on the basis of a sample dated from a 150-ft-elevation marine terrace ca 13 mi southeast of this site, U. S. Geological Survey (Rubin and Alexander 1958) age determination (W-405, 3250±200), is ca 4.6 ft/century. Comparison with the Southeast Lituya Bay sample age and elevation suggests a rate of regression between the 150-ft and 100-ft stands southeast of the bay as ca 10.9 ft/century. Also, comparison of Southeast Lituya Bay age and that from Lower Northwest Lituya Bay (this date list), both sites at nearly the same elevation, reveals that the ocean withdrew from the latter site much earlier. Such a difference between sites at practically the same elevation northwest and southeast of the bay suggests variations in local tectonic activity.

L-106B. Lemon Creek, Alaska 3500±250

Wood intercalated in ligneous peat in a muskeg on Sunny Point on Gastineau Channel at Milepost 7.5 along Glacier Highway northwest of Juneau; sample elevation ca 5 ft (58°22′N, 134°32′W). Sample was removed from a 0.5-m-thick ligneous stratum exposed in a freshly cut section, 2.6 m thick, in which the stratum is overlain by 2 m of sedge and moss peat and underlain by 0.1 m of sedge remains. Sample age (Kulp *et al.* 1952) is the close of the Hypsithermal (Fig. 24), essentially as previously interpreted (Heusser 1953). *Comment:* this interpretation is in accord with dated samples of interfluctuational wood from nearby Mendenhall Glacier. Ages of 1790±285 B. P. (Kulp *et al.* 1951) and 2790±130 B. P. (Preston *et al.* 1955) for this wood indicate that the glacier was advancing at ca 50-ft elevation after having been rejuvenated under a post-hypsithermal, cool, humid climate (Heusser 1952).

L-297B. Lemon Creek, Alaska 6100±300

Basal sedge peat from 4.8-m depth in a muskeg at Sunny Point, previously located; sample elevation ca 0 ft. Sample dates from the Hypsithermal (Fig. 24) and discloses, along with the section pollen and peat stratigraphy, that the relationship between land and sea level has not changed within the last ca 6100 yr. Since marine fossils are found up to an elevation of ca 500 ft in the Juneau area (Twenhofel 1952) and marine shells have already been reported from beneath the muskeg (Dachnowski-Stokes 1941), peat evidently began forming following the withdrawal of tidewater.

L-297A. Upper Lemon Creek, Alaska 10,300±600

Basal ligneous peat from a depth of 5.8 m in a muskeg situated 6 mi north of Juneau, ca 1000 ft from the position attained by the tongue of Lemon Creek Glacier in the mid-eighteenth century; sample elevation ca 750 ft (58°23′N, 134°25′W). Age of the sample is the latter part of the Late-glacial; age provides proof that Lemon Creek Glacier has not extended far beyond its mid-eighteenth century position, if at all, for at least the last 10,000 yr. No pollen diagram has been prepared for the overlying section, although samples have been taken. *Comment:* this age is practically identical with Upper Montana Creek age (Broecker and Kulp 1957; L-297D, 10,300±400; also this date list).

L-297E. Mendenhall River, Alaska 6650±250

Sedge peat from a 2.9-m depth at the bottom of a muskeg near Milepost 11.5 along the Glacier Highway northwest of Juneau; sample elevation ca 40 ft (58°22′N, 134°37′W). The sample age, pollen content, and pollen stratigraphy for the overlying section indicate muskeg formation began during the Hypsithermal. Arboreal-conifer pollen diagram has been published previously (Heusser 1952). *Comment:* Lemon Creek sample (L-297B, 6100±300, this date list) shows a close relationship. Both peat deposits appear to owe their formation to withdrawal of tidewater. A change of land–sea-level relations of ca 40 ft in 550 yr or ca 7.3 ft/century between 6650 and 6100 B. P. is indicated.

L-297G. Lower Montana Creek, Alaska 7800±300

Basal ligneous peat from a depth of 5.9 m in a muskeg along Montana Creek Road, 11 mi northwest of Juneau; sample elevation ca 150 ft (58°25′N, 134°37′W). Pollen record shows the sample to be the early part of the Hypsithermal in age (Fig. 24). Fossiliferous marine till to ca 400 ft in Montana Creek valley (D. J. Miller, personal communication) and truncated pollen profiles at this site and Mendenhall River (this date list) compared with those from Upper Montana Creek support the belief that peat began to form after the regression of sea level. *Comment:* regression rate between elevations of ca 150 and 40 ft appears to have been 9.6 ft/century on the basis of data from Lower Montana Creek and Mendenhall River (this date list).

L-297D. Upper Montana Creek, Alaska 10,300±400

Muskeg sample of basal sedge peat is from a depth of 3.8 m. Locality is 3 mi from the end of Montana Creek Road northwest of Juneau; sample elevation ca 750 ft (58°27′N, 134°40′W). Pollen in the sample is mostly alder, willow, and lodgepole pine (Fig. 24). This assemblage and sample age (Broecker and Kulp 1957) are interpreted as representing the latter part of the Late-glacial. Volcanic ash near the base of the peat section overlying the dated sample is presumably from Mt. Edgecumbe on Kruzof Island, situated in the outer part of the Alexander Archipelago, ca 100 mi distant. The eruption of this volcano is estimated at 9000 B. P.

L-297C. Langara Island, British Columbia 10,850±800

Limnic peat from a depth of 6.6 m at the base of a muskeg situated toward the southern end of the island, the northernmost member of the Queen Charlotte Islands; sample elevation ca 140 ft (54°12′N, 133°00′W). Pollen assemblage (Heusser 1955b) and age (Broecker and Kulp 1957) date the sample from the Late-glacial. Vegetation at this time consisted of park tundra, where lodgepole pine grew with willow, heath, sedge, and fern. Previously the sample had been assigned to the "very early postglacial" (Broecker and Kulp 1957). *Comment:* sample shows good correlation with Munday Creek, Alaska (this date list; 10,850±800 B. P.).

I(AGS)-15. Seaview, Washington 2950±150

Bottom sedge peat at a depth of 3.3 m in a bog situated at the end of an abandoned dirt road that leads off the south side of State Highway 12, ca 1.25 mi east of Seaview; sample elevation ca 0 ft (46°19′N, 124°03′W). Location is north of the mouth of the Columbia River in Pacific County. Pollen profiles from a section of the muskeg show an increase upward of lodgepole pine at the expense of forest conifers, Sitka spruce and western hemlock; fern and sphagnum profiles also increase upward (Fig. 42). A period of storminess and dune instability and of cool, moist climate with fluctuations is inferred to have occurred after the time of this sample age. Muskeg resting at present-day sea level may have begun to form with the laying down of the southern part of Long Beach spit, and accordingly sample age may date that event. *Comment:* arboreal pollen profiles by Hansen (1944) from nearby Ilwaco show essentially similar form to Seaview profiles.

I(AGS)-16. Devils Lake, Oregon 6300±275

Peat consisting of limnic and ligneous remains from a depth of 11.7 m in a section removed from a wooded bog found on the western shore of Devils Lake, ca 1 mi northeast of the outlet, and less than 1 mi east of the village of Oceanlake, Lincoln County; sample elevation ca −24 ft (44°58′N, 124°00′W). Approximately 7 m of the section are below present-day sea level. Pollen profiles for the section show prominences for two brackish-water indicators, *Ruppia* and Chenopodiaceae, with two intervals of nondeposition of pollen between ca 6.5 and ca 9 m (Fig. 43). This part of the section is interpreted as representing a time when Devils Lake was a saltwater lagoon. Below the 9-m level in the section, some sediments appear to have formed in slightly brackish water, but above the ca 6-m level essentially freshwater conditions are manifest. *Comment:* sample age and section stratigraphy suggest eustatic sea-level rise during the Hypsithermal, reaching a maximum ca 5000 B. P. between ca 6.5 and ca 9 m in the section. Moreover, it appears likely that the inception of the Devils Lake deposit is related to the early phase of the eustatic rise of the Pacific Ocean that ultimately resulted in the formation of the Older Peron Terrace, Australia, which dates from ca 5000 B. P. (Fairbridge 1958). If the two levels of nondeposition at this site represent two separate transgressions, the lower level may be related to the Older Peron Terrace whereas the upper one may bear a relationship to the Younger Peron Terrace, dating from ca 3600 B. P. (Fairbridge 1958).

I(AGS)-17. Garrison Lake, Oregon 6720±250

Basal limnic-ligneous peat from a depth of 13.0 m in a section from the northwestern arm of Garrison Lake, less than 0.5 mi from the ocean, 6 mi south of Cape Blanco, and 1.5 mi northwest of Port Orford, Curry County; sample elevation ca −38 ft (42°06′N, 124°31′W). Practically the entire section is beneath present sea level. Although it is largely a freshwater deposit, the pollen profiles reveal several possible mildly brackish intervals of deposition with one strongly brackish from ca 10 to ca 11 m, this latter as indicated by the *Ruppia* profile (Fig. 45). Using the sample age as a datum from which to estimate, this strongly brackish interval is dated at ca 5000 B. P. and suggests eustatic transgression. *Comment:* age of the sample and position of the *Ruppia* zone in the overlying sediments in this section generally corroborate the data from Devils Lake (this date list). If, in reality, two separate transgressions have occurred at Devils Lake, pollen profiles from Garrison Lake show that the single *Ruppia* peak is related to the older transgression. No evidence of a younger transgression is apparent at this site.

Chapter VII

PEAT AND POLLEN STRATIGRAPHY OF THE SECTIONS

A consistent system is adhered to throughout the diagrams (Figs. 13–46)*. Peat stratigraphy for each section appears in a column at the extreme left, and the environmental sequence, as a succession of zones, is at the extreme right. Symbols for the sedimentary types are given in Figure 12. Environmental zones begin with the Late-glacial (LG), which is subdivided tripartitely into LG-1 (oldest), LG-2, and LG-3 (youngest). The Postglacial lying above the Late-glacial in zonation is also represented by a three-fold subdivision, beginning with the Early Postglacial (EP) and followed by the Hypsithermal (HTL) and Late Postglacial (LP). The symbols for the three late-glacial zones are synonymous, in the order given, with the terms Older Dryas, Alleröd, and Younger Dryas (Hammen 1957). The terminology applied to the Postglacial is respectively synonymous with the Anathermal, Hypsithermal, and Hypothermal (Cooper 1958a).

The pollen profiles make up the central part of each diagram. In the profiles, arboreal pollen is grouped on the left-hand side and nonarboreal on the right. The arboreal assemblage begins with the conifers and ends with the angiosperms. Nonarboreal pollen begins with the monocots and proceeds through the lower and thence taxonomically higher dicots. The ferns and fern allies follow these. Diagrams for southwestern and south-central Alaska summarize the arboreal species and genera in collective AP profiles. The sums of nonarboreal groups for these Alaskan districts are depicted by NAP profiles. The genus *Sphagnum* occupies the right-hand flank of the profiles. A meter scale to the left of the profiles indicates depth, and a scale at the lower left of each diagram is included for measuring, in conjunction with unlabeled scales under important profiles, the percentage of pollen representation at each level in the section. Where plus signs appear in a profile, representation is less than 2 per cent. Radiocarbon dates, in years B. P. (Before Present), appear to the left of the peat stratigraphic column in certain sections where age determinations are available.

PEAT STRATIGRAPHY

Alaska

Southwestern District

Inspection of Table 2 reveals that the sections (1–8) taken from the Southwestern District of Alaska are over 1 m, but less than 3.5 deep (average 2.1). The only two peat types observed are bryophytic and sedge. Generally, bryophytes are predominant in the upper or surface peat whereas sedge predominates in the lower parts of the deeper sections. The abundance of *Sphagnum* in the bryophytic peat at and near the surface is indicative of cooling and greater humidity during recent millennia

*These figures will be found at the end of the chapter.

TABLE 2—STRATIGRAPHIC DATA FOR SECTIONS BETWEEN KODIAK ISLAND AND THE COPPER RIVER, ALASKA.

SECTION	DEPTH M	SEDIMENTARY TYPES*	LIGNEOUS HORIZONS MAJOR	LIGNEOUS HORIZONS MINOR	ASH HORIZONS MAJOR	ASH HORIZONS MINOR	SECTION BASE
(1) Karluk	1.1	Sp,Sg	–	–	–	1	Gravel
(2) Cape Chiniak	1.2	Sp,Sg	–	–	1	–	Silt-clay
(3) Cape Greville 1	1.5	Sp,Sg	–	–	2	–	Silt
(4) Cape Greville 2	3.4	Sp,Sg	–	–	3	–	Silt-clay
(5) Kodiak 1	2.5	Sp,Sg	–	–	2	–	Gravel
(6) Kodiak 2	2.1	Sp,Sg	–	–	3	–	Gravel
(7) Kodiak 3	2.2	Sp,Sg	–	–	3	–	Gravel
(8) Afognak	2.5	Sp,Sg	–	–	3	–	Silt
(9) Homer 1	6.5	Sp,Sg	–	–	3	3	Clay/coal
(10) Homer 2	3.5	Sp,Sg	–	–	3	–	Silt-clay
(11) Homer 3	4.1	Sp,Sg	–	–	3	–	Clay
(12) Windy Bay	2.1	Sp,Sg	–	–	3	–	Gravel
(13) Port Chatham	1.5	Sp,Sg	–	–	3	–	Gravel
(14) Seward	3.7	Sp,Sg,Lg	–	1	2	–	Gravel
(15) Moose Pass	1.5	Sp	–	–	2	–	Clay-silt
(16) Saxton	2.0	Sp,Sg	–	–	2	–	Sand-silt
(17) Girdwood	1.4	Sp,Sg	–	–	2	–	Silt
(18) Hinchinbrook I.	1.3	Sp,Sg	–	–	–	2	Silt
(19) Montague I.	1.1	Sp,Sg	–	–	–	–	Sand-silt
(20) Perry I.	4.1	Sp,Sg,Lc	–	–	2	–	Clay-silt
(21) Cordova	3.0	Sp,Sg,Lg	1	–	2	–	Bedrock
(22) Alaganik 1	2.1	Sp,Sg	–	–	–	2	Gravel
(23) Alaganik 2	1.9	Sp,Sg	–	–	–	2	Gravel

*Sp—bryophytic (moss)
Sg—sedge (fibrous)
Lg—ligneous (wood)
Lc—limnic (lake)

(Figs. 13, 14). The change, which is of common occurrence along the coast, is borne out also by the trends of certain pollen profiles not in this district alone but elsewhere as well. Bases of the sections are either silt-clay or gravel. Fine clastics form much of the Cape Greville 2 section below 1 m, and although not shown in Figure 13, many fine particles of volcanic ash were observed at a depth of 3.2 m. Charred peat was noted only in the Afognak section in the sample from 0.7 m.

Volcanic-ash horizons in four of the sections (Afognak, Kodiak 2 and 3, Cape Greville 2) number three. The remaining sections disclosing two or only one are younger or were so situated as to lie beyond the area encompassed by the ashfall. The uppermost Katmai ash of 1912 is present in all the sections, although Karluk contains very little of this material since it was marginal to the area of fall, which was generally southeastward from the volcano (Fig. 13). Katmai ash, appearing as glass shards and vesicular fragments under the microscope, occurs in the upper 0.5 m, largely as a layer 1–2 dm thick. The lower part is gritty, gray pumice; the upper is fine and pink colored. Presumably in time it will become compacted like the two

TABLE 3—STRATIGRAPHIC DATA FOR SECTIONS BETWEEN THE COPPER RIVER, ALASKA, AND BRITISH COLUMBIA.

SECTION	DEPTH M	SEDIMENTARY TYPES*	LIGNEOUS HORIZONS MAJOR	LIGNEOUS HORIZONS MINOR	ASH HORIZONS MAJOR	ASH HORIZONS MINOR	SECTION BASE
(24) Upper Katalla	2.3	Sp,Sg	–	–	1	1	Sand-silt
(25) Lower Katalla	1.9	Sp,Sg	–	–	2	–	Sand-silt
(26) Martin Lake	1.3	Sp,Sg	–	–	1	1	Sand-silt
(27) Bering Lake	3.5	Sp,Sg,Lg	1	–	2	–	Silt
(28) Munday Creek	7.2	Sp,Sg	–	–	–	2	Sand-silt
(29) Grand Plateau Glacier	2.0	Sp,Sg	–	–	–	–	Sand-silt
(30) Upper NW Lituya	3.2	Sp,Sg,Lg	1	2	–	1	Sand-silt
(31) Lower NW Lituya	2.2	Sp,Sg,Lg	1	2	–	1	Gravel
(32) SE Lituya	1.2	Sp,Sg	–	–	–	–	Sand-silt
(33) Icy Point	1.4	Sp,Sg	–	–	–	–	Sand
(34) Upper Montana Creek	4.0	Sp,Sg,Lg	1	–	1	1	Silt
(35) Lower Montana Creek	6.0	Sp,Sg,Lg	2	–	–	1	Gravel
(36) Lemon Creek	5.0	Sp,Sg,Lg	2	1	–	1	Sand-silt
(37) Whitestone Harbor	3.9	Sp,Sg,Lg	1	–	1	–	Silt
(38) Gull Cove	2.5	Sp,Sg,Lg	–	2	–	1	Silt
(39) Mite Cove	1.5	Sp,Sg	–	–	–	1	Silt
(40) Threemile Arm	4.0	Sp,Sg,Lg	2	1	–	–	Silt-clay
(41) Suloia Lake	1.5	Sp,Sg	–	–	1	1	Volcanic ash
(42) Port Krestof	1.3	Sp,Sg	–	–	1	1	Volcanic ash
(43) Hasselborg Lake	7.4	Sp,Sg,Lc,Lg	–	3	1	–	Clay
(44) Hobart Bay	7.5	Sp,Sg,Lg	1	2	–	–	Silt-sand
(45) Salmon Bay	3.2	Sp,Sg,Lg	2	1	–	–	Sand-silt
(46) Hamilton Bay	3.3	Sp,Sg	–	–	–	–	Silt-clay
(47) Sarkar Lake	4.8	Sp,Sg,Lc	–	–	–	–	Marine shells
(48) Hollis	6.1	Sp,Sg,Lg	2	1	–	–	Sand-silt
(49) Kendrick Bay	4.1	Sp,Sg,Lc	–	–	–	–	Silt-clay
(50) SE Gokachin Lakes	4.9	Sp,Sg,Lc	–	–	–	–	Silt-clay

*Sp—bryophytic (moss)
Sg—sedge (fibrous)
Lg—ligneous (wood)
Lc—limnic (lake)

underlying ash horizons. Because it is unknown to what extent compaction will take place in time, it is difficult to compare the three eruptions represented in the sections. It does appear, however, that the Katmai eruption caused more ash to fall on Kodiak than the two previous eruptions. Sources of the two earlier eruptions of fine, gray ash are unknown.

South-Central District

The stratigraphic characteristics of the sections (9–28) from the South-Central District of Alaska are summarized in Tables 2 and 3. Depths range from 1.1 to 7.2 m and average 2.8, which is deeper than the average for the Southwestern District. Deep sections of particular value for late-Pleistocene study are those at Homer 1 (6.5

m) and at Munday Creek (7.2). In general, peat types in this district are similar (bryophytic peat predominant at upper levels and sedge peat at lower), except for the sections from Seward, Cordova, and Bering Lake, where a ligneous horizon is intercalated; the section from Perry Island, where limnic peat forms the lower 2 m; and the section from Moose Pass, where no sedge is evident (Figs. 15–19).

The ligneous horizon in the Bering Lake section and the horizon at Cordova do not appear to correlate, whereas the horizon at Seward seems to be correlated with that at Cordova. The Bering Lake horizon almost certainly predates any of the "recurrence surfaces" (Swedish *Rekurrensytor*, RY; also called in German, *Grenzhorizonten* and *Rekurrenzflächen*) studied in Europe by Granlund (1932) and more recently discussed by Godwin (1954). The position of the Seward ligneous peat and that at Cordova, in relation to other features of the diagrams, suggests the Alaskan equivalent of the classic *Grenzhorizont* (Granlund's RY III). This is the most prominent recurrence surface studied by Granlund and in Europe marks the Sub-Boreal–Sub-Atlantic and Bronze Age-Iron Age boundaries. As will be seen, many muskeg sections from the Southeastern District and from British Columbia also exhibit ligneous horizons (recurrence surfaces). An attempt to answer the question of why these horizons are present in only certain sections may require a detailed analysis of many factors, and even with this analysis the question might still remain unanswerable.

Two major or minor levels of volcanic ash show up in most of the sections with the exception of those from the southwestern and northwestern Kenai Peninsula (Tables 2,3). This excepted group contains three levels, excluding Homer 1, which registers six (Fig. 15). It is difficult to say with certainty that the three ash levels in Kodiak and Afognak sections are correlated on the Kenai Peninsula or elsewhere in the district; however, pollen profiles seem to indicate that they are, in fact, correlative. The position and prominence of the uppermost ash in all the Kenai sections points to the Katmai eruption. The lowermost ash levels at Homer 1, 2, and 3 also appear to be correlative. The lowermost ash at Homer 1 is coarse and gritty whereas that correlated with Kodiak and Afognak is finer. If this basal ash is the same in these two districts, it would seem that the source volcano was relatively near the Kenai site. The middle horizons at Homer 2 and 3 and the lower at Seward seem correlated with the major horizon at 1.2–1.5 m in Homer 1. In addition, the three ash levels in Windy Bay and Port Chatham sections, on the basis of position and pollen profiles, show a stratigraphic relationship to the upper three (or possibly four) levels at Homer 1.

Whereas the middle ash at Kodiak may be correlated on the Kenai Peninsula, in Prince William Sound (Perry Island), and as far as Icy Cape (Munday Creek), Katmai ash is not clearly distinguishable beyond the Kenai except perhaps in the Katalla region. Because of the nearness of the volcanoes of the Wrangell Mountains, this upper ash about Katalla is more probably derived from the Wrangell area. Upper ash at Perry Island and at Munday Creek is tentatively correlated and also seems to have come from the Wrangells. It is necessary because of the uncertain correlation of ash from place to place to speculate somewhat in the interpretation of the ash stratigraphy. This requirement unfortunately limits the value of the horizons as a means for teleconnection. If, ideally, the ash levels could be assigned radiocarbon dates, they might be more readily "unscrambled."

Southeastern District

A digest of the section stratigraphy from the Southeastern District of Alaska is found in Table 3. Sections 29 through 50 are in this district and display greater complexity than those previously discussed. Their depths on the average are more than the preceding, ranging from 1.2 to 7.5 m (average 3.7). Characteristically, almost all the sections show bryophytic peat predominantly composing surface and upper parts and sedge peat making up much of the underlying plant material (Figs. 23–31). Ligneous-peat layers, from one to three in number, are present in more than half of the sections, and limnic peat forms the lower part of four. Volcanic-ash horizons are far less frequent and less prominent than those noted in the South-Central District.

Of particular interest in the stratigraphy of these sections are the ligneous-peat levels. Many of these undoubtedly are recurrence surfaces and, therefore, of considerable value in disclosing intervals of drying (humification) or regeneration (nonhumification) of the peat. But correlation of these ligneous levels is difficult for a number of reasons. Local conditions can dictate whether sufficient desiccation will occur to allow invasion by trees and shrubs, which give rise to ligneous peat. Consequently, a climatic shift may be insufficient to exceed a controlling threshold at one site whereas at another it may easily bring about the required change. Moreover, since the stratigraphy shown for the sections is by and large from a single peat core, the relative importance of the ligneous horizons is difficult to assess in terms of the entire peat deposit. The result is a complex problem in correlation that must depend upon the pollen profiles and available radiocarbon-dated horizons for its solution.

Certain ligneous-peat levels in the sections about Juneau appear to be correlated (Fig. 24). The dated middle level at Lemon Creek seems certainly related to the upper level at Lower Montana Creek. Both occur below the rise of the Ericales in the pollen profiles. The lower ligneous peat at Lower Montana Creek and the ligneous horizon at Upper Montana Creek also show a stratigraphic relationship. Both are identified by a peak in the alder pollen profile. It appears a possibility, in addition, that the lower ligneous level at Lemon Creek is likewise correlated with upper parts of this peat type in the other two sections.

By assuming that the Lower Montana Creek section is typical of the two major ligneous-peat levels in the Juneau area, further correlations can be attempted elsewhere in the district. On the basis of their radiocarbon dates, the lower ligneous peat at Upper Northwest Lituya Bay (Fig. 23) was formed at about the same time as that at Montana Creek. The upper part of the basal ligneous peat at Lower Northwest Lituya Bay (Fig. 23) may be correlated with the upper level at Montana Creek.

No distinctive horizons are evident at Whitestone Harbor (Fig. 25), and the woody peat in the entire lower half of the section is in the same time zone as the upper and lower levels in the Juneau area. At Threemile Arm (Fig. 26)and at Hobart Bay (Fig. 28), the lower woody peat is correlated with the lower level at

Montana Creek, and the two lower horizons at Salmon Bay (Fig. 29) and Hollis (Fig. 30) appear to correlate with those at Montana Creek.

The minor horizon in the upper part of the Lemon Creek section also appears to have correlative horizons in the district; these are based on the position of the minor horizon above the peak of the Ericales profile. Thus, the upper woody levels at Gull Cove (Fig. 25), Threemile Arm (Fig. 26), Salmon Bay (Fig. 29), and Upper and Lower Northwest Lituya Bay (Fig. 23) are probably contemporaneous. Correlation of the upper level at Hollis (Fig. 30), the three levels at Hasselborg Lake (Fig. 27), and the upper two levels at Hobart Bay (Fig. 28) is uncertain.

Volcanic ash in these sections (29–50) is found at two positions. A lower ash, appearing as a major or minor horizon, is considered everywhere to represent the eruption of Mt. Edgecumbe. In its correct stratigraphic position (Hasselborg Lake, Fig. 27), it occurs directly above or in the upper part of the basal lodgepole pine deposits. An upper ash, as only a minor horizon, is of unknown origin. Five sites, Upper Montana Creek, Whitestone Harbor, Suloia Lake, Port Krestof, and Hasselborg Lake, reveal major deposits of Mt. Edgecumbe ash. Four sites—Gull Cove, Mite Cove, and two, Upper and Lower, at Northwest Lituya Bay—contain minor amounts of what is interpreted to be Mt. Edgecumbe ash. The minor ash horizons at Upper and Lower Montana Creek, Lemon Creek, Suloia Lake, and Port Krestof are the ones whose origins have not been determined.

The stratigraphy of the Sarker Lake section is diagramed only to the depth of the pollen profiles at 3.5 m (Fig. 30). Because of the importance of the section in determining land–sea-level changes, the underlying material is described here from determinations kindly made by Allyn G. Smith of the California Academy of Sciences (personal communication, 11 November 1957). Below 3.5 m the sediments become increasingly marine and from 3.9 to the base of the section at 4.8 are almost entirely marine. From 3.9 to 3.5 m the evidence consists of barnacles, pelecypod-mollusk remains, echinoderm spine fragments, and some Foraminifera. At and below 3.9 m these forms are still present, in addition to gastropod-mollusk fragments; however, the predominating material seems to be barnacles. According to Mr. Smith, "The marine fauna represented is shallow-water, equivalent to what one normally finds in pockets in tide pools, between tides (i.e. between high and low tide)."

Charred-peat levels observed on numerous occasions are at various depths in the sections throughout the district. The sites and depths of such evidence are: Upper Northwest Lituya Bay (various levels between 0.6 and 2.8 m), Lower Northwest Lituya Bay (various levels between 0.1 and 1.4), Southeast Lituya Bay (between 0.3 and 0.7), Gull Cove (various levels between 0.1 and 1.4), Whitestone Harbor (various levels between 0.1 and 1.3), Lemon Creek (0.1 and 0.7), Suloia Lake (0.1), Threemile Arm (various levels between 0.1 and 2.3), Salmon Bay (various levels between 0.5 and 2.7), Hobart Bay (2.5 and 4.6), and Hollis (0.4).

British Columbia

Sections 51 to 65 are from the British Columbia coast (Figs. 32–37). Their stratigraphic features appear briefly in Table 4. In many ways they are similar to the

TABLE 4—STRATIGRAPHIC DATA FOR SECTIONS FROM BRITISH COLUMBIA, WASHINGTON, OREGON, AND CALIFORNIA.

SECTION	DEPTH M	SEDIMENTARY TYPES*	LIGNEOUS HORIZONS MAJOR	LIGNEOUS HORIZONS MINOR	ASH HORIZONS MAJOR	ASH HORIZONS MINOR	SECTION BASE
(51) Masset, B. C.	8.0	Sp,Sg,Lg	2	1	–	–	Clay
(52) Prince Rupert, B. C.	5.8	Sp,Sg,Lg	1	–	–	–	Sand-clay
(53) Rainbow Lake, B. C.	4.0	Sp,Sg,Lg	1	–	–	–	Bedrock
(54) Summit, B. C.	2.8	Sp,Sg,Lg	1	–	–	–	Sand
(55) Pitt Island, B. C.	0.9	Sp,Sg	–	–	–	1	Sand
(56) Susan Island, B. C.	1.9	Sp,Sg,Lg	–	2	–	–	Sand
(57) Fitzhugh Sound, B. C.	1.6	Sp,Sg,Lg	–	1	–	–	Sand
(58) Cape Caution, B. C.	1.5	Sg,Lg	–	1	–	–	Sand
(59) Upper Hope Island, B. C.	3.5	Sp,Sg,Lg	1	–	–	–	Sand
(60) Lower Hope Island, B. C.	1.5	Sp,Sg,Lg	1	–	–	–	Sand
(61) Port Hardy, B. C.	2.0	Sp,Sg	–	–	–	1	Sand
(62) Harbledown Island, B. C.	4.0	Sp,Sg,Lg,Lc	–	1	–	–	Clay
(63) Menzies Bay, B. C.	4.8	Sp,Sg,Lg,Lc	–	1	–	–	Sand
(64) Little Qualicum Falls, B.C.	1.9	Sg,Lc	–	–	–	–	Sand
(65) Malahat, B. C.	7.4	Sp,Sg,Lc	–	–	1	2	Clay
(66) Pangborn Lake, Wash.	9.5	Sg,Lc	–	–	1	3	Sand
(67) Whidbey Island, Wash.	15.0	Sp,Sg,Lg,Lc	2	8	1	–	Sand-clay
(68) Ozette Lake, Wash.	4.2	Sp,Sg,Lg	1	3	–	–	Gravel
(69) Wessler, Wash.	10.0	Sp,Sg,Lg	2	3	–	–	Sand-silt
(70) Humptulips, Wash.	4.2	Sp,Sg,Lg	–	1	–	–	Silt-clay
(71) Seaview, Wash.	3.3	Sp,Sg,Lg	1	–	–	–	Sand
(72) Warrenton, Ore.	2.5	Sg,Lc	–	–	–	–	Silt-sand
(73) Devils Lake, Ore.	13.0	Sp,Sg,Lg,Lc	–	3	–	–	Sand-clay
(74) Tahkenitch Lake, Ore.	8.0	Sg,Lc	–	–	–	–	Silt-sand
(75) Garrison Lake, Ore.	13.0	Sp,Sg,Lg,Lc	–	6	–	–	Sand
(76) Lake Earl, Calif.	4.0	Sg,Lg,Lc	1	2	–	–	Sand
(77) Capetown, Calif.	5.8	Sg,Lg,Lc	–	2	–	–	Silt-sand
(78) Fort Bragg, Calif.	3.5	Sp,Sg,Lg	–	1	–	–	Sand

*Sp—bryophytic (moss)
Sg—sedge (fibrous)
Lg—ligneous (wood)
Lc—limnic (lake)

sections from the Alaskan Southeastern District. Their average depth (3.4 m) is comparable, ligneous peat is interbedded between sedge and bryophytic types, bryophyte peat is prevalent in the upper and surface levels, and volcanic ash is of limited occurrence. Of all the muskeg sections taken for the entire study, the one from Masset on the Queen Charlotte Islands (Fig. 32) is the deepest (8.0 m) and contains one of the finest peat- and pollen-stratigraphic records. This section correlates well with Alaska sites to the northwest and with other sections from coastal British Columbia.

The two major woody peat levels at Masset (the lower one although bipartite is considered a single unit) in conjunction with the pollen profiles assure correlation with the Juneau area. In sections from these two localities (Figs. 24,32) the higher level is directly below the sharp increase of Ericales pollen and the lower level rests above a peak of lodgepole pine pollen. Both levels are separated by sedge, or predominantly sedge, peat, and the lower level is underlain by sedge peat. In some sections from British Columbia (Summit, Rainbow Lake, Upper Hope Island), the levels grade together, but correlations can still be drawn readily (Figs. 33,35). Only the upper level at Masset seems to be correlated with the Prince Rupert section (Fig. 33). These are the only ligneous horizons, considered recurrence surfaces, that appear to correlate satisfactorily in British Columbia. Some of the late-postglacial levels (for example, Susan Island, Fitzhugh Sound, and Lower Hope Island; Figs. 34, 35), however, are undoubtedly related, but in the absence of surfaces in muskeg areas located south of Hope Island on the British Columbia coast, this feature of the peat stratigraphy is only of partial value for correlation.

Three sections, Susan Island, Port Hardy, and Malahat, contain volcanic ash (Table 4, Figs. 34, 35, 37). The only major layer is found at Malahat at a depth of 4.2–4.3 m. This ash is almost certainly from Glacier Peak in Washington, as will be discussed subsequently (Rigg and Gould 1957). Since Glacier Peak ash has been radiocarbon dated, it is an excellent time marker in the bogs of southern coastal British Columbia and about Puget Sound. The minor ash horizon below the major layer at Malahat because of its proximity may also be related to Glacier Peak but this is uncertain. The relationship of the other minor horizon at ca 2.0-m depth and of the ash at the base of the Port Hardy section is unknown. It is peculiar that this minor level does not show up in the deep sections from Menzies Bay and Harbledown Island, which lie between the Malahat and Port Hardy sites, particularly since Hansen (1950a) found ash in intervening sites in the vicinity of Qualicum Beach and Black River. Ash at Pitt Island is quite recent and may have come from the volcanic area about the Nass River in the northern British Columbia Coast Mountains.

Fires have been widespread and have occurred repeatedly as indicated by the numerous levels of charred peat examined in the course of the study. The following sites and their horizons of burned peat attest to the incidence of fire: Prince Rupert (various levels between the surface and 4.4 m), Rainbow Lake (0.3), Summit (the surface to 0.3), Masset (6.7 and 6.9 and various levels between the surface and 4.8), Susan Island (various levels between 0.1 and 1.1), Fitzhugh Sound (various levels between the surface and 1.0), Upper Hope Island (various levels between the surface and 2.0), Lower Hope Island (various levels between 0.2 and 1.5), Harbledown Island (various levels between the surface and 0.8), Menzies Bay (0.2), and Little Qualicum Falls (various levels between 0.3 and 1.6).

Washington, Oregon, and California

The remaining sections, 66 through 78, in Washington, Oregon, and California (Table 4), not only have the greatest average depth, 7.4 m, in the study region but are also the most difficult to interpret stratigraphically (Figs. 38–46). Four of the sections, Whidbey Island, Wessler, Devils Lake, and Garrison Lake, are between 10.0 and 15.0 m deep, and of those remaining, none is less than 2.5 in depth. All peat types encountered previously are present. Limnic, sedge, and ligneous types are most abundantly represented whereas bryophytic peat is far less important in this coastal segment than it is to the northwest. Woody surfaces are numerous in some sections; for example, ten at Whidbey Island. Volcanic ash of the Glacier Peak eruption was located at only two sites, Pangborn Lake and Whidbey Island in Washington.

It is unfortunate that Glacier Peak ash does not occur in more sections of this study. Its presence only at Malahat in British Columbia and at Pangborn Lake and Whidbey Island (Figs. 37–39) limits its usefulness, but in these places it serves as an excellent guide for correlation. Where it is found in close association with ligneous peat at Whidbey Island, its value is even further enhanced. Because the major ash-fall has been bracketed by radiocarbon dates, the interpretation of the ligneous peat stratigraphy and of the pollen stratigraphy has a firm basis. The three ash levels between 5.5 and 7.5 m at Pangborn Lake, tentatively designated the Glacier Peak eruption interval, may be correlated with the two levels between 4.2 and 4.9 m at Malahat. The minor level at the base of the Pangborn Lake section is not in place in all likelihood and has probably been reworked by glaciofluvial action from an earlier eruption.

The positions of the major ligneous surfaces at Vhidbey Island show a parallelism with those at Masset and those in Southeastern Alaska. The two and possibly three surfaces above the ash and below the prominent interval of Ericales pollen appear to correlate with the upper wood peat at Masset and at Lower Montana Creek in the Juneau area (Figs. 24, 32). The position of the ligneous remains below the ash suggests correspondence with the lower wood peat at these places. Besides showing a parallelism, the surfaces may be roughly synchronous as well. At Whidbey Island, the ash, given a radiocarbon age of ca 6700 yr (Rigg and Gould 1957), is between ligneous horizons that are correlated with Juneau horizons having radiocarbon ages 3500 yr and less than 7800 yr.

Further stratigraphic relationships appear between the wood surfaces at Whidbey Island and those at other sites studied in the western United States. The wood peat in the lower half of the section at Ozette Lake (Fig. 41), below the slight prominence in Ericales pollen, seems connected with some or all of the Whidbey Island wood layers resting below a similar Ericales-pollen peak. The Wessler (Fig. 40) stratigraphy is complex but a like connection can be drawn with the upper major horizon at this site. Also, the Whidbey Island minor horizon just below 9.0 m may be correlated with the upper horizon at Devils Lake (Fig. 43) and probably with the wood peat at Seaview (Fig. 42), since all occur at or above the Ericales prominence. To attempt additional correlations seems risky.

As in the other sections of the study region, fire is in evidence here as well. At Whidbey Island charred peat is found at 0.1, 0.2, and 0.3 m; at numerous levels between 1.2 and 5.7; at 7.1 and 9.3; and between 10.4 and 10.7. In the Wessler section it occurs at 4.4, 4.5, and 8.5 m; at Ozette between 1.0 and 1.5; at Humptulips, at 1.1 and 1.2; and at Seaview at all levels between 0.3 and 2.1. In Oregon, charring at Devils Lake is at 0.1, 0.2, 0.9, 1.0, 1.1, and 7.2 m; at Tahkenitch Lake, 0.6, 0.7, 2.7, 4.6, 4.8, 6.4, and 7.2; and at Garrison Lake at 0.9 and 1.0, between 4.7 and 4.9, and at all levels between 5.9 and 6.9. In California it occurs in the Capetown section at 2.0 and 3.2 m and in that at Ft. Bragg at numerous levels between 0.4 and 3.4.

Many of the sections contain varying amounts of nonorganic, undifferentiated sediments (largely sand, silt, and clay-size particles). In the sections close to present sea level, these sediments corroborate pollen-profile evidence of previous marine incursion. This is seen in the Devils Lake section (Fig. 43) at depths between 6.5 and ca 9.0 m where sand and clay-size particles form the bulk of the deposit; pollen is generally absent or in small quantities at these depths, where *Ruppia* and the Chenopodiaceae indicate a brackish-water environment. At Tahkenitch Lake (Fig. 44), sediments principally of silt and varying quantities of sand make up the deposit below 4.5-m depth. Again, *Ruppia* and the Chenopodiaceae are associated. In the Garrison Lake section (Fig. 45) the nonorganic sediments found at lower levels (mostly sands) also contain *Ruppia* pollen and delimit what appears to be this same episode of incursion. The Lake Earl section (Fig. 46) shows silt, presumably resulting from tidal action, in the lower part, although the peculiar distribution of *Ruppia*, as well as several other groups, indicates brackish conditions through most of the deposit.

Erosion following fires may account for the large amounts of silt in some sections. Wessler, Humptulips, and Fort Bragg (Figs. 40, 41, 46) contain silt that may have originated in this manner. Silt at the top of the Capetown section (Fig. 46) was formed recently when the lake was artifically but only temporarily drained.

POLLEN STRATIGRAPHY

Alaska Pollen Profiles

Southwestern District

Sitka Spruce (*Picea sitchensis*)

Perhaps the most striking profile from Kodiak and Afognak sections (Figs. 13, 14), in the Southwestern District of Alaska, is that of Sitka spruce. Pollen of this conifer is rare below 1-m depth but gradually increases in number from above this depth to below the Katmai ash. Above the ash, its proportion in almost every case is suddenly greater than any of the other plants depicted in the profiles. It appears to be overrepresented, particularly at localities where it is an important member of the flora at the site (for example, Cape Chiniak, Cape Greville 1 and 2, and Afognak; Figs. 13, 14). Nevertheless, the recency of the arrival of spruce on these islands, its rapid spread, and its increase in proportion to other species during the Late Postglacial are documented by historical accounts and vegetation studies (Griggs 1934). Its major ascendency seems to have occurred following the eruption of Mt. Katmai in 1912. Griggs points out in this regard that its vigor following the ashfall resulted from a decrease in competition between species, although a highly mineralized seed bed also seems to have been favorable for its rapid spread.

At Karluk (Fig. 13) only a single spruce grain was observed, and this was below a thin band of Katmai ash. The nearest spruce trees from which the pollen probably came are 20–25 mi eastward at Uyak Bay. No apparent change in spruce resulted following the ashfall at Karluk, but the small quantity of ash that fell on this part of the island may have been insufficient to influence the extension of spruce. Nonedaphic factors are no doubt registering more of a control of the spruce vanguard on Kodiak. From what is known of the autecology of this important forest tree, cool, moist summers and rainy or snowy winters lacking the temperature extremes of the interior are optimum for its growth and reproduction. From evidence contained in the pollen profiles, the establishment and western migration of spruce, Katmai ash notwithstanding, seems to be largely the result of cooling and an increase in humidity during the last few thousand years. A case in point is the fact that spruce appears to have been established on the islands prior to a pre-Katmai ashfall, but no significant change in spruce was registered after this ash was deposited.

Poplar (*Populus*)

The pollen of the genus is recorded at a number of levels in Southwestern Alaska sections. Usually never present in amounts of more than one or two grains, poplar at two sites (Cape Chiniak and Kodiak 3; Figs. 13, 14) formed 25 per cent or more of the pollen sum. Bowman (1934) identifies small amounts of poplar pollen to a depth of ca 4.0 m in his deepest section whereas in this study the genus is not recorded in spectra below 2.2. As previously mentioned, the preservation of poplar pollen is rather fortuitous, and when occasionally encountered under the microscope, the grains are usually badly damaged. It is impossible, unfortunately, to translate anything of value from such meager and questionable profiles.

Willow (*Salix*)

The genus is found in quantities of only a few per cent or less from the bottom to the surface of the oldest sections studied on both Kodiak and Afognak. No value can be ascribed to the profiles, other than a record of the presence of the plant. Greater amounts of willow were expected in the Karluk profile, but such were not found. Willow may have exhibited a greater proportion during the Late-glacial, which does not seem to be represented in the material collected on these islands.

Birch (*Betula*)

The general trend of the birch profiles is registered by the higher percentages during the Late Postglacial (for example, Cape Greville 1 and 2, Kodiak 3, and Afognak; Figs. 13, 14). Karluk and Cape Chiniak profiles (Fig. 13) are too young to serve for purposes of comparison. In all profiles, the importance of birch is far less at the top.

To properly interpret this behavior, individual profiles for the representative species (*Betula kenaica* and *B. nana* subsp. *exilis*) are essential. Short of this information, generalizations only can be made. However, one favorable point bearing on an interpretation is that both species range mostly northward into the interior of Alaska and only reach southerly stations on Kodiak. This is indicative of their ecological character, that is, both grow under a climate of greater continentality—temperatures over these latitudes are low in winter and cool in summer and precipitation is low. An increase in the amount of birch during the Late Postglacial would, therefore, imply a lowering of temperature. In view of the fact that spruce, indicative of moisture and moderate temperatures, is the predominant pollen at the top of the profiles where birch declines, a recent trend toward oceanity seems apparent.

Alder (*Alnus*)

Only a single species of alder (*Alnus crispa* subsp. *sinuata*) grows on the Kodiak-Afognak archipelago. It is principally coastal around the Gulf of Alaska and southward, but is also known to occur at a number of scattered stations in the Alaskan interior. Its position in succession is that of an early woody invader, and the sites where it is now found producing good growth in the absence of conifers in this coastal region are probably able to support Sitka spruce. Spruce does not seem to occupy these potentially suitable areas because of a slow rate of migration, which causes it to lag behind the alder. Ecologically, alder requires a moist climate with moderate temperature. Where winter snowfall does not cover the plant, exposed branches are commonly killed by snow blasting under cold conditions. Alder appears to suffer less under high temperature, which periodically prevails in summer.

Alder is recorded in small amounts below the bottom ash layers at the bases of the older sections but in the lower part, between the lower and middle ash horizons, it achieves supremacy in the hypsithermal deposits. Subsequently, it declines. In some cases (Cape Greville 1 and 2, Fig. 13) this decline is well developed; in others (Kodiak 1, 2, and 3, and Afognak; Fig. 14) it is only gradual. If it were not for the strong representation of spruce at upper levels, alder would appear to increase over this part of the section. For example, at Karluk (Fig. 13) where spruce does not grow, a slight increase in the amount of alder occurs; moreover, at Kodiak 1, alder appears to be more abundant in the upper profile, where the amount of spruce is relatively low, than at midprofile.

Alder behaves for the most part out of phase with birch and is generally more abundant than birch. From what has been said about its autecology, the climatic conditions that prevailed when the lower sediments of the profile below the bottom ash were deposited appear to have been colder than the present. Later, between the deposition of the bottom and middle ash, conditions became moderate, but above the middle ash a reversion occurred, which has ended only recently.

AP-NAP

The climatic succession outlined above is also borne out by the profiles for arboreal and nonarboreal pollen. These developed reciprocally so that the fluctuation in one is reflected by the fluctuation of the other. They are of questionable value, mainly because it is difficult to strictly categorize entire plant groups as nonarboreal or arboreal, although in this case they substantiate the implications of a number of the individual profiles.

Grass (Gramineae)

Pollen of the grass family is distributed throughout the sections. The profiles, however, display no prominent changes. At Karluk (Fig. 13), where tundra covers considerable area and the family is well represented, its profile is somewhat better developed than at the other sites where tundra is less extensive.

Sedge (Cyperaceae)

A consistent feature of the sedge profiles in the older sections is the prominence below the lower ash layer in the early-postglacial zone. Upward in the profiles, the amount of sedge pollen becomes less, except for the sharp peak below the middle ash at Cape Greville 2 and the gradual increase in the upper levels at Kodiak 3 and Karluk (Figs. 13, 14). These exceptions appear to be the result of variations in local conditions. The occurrence of an abundance of sedge, an important tundra plant, in the general absence of arboreal species at lower levels is indicative of a colder environment, characteristic of tundra. With later amelioration, the tundra was reduced in area by colonies of alder and birch.

Sweet Gale (*Myrica*)

The profile is similar to that of birch; both show greater abundance in late-postglacial sediments. The profile of sweet gale is best developed at Afognak (Fig. 14), whereas in the other sections it is fragmentary. Nevertheless, a peak just above the middle ash at Afognak appears in four other sections. At Cape Greville 1 and Karluk (Fig. 13), grains of the genus are rare.

Umbellifer (Umbelliferae)

As profiles from Afognak, Cape Greville 2, and Kodiak 1, 2, and 3 (Figs. 13, 14) disclose, umbellifer pollen is found chiefly in early-postglacial sediments at lower levels, where sedge is generally abundant. This is of significance for it supports the interpretation that tundra communities flourished on this landscape during the Early Postglacial preceding the invasion by birch and alder.

Heath (Ericales)

The evident strengthening of the Ericales profile above the middle ash stratum but below Katmai ash is rather conspicuous. In this respect, the heath profile develops and weakens much like birch and to some extent like sweet gale. Maxima for birch and Ericales appear more or less synchronous whereas most sweet gale maxima precede these. As will be seen, the form of the Ericales profile in Kodiak-Afognak sections is found in most sections elsewhere in the study region.

Since the Ericales is largely an entomophilous order, its pollen is derived mostly from plants growing at the sites. A greater proportion of the heath pollen in the upper levels accordingly would result from local invasions by members of the group, which being arctic-alpine in character, ecologically reflects a cold environment. The relatively large amount of Ericales pollen found at Karluk in the tundra is cogent evidence of a cold environment (Fig. 13). This interpretation corroborates that made of the birch profiles.

Fern (Polypodiaceae)

What climatic-indicator value can be attributed to the apparent abundance of fern spores in the basal levels of older sections is uncertain. For one thing, the tremendous production of spores by the family has resulted in overrepresentation. For another, the high percentage is probably caused only by a local fern cover growing under the wet conditions of the site and does not necessarily reveal a prevalence of fern in the surrounding plant communities. The Polypodiaceae was undoubtedly represented in the regional vegetation, but sedge was the major plant cover along with the umbellifers and several other known groups. To conclude that the prevailing early-postglacial climate was cold but undergoing mollification seems reasonable.

Sphagnum

The *Sphagnum* profile develops much like the Ericales profile but it tends to reach a prominence higher in the section. In almost every case, this prominence weakens at the surface. Since the profile is derived independently of the others, it is unaffected by the sudden predominance of Sitka spruce at and near the surface. *Sphagnum* is considered a fairly reliable climate indicator of cooling and a rise in humidity. The form of its profile in the Kodiak-Afognak sections is repeated all along the coast and parallels the evidence from the peat stratigraphy previously discussed.

Other Profiles

Sanguisorba, although present by no more than a few per cent, is consistently found in the basal sediments of the older sections and in the section from Karluk (Figs. 13, 14). It is an important member of the present tundra on Kodiak and, apparently, was also a constituent of this type of vegetation when the older sections were first being formed. Another important profile, although also weak and fragmentary, is that of *Rubus chamaemorus*. Almost unfailingly this profile is best formed in the upper levels in association with *Sphagnum*, the Ericales, and birch. A typically arctic species, its presence with these plants of similar arctic affinity points convincingly to cooling during the formation of this part of the sections. Two of the deposits, Cape Greville 2 and Kodiak 2, underwent hydrarch succession early in their formation, as indicated by the amount of *Potamogeton* at low levels.

South-Central District

Lodgepole Pine (*Pinus contorta*)

The northwestern coastal limit of lodgepole is on the Yakutat foreland (Johnson and Sandor 1957), but the Cordova, Alaganik 1 and 2, Upper Katalla, Bering Lake, and Munday Creek sections from the South-Central Alaska District show solitary grains from this tree (Figs. 16–18). These are believed to have been transported by wind from the southeastern panhandle, where lodgepole is found thriving chiefly on muskeg. During the Late-glacial and Early Postglacial the tree occupied an important position in the vegetation of this part of the coast. Its occurrence in the lower sediments of the Munday Creek section and near the bottom of the Alaganik 1 section, both dated over 10,000 yr B. P., is almost certainly a result of long-distance transport from the forest to the southeast, where it abounded at this same time. Lodgepole at present is ca 100 mi from the Munday Creek site, which is nearest the limit of its range at Yakutat; 10,000 yr ago it was probably about 250 mi distant from this site. This latter approximation is made on the basis of the Excursion Inlet section in the Southeastern District (Heusser 1954c), the nearest early-postglacial site exhibiting lodgepole predominantly at its base. Interestingly, the grains in the Munday Creek section are distributed toward the base and toward the top, which corresponds to the lodgepole profile in the Southeastern District. The grain at the surface at Cordova represents a transport distance of at least 225 mi.

Spruce (*Picea*)

Three species of spruce, white (*P. glauca*), Sitka (*P. sitchensis*), and black (*P. mariana*), and an unknown number of hybrids (for example, *P. lutzii* Little) are treated in the profiles of the South-Central District. Where all of these are present on the Kenai Peninsula, only black spruce could be separated. At the sites of most of the sections Sitka spruce is the solitary species. Profiles from the Kenai, Prince William Sound, and those southeastward will be examined in that order.

Spruce profiles from the Kenai exhibit certain characteristics. Spruce is best portrayed in late-postglacial deposits; older sections do not disclose spruce pollen at depth (below 4.0 m and mostly less). The white spruce-Sitka spruce complex about Homer, at Saxton, and at Moose Pass (Figs. 15, 16, 18) begins to appear much earlier than black spruce. At Seward, Sitka spruce is somewhat more important at depth than the spruce complex at Homer (Figs. 15–17). From the evidence contained in the Homer 1 and Seward sections, spruce forest (or enclaves) has existed for a longer time on the gulf coast of the Kenai Peninsula than on the "inside" coast along Cook Inlet.

Gulf of Alaska coastal stations (Seward, Windy Bay, and Port Chatham; Fig. 17) generally display stronger spruce profiles through the upper ca 1 m of the sections. The oceanic climate has apparently been more conducive to the development of Sitka spruce in recent millennia. About Kachemak Bay in the vicinity of Homer, increased continentality of the climate seems to have withheld its advance.

Southwestward migration of Sitka spruce, evidenced by a comparison of the profiles from Seward, Windy Bay, and Port Chatham, has taken place quite recently and is reminiscent of the rise of spruce on Afognak and Kodiak. Sitka spruce has grown in the vicinity of Seward since at least the Late-glacial, but only over the last several thousand years has it been able to extend its range. The extension is attributed to some cooling and an increase in atmospheric moisture.

In Prince William Sound spruce is displayed best in the upper levels of profiles at Hinchinbrook Island and Cordova, less at Alaganik 1 and 2, still less at Montague Island, and least at Perry Island (Figs. 19, 20). Thus, spruce decreases in the pollen record from the eastern sound about Cordova toward the Copper River mouth in one direction, and toward the western and northwestern sound in another. The pattern of existing vegetation is in keeping with the relative abundance of spruce recorded in the profiles. Some of the best forest cover in the sound is in the neighborhood of Cordova. In the western sound and about Alaganik, on the other hand, generally a poor class of forest cover exists in the immediate coastal areas; inland, shallow and treeless muskeg covered with tundra species occupies much of the low, sloping, hilly terrain.

Southeastward from the Copper River mouth at Upper and Lower Katalla, Martin Lake, and Bering Lake (Fig. 21), a weak spruce profile is quite similar to that at Alaganik. Spruce as well as other forest growth is poor and occurs in limited areas at these places. At Munday Creek (Fig. 22) the strongest profile of the South-Central District is seen. It begins ca 2 m above the base of the section and fluctuates upward in phase with the other coniferous species. Since these fluctuations, peculiar to this section, are in phase with other conifers but out of phase with alder, periodic disturbances resulting in repeated plant successions seem to have caused the changes. What the periodic disturbances may have been is not definitely known. The location of the Munday Creek section suggests two possibilities or combinations of these: (1) land–sea-level changes resulting in terrace formation, and (2) glacier variations.

The Munday Creek deposit, considered to be resting on a marine terrace, is situated above three other terraces (D. J. Miller, personal communication). Since the three lower terraces postdate the Munday Creek level and each has undergone plant succession (alder followed by spruce and other conifers) while becoming subaerial, it is likely that pollen produced by succeeding species during the formation of each terrace would become incorporated in the Munday Creek section. The emergence of the major terrace of the three is dated at about 1050 B. P. (Rubin and Alexander 1958), and the latest peaks for alder and spruce may record this event. The upper minor terrace resting between this major level and Munday Creek may be represented by the preceding peaks. The remaining lower minor terrace appears to be too insignificant and too recent to have possibly left any evidence in the pollen profiles.

Glacier variation is considered the other possible causal factor because of the location of the section and what is known about the recent glaciation nearby. Munday Creek is on a relatively short stretch of coast between the great piedmont tongues of Bering and Malaspina Glaciers. The recent advance of the Malaspina and neighboring glaciers that filled nearby Icy Bay is dated at its culmination between 600 and 920 A. D. (Plafker and Miller 1958). Pollen from alder and spruce, which succeeded as the ice front withdrew, may have caused the uppermost changes in the Munday Creek profiles. The recent history of the Bering Glacier is little known, but a corresponding interval of advance and plant succession is considered a likelihood along at least part of its front. Previous fluctuations in the profiles suggest the possibility of advances before that which reached its maximum between 600 and 920 A. D.

Western Hemlock (*Tsuga heterophylla*)

The northwestern coastal limit of the range of western hemlock is western Prince William Sound or the southeastern part of the Kenai Peninsula. As would be expected, Kenai sections do not reveal this conifer, with the exception of Port Chatham, which contains individual grains at and near the surface (Fig. 17). In the remainder of the district, the profiles are developed in the upper levels later than spruce, but the degree of development in each area follows the pattern for spruce. About Prince William Sound, for example, the best development is at Cordova and Hinchinbrook Island, while the poorest is at Perry and Montague Islands (Figs. 19, 20). Munday Creek, like Cordova, shows an abundance of western hemlock in the upper half of the section; Alaganik 1 and 2, Upper and Lower Katalla, and Martin and Bering Lakes register only small amounts (Figs. 21, 22).

When Sitka spruce succeeds on a landscape where western hemlock is present, hemlock usually will in turn predominate over spruce under conditions of physiographic stability and in the absence of fire. This is so because of hemlock's high degree of shade tolerance and the alteration, during preceding succession, of soil factors favorable to its growth and reproduction. Where hemlock is at the end of its range, however, its numbers being relatively few and conditions less favorable, succession proceeds slowly. The replacement of spruce by hemlock, which has hastened recently, is well portrayed by the profiles. It has taken place over an interval of an estimated several thousand years when the environment was suitable for the establishment of hemlock as an important member of the forest in this district. Spruce and western hemlock appear to have been present for a longer time, though not in extensive forest stands. Their rise in importance in many sectors is associated with the late-postglacial climatic change toward coolness with greater humidity.

Mountain Hemlock (*Tsuga mertensiana*)

Mountain hemlock extends farther westward than western hemlock, reaching to Cook Inlet in the vicinity of Turnagain Arm. It is present in the Kenai profiles in greater numbers than western hemlock, as expected. In sections about Homer and at Windy Bay (Figs. 15–17) only individual grains are recorded at a few levels, but at Seward, Moose Pass, Saxton, and Girdwood (Figs. 17, 18) the species forms profiles comparable to, or even more prominent than, spruce. The finest development of the mountain hemlock profile in the entire district is at Cordova (Fig. 20).

In most instances, the bulk of the pollen began to appear later than spruce and in this regard, mountain hemlock behaves very much like western hemlock. However, in several places, most notably at Cordova and Perry Island (Figs. 19, 20), it appeared in greatest abundance before spruce had gained in importance. Mountain hemlock, being able to endure under climatic conditions of increased continentality (less humidity and greater temperature extremes), had pioneered on such sites before spruce could achieve importance. Mountain hemlock is not capable of enduring the extremes of the interior to the extent white spruce or birch are, but it is considered the most "continental" of the coastal conifers. In this respect, the form of its profile discloses that late-postglacial coolness and wetness at some places was preceded to a greater extent by temperature lowering than by humidity change.

Willow (*Salix*)

Grains are scattered individually or in small numbers throughout the sections. At the sites where they are recorded in greater quantities in basal sediments (Homer 1, Saxton, Perry Island, Alaganik 1, Bering Lake, Munday Creek; Figs. 15, 18–22), late-glacial tundra environments are interpreted.

Birch (*Betula*)

Where they are best developed, birch profiles for the Kenai sections show the form of those from Kodiak and Afognak but, in addition, reveal a basal prominence (for example, Homer 1 and Seward; Figs. 15, 17). It is apparent from this that Kodiak-Afognak sections are truncated below and do not possess a late-glacial record. On the Kenai the Late-glacial is associated with the lower birch peak as well as peaks for other indicator groups (for example, *Salix*). In western Prince William Sound, the birch profile on Perry Island (Fig. 19) is weak, although during the Late-glacial it had been strengthened. Farther eastward in the district birch grains were encountered only occasionally.

Alder (*Alnus*)

Alder has the most robust profile in almost every section in the district. The characteristic shape of its profile is much the same as it is for Kodiak and Afognak; that is, maximum quantities of alder are encountered in the hypsithermal zone and in the Late Postglacial amounts decrease, and markedly so, at most sites.

The interpretation of the profile changes for this district is the same as that for the Kodiak area. Alder supremacy at lower levels occurred under a climate somewhat warmer and drier than that which followed. Although there are many instances where conifers developed profiles during this episode, they failed to succeed alder because, it is thought, they were not able to advance from areally limited and microclimatically controlled habitats where suitable higher humidity and coolness prevailed. The fluctuations of the alder profile at Munday Creek (Fig. 22), as previously discussed, are presumably a peculiar case probably resulting from the formation of marine terraces and/or from glacier variations.

AP-NAP

Since alder is considered an arboreal-pollen type and dominates at least a part of almost every set of profiles, the AP profile shows a striking similarity to it. Alder controls large parts of the NAP profile as well, owing to the reciprocal nature of the AP and NAP profiles.

These profiles are not necessary in the diagrams, as they merely represent the sums of two groups of plants with different life forms whose profiles can be studied individually. Their value lies in the picture they provide of the general trends in particularly old sections. In the Munday Creek section (Fig. 22), for example, the gradual replacement of nonarboreal groups can be seen at a glance. For a more definitive interpretation, however, every profile must be examined.

Grass (Gramineae)

In the vegetation of this district, grass is relatively unimportant except in the western Kenai Peninsula. The grass profiles are likewise of little consequence with the exception of this part of the Kenai. Percentages are low, generally less than 5 per cent, but appear to be highest at the level of alder predominance, prior to the invasion by conifers and the rise of the Ericales profile. The oldest section, Homer 1, shows this feature of the Gramineae profile best; in Homer 3 it is also seen but less convincingly (Figs. 15, 16). Contrary to what might be expected, the Gramineae occur only occasionally in the late-glacial sediments.

Sedge (Cyperaceae)

The most consistent trend of the sedge profiles, as depicted by diagrams from the oldest sections, is from high proportions at basal levels, to lower at midprofile, to higher again in upper areas. Kodiak-Afognak profiles in the Southwestern District show a basal abundance, but no strengthening of the profiles is distinguishable in the other districts. The very marked appearance of Sitka spruce in the upper parts of the South-Central sections may have masked any later increase of sedge.

Sedge in the absence of arboreal species is clearly a member of the pollen assemblage that designated tundra during the Late-glacial. During the Late Postglacial it again came into prominence, reflecting the surface vegetation of the section site, in itself a diminutive tundra at that time. The increase of the proportion of sedge pollen, along with increases of the Ericales and *Sphagnum* (as will be seen), is indicative of the rejuvenation of these plants on the surface of the peat as climate became cool and moist. The surface flora varied from site to site, but the changes noted during the Late Postglacial represent individual responses to an over-all climatic alteration.

Skunk Cabbage (*Lysichitum*)

The species *L. americanum* is only rarely encountered in the peats of the Kenai Peninsula. In Prince William Sound, particularly on Montague and Hinchinbrook Islands where it registers short but sharp prominences, and at Cordova, the species is better represented (Figs. 19, 20). Eastward it has developed peaks in profiles at Upper Katalla and Munday Creek (Figs. 21, 22).

Skunk cabbage is valuable as an indicator of a high degree of humification, characteristic of a static or retrogressive peat surface. A peak for the species is usually followed by increases in the sedge, heath, and *Sphagnum* profiles. This change ensues as a response to the late-postglacial climatic fluctuation favoring anew the formation of peat. In many cases a decline of the skunk cabbage profile marks the close of the Hypsithermal.

Sweet Gale (*Myrica*)

The profile in this district is similar to Kodiak and Afognak profiles, although it is commonly weak or nonrepresented. Its best expression is found at Homer 2 (Fig. 16). Where the profile attains any degree of distinctiveness at higher levels, an association with *Sphagnum* is commonly seen.

Umbellifer (Umbelliferae)

The Umbelliferae occur in amounts of a few per cent or less in many of the sections. Only on the Kenai Peninsula at Homer 1, however, are they identified with the Early Postglacial as in the Southwestern District (Fig. 15). The group is a constituent of early tundra vegetation.

Heath (Ericales)

At almost every site Ericales gains greater representation in the upper parts of the sections. In this respect, it shows no dissimilarity to heath profiles in the Southwestern District. In another, however, the profile differs: at the bottom of several older sections heath pollen is more abundant during the late-glacial and early-postglacial intervals (for example, Homer 1, Seward, Alaganik 1, and Munday Creek; Figs. 15, 17, 20, 22).

The Late-glacial is not in evidence on Kodiak and Afognak in the Southwestern District. This conclusion is reached not only because heath is absent from basal sediments, but also because birch and willow are not found. Heath profiles for the Late Postglacial in the Southwestern District are distinctly stronger than those from the South-Central District.

Fern (Polypodiaceae)

Fern spores continue to be found in profusion in the lower sediments of the older sections. This interval succeeded during early-postglacial time as amelioration of the late-glacial climate occurred. It is considered to be a consequence of the local establishment of the family under the moist conditions at the site, but does not wholly reflect regional vegetation.

Higher in the profile, the number of fern spores declines, although variations occur (for example, Homer 2, Perry Island, and Lower Katalla; Figs. 16, 19, 21), which are presumably dependent upon local vegetation dynamics and water relations.

Sphagnum

The general form of the profile is strengthened in the upper parts of the sections. Heath and sedge, in many cases, parallel this trend. When the upper sediments of these sections were deposited, the growth of these plants was enhanced by a climate favorable for their invigoration. Recently the *Sphagnum* profiles at most sites have weakened after the attainment of maxima. Parallelism is seen with the profiles of the Southwestern District.

There is some indication that during late-glacial time this bryophyte was somewhat more abundant (Homer 1, Perry Island, and Munday Creek; Figs. 15, 19, 22). Since *Sphagnum* is a common member of tundra communities, its presence during this interval is not unusual.

Other Profiles

Sanguisorba, included in the list of tundra elements of the Late-glacial and Early Postglacial, appeared in the Homer 1, Perry Island, Alaganik 1, Bering Lake, and Munday Creek sections (Figs. 15, 19–22) during either or both of these episodes. Munday Creek section is particularly valuable since it reveals an additional assemblage of typical tundra plants, not previously mentioned, of the Late-glacial and/or Early Postglacial: *Fritillaria*, *Rubus*, *Polemonium*, Tubuliflorae, *Lycopodium annotinum*, *L. selago*, and *Selaginella selaginoides*.

Hydrarch succession early in the history of Homer 1 and 2, Seward, Perry Island, Cordova, and Bering Lake deposits (Figs. 15–17, 19–21) is disclosed by transitory increase in *Nuphar* and *Potamogeton* at lower levels.

Southeastern District

Lodgepole Pine (*Pinus contorta*)

In the earliest pollen spectra in the Southeastern District of Alaska, the quantity of lodgepole pine present is no more than a few per cent (for example, Hasselborg Lake; Fig. 27). Subsequently, lodgepole achieves in most instances the highest percentages in its profiles (for example, Hasselborg Lake, Upper Montana Creek, and

Salmon Bay; Figs. 24, 27, 29). During the Late-glacial when lodgepole occurred as the only coniferous species with sedge, willow, and alder, a parkland-type vegetative cover is suggested. Later, as pine reached its major peak, it became the featured early-postglacial invader participating in succession. Climatic amelioration, which favored its advance, and its ability to persist under the adversity of physiographic instability following glaciation (avalanching, flooding, earth movement, and other catastrophic changes) are the reasons for its high proportion in the pollen record at that time.

The proportion of pine subsequently declined as the landscape became relatively stabilized, and shade-intolerant pine was replaced by Sitka spruce and western and mountain hemlocks. In a number of instances, the decline was so pronounced that lodgepole was not represented for a time. This condition prevailed during the Hypsithermal when peat accumulation at the sites was retarded, and the surfaces became suitable for invasion by forest conifers. The buried ligneous-peat horizons in most of the sections attest to this invasion and temporary occupancy by forest species. Not only was pine displaced locally at the site of deposition but also regionally, so that its survival was seriously threatened. The only localities where it was likely to have survived are near the forests edge on cliffs bordering the ocean and along the fiords where survival was not endangered by competition for light by the other conifers.

During the latter part of the Postglacial, following the climatic shift to coolness and wetness, forest trees, unable to thrive at the sites, were killed, and their remains were later buried by sedge and bryophytic peat. In this manner the prominent recurrence surface or *Grenzhorizont*, dated at ca 3500 B. P. in this district, was formed. As climate began to change and openings appeared in the forest cover on the muskeg sites, lodgepole again became established. Through the Late Postglacial pine has risen in importance in its profiles, more so at sites near sea level than at higher elevations. The late-postglacial growth and spread of muskeg and the regional displacement by muskeg of terrain occupied by forest during the Hypsithermal are responsible for the increase of pine in the profiles and its more secure position in the vegetation.

At Grand Plateau Glacier (Fig. 23), just southeast of the Yakutat coastal plain, where pine is very near the northwestern coastal limit of its range, the species is prominently displayed in the upper part of its profile. Pine has been present in the neighborhood of this site for the last ca 1000 yr but has not been able to migrate much farther to the northwest. If it were not for the barriers imposed by the Malaspina and Bering Glaciers, it is likely that lodgepole might have been able to extend its range farther northwestward along the coast.

Sitka Spruce (*Picea sitchensis*)

Following the lodgepole maximum during the Early Postglacial, Sitka spruce gained superiority among the conifers. This succession, which is illustrated by the sequence of dominants in the profiles, is quite similar to that occurring on modern moraines and outwash as glaciers recede. Sitka spruce, being a poor competitor of the highly tolerant western hemlock, registered only a transient peak and was replaced by hemlock to a large extent. But periodic disturbances maintained the species by way of glacier recession, avalanches, blowdowns, floods, and fires, so that spruce was repeatedly participating in succession. These disturbing influences account for the maintenance of the spruce profile after its maximum had been reached.

Western Hemlock (*Tsuga heterophylla*)

The early-postglacial succession following lodgepole predominance was from alder to Sitka spruce to western and mountain hemlocks in association with Sitka spruce. The invasion of Sitka spruce forest by hemlock followed in the Southeastern District, as in the Prince William Sound region to the northwest. Before hemlock was able to become established permanently, however, even under a favorable climate, edaphic requirements had to be satisfied and alder and Sitka spruce altered the edaphic environment advantageously for hemlock invasion.

Following the Hypsithermal, the climate again became cooler and more humid. This change appears to have been most favorable to western hemlock, for the greatest proportion of the species is exhibited in its profiles at this time. At Hobart Bay and at Hollis (Figs. 28, 30), where the amount of peat accumulation has been extraordinary during the Late Postglacial, its characteristic maximum is well illustrated.

Mountain Hemlock (*Tsuga mertensiana*)

Of the four coniferous species represented by profiles—lodgepole pine, Sitka spruce, western hemlock, and mountain hemlock—mountain hemlock is usually the last to develop in any great proportion, following the appearance of western hemlock. The species is recorded at the time of the pine maximum, but only in amounts of a few per cent or less. Mountain hemlock has ecological requirements in many respects similar to those of western hemlock; until they could be satisfied, the tree was unable to succeed.

Its profile is weak in most sections. Characteristically, a peak is registered soon after the appearance of the species at depth, after which a gradual decline takes place. This form is best seen at Upper Montana Creek, Whitestone Harbor, and Southeastern Gokachin Lakes (Figs. 24, 25, 31). Representation is best in the late-postglacial deposits.

Willow (*Salix*)

Grains of willow occur sporadically in almost all the sections, and sharp peaks of brief duration appear in the profiles from the lower sediments of the older deposits. These peaks identify the Late-glacial where they precede the basal prominence in the lodgepole pine profiles and occur with small amounts of lodgepole. The Late-glacial, when a cold and moderately moist climate appeared, is represented in this district at Upper Montana Creek and Hasselborg Lake (Figs. 24, 27).

Alder (*Alnus*)

Alder, as a pioneer participating in succession, appears most abundantly at the lower levels of older sections. Its maximum is contemporaneous with either the Late-glacial or Early Postglacial and occurred prior to the Sitka spruce maximum. Except for this peak early in the profile, the proportion of alder is small and generally less than in the profiles from the South-Central District. The largest proportion in the Southeastern District is found in sections about Lituya Bay (Fig. 23).

Ditch Grass (*Ruppia*)

The Sarkar Lake section (Fig. 30) is underlain by a brackish-water deposit that grades upward through lagoonal sediments into freshwater peat. This succession is borne out by the pollen profiles, in which *Ruppia* is the most distinctive brackish-lagoon indicator. *Ruppia* produced large quantities of pollen (maximum 82 per cent) through almost 1 m of sediments in the lower part of the section. Since its profile abruptly gains prominence several decimeters above the base, and below this, pollen is from plants indicating varying degrees of brackishness, fluctuations in the tidal range affecting the site are suggested. *Potamogeton* and the Chenopodiaceae, evident below the height of the *Ruppia* profile, include species of brackish affinity, and the sequence may have resulted from physical changes and plant succession in a tidal environment that terminated with *Ruppia* predominance. The sudden decline of *Ruppia* indicates an abrupt fall in tide level with no greater subsequent incursion.

Sedge (Cyperaceae)

Sedge profiles, depicting mainly *Carex*, *Scirpus*, and *Eriophorum*, but probably to some extent also *Rynchospora* in certain sections, do not display a consistent form in the Southeastern District. In the late-glacial deposits, sedge is usually represented, and before and after the peak of the skunk cabbage profiles, sedge may rise in proportion. Subsequently, it often fluctuates with the Ericales and *Sphagnum*. Its behavior appears to be a response to the local conditions affecting plant succession on the surface of the deposit. It is believed that the pollen contributed to its profile has been derived almost entirely from local sources.

Skunk Cabbage (*Lysichitum*)

This plant attains a position of predominance in most sections during the Hypsithermal. In certain instances it is also found during the Early Postglacial, although never as early as the Late-glacial, as in the South-Central District. Since the species is frequently found together with ligneous-peat horizons in the diagrams (for example, Upper and Lower Montana Creek, Lemon Creek, Upper Lituya Bay, Hobart Bay, Whitestone Harbor, Threemile Arm, and Hollis; Figs. 23–26, 28, 30), forest with skunk cabbage forming most of the ground cover is visualized during this time. Drainage in these localities was no doubt impeded and conditions may have even been swampy in the spring and fall, but under the hypsithermal climate, water relations were apparently favorable for tree growth. Later, however, as the Hypsithermal closed and climate became more humid, the increase in ground water presumably precluded further tree growth. As a result the forest began to perish and the cover of skunk cabbage was practically eliminated. At present, skunk cabbage in the district occurs infrequently on muskeg, but in damp lowland forest the plant commonly grows luxuriantly.

Sweet Gale (*Myrica*)

In three sections, Kendrick Bay, Lower Northwest Lituya Bay, and Grand Plateau Glacier (Figs. 23, 31), the profile for the species *M. gale* accentuates sharply in the late-postglacial zone. Grains of sweet gale are recorded for previous intervals, but not until the Late Postglacial did they become abundant. The form of the profile is similar to that shown in sections in the two preceding districts. Although the autecology of the plant is little known, its behavior in coastal Alaska in conjunction with cool-climate indicators would accord it the same indicator value. Strengthening of its profile at Kendrick Bay appears to represent a transient stage in hydrarch succession at this site.

Heath (Ericales)

Southeastern Alaska heath profiles parallel those from the South-Central District, except for the fact that pollen of the group is not a part of the late-glacial spectra. Heath pollen, instead, first appeared during the Early Postglacial, but its trend from that time to the present follows the trends of the South-Central Alaskan profiles. The proportion of heath is much greater in Southeastern Alaska, however, and the profiles are some of the best developed in the diagrams. The greatest abundance of heath is found above the *Lysichitum* peak, and thereafter a decline, more rapid at the onset, is evident. This decline is interpreted primarily as a response to cooling, but climate was also less humid during the time the Ericales were preponderant. Later the climate must have become increasingly humid, for the group declined in importance, and *Sphagnum* and/or sedge rose briefly, or continued to rise to superiority among the plants forming the cover on muskeg. Recently, the tendency at a number of sites (for example, Lower Montana Creek, Lemon Creek, Hobart Bay, and Whitestone Harbor; Figs. 24, 25, 28) is toward the reinvigoration of heath and a weakening of *Sphagnum* profiles, suggesting decreased humidity and some cooling in the climatic regime.

Fern (Polypodiaceae)

The prevalence of spores of the Polypodiaceae in bottom sediments of the sections, regardless of their age, is readily apparent. For example, all the radiocarbon-dated sections in the Cape Fairweather sector (Fig. 23) reveal this prevalence. Sections from the South-Central District also suggest this to be the case, but without a chronological control conclusive remarks about this district are not possible. Because of the local succession of ferns at sites formed at different times, the stratigraphic correlations of sections using pollen data alone is not possible in some instances. Thus, the inclusion of the Polypodiaceae in the basic pollen sum may be open to question.

Ferns in the oldest sections were usually most abundant during the Early Postglacial and only moderate to infrequent in abundance during the Late-glacial. The profiles otherwise are mostly weak, except where ferns temporarily prevail locally during the inception of sedimentation and in three special cases involving lake deposits, where the profiles behave somewhat inversely. The special cases are Hasselborg Lake, Kendrick Bay, and Southeastern Gokachin Lakes (Figs. 27, 31). Hydrarch succession prevailing during the filling of the basin is apparently the underlying cause for the distinctiveness of these profiles. In each the abundance of ferns declined as limnic sediments became increasingly overlain by sedge and bryophytic

peat. Certain stratigraphic correlations are seen with the profile from Perry Island in the South-Central District (Fig. 19).

Sphagnum

Some anomalous trends are evident in the *Sphagnum* profiles, but the over-all direction of change is toward high percentages upward in the sections, followed by a decline at or near the surface. In several cases, rather sharp fluctuations tend to obscure the directional trends.

Limnic deposits contain low percentages of *Sphagnum* (for example, Hasselborg Lake, Kendrick Bay, and Southeastern Gokachin Lakes; Figs 27, 31), indicating that the source of large amounts in muskeg is the local surface *Sphagnum*. Although in many instances macroscopic remains of this bryophyte occur in abundance in the peat, only few spores were counted. In one extreme case at Hamilton Bay in the Alexander Archipelago (Fig. 29), not a single spore is evident although *Sphagnum* peat composes a part of the upper section.

Other Profiles

Following the pattern set in the two other Alaskan districts, the Umbelliferae appear in early-postglacial sediments (for example, Upper Montana Creek and Hasselborg Lake; Figs. 24, 27). *Sanguisorba* is found in late-glacial deposits at Hasselborg Lake. It is well distributed in a number of the sections but is most prevalent at upper levels.

Profiles for *Rubus chamaemorus*, in the main, range with those for the Ericales (for example, Hollis and Hobart Bay; Figs. 28, 30). *Lycopodium annotinum* also discloses a relationship with the Ericales, but appears later than *Rubus chamaemorus*. Spores of *Lycopodium inundatum*, observed only at Hollis in this district, were found in amounts as high as 16 per cent. The profile, which extends over more than 3 m of the section, is asymmetric to that for the Ericales. It reaches to within less than 1 m of the surface but halts abruptly for reasons unknown.

British Columbia Pollen Profiles

Lodgepole Pine (*Pinus contorta*)

Profiles for lodgepole pine in northern coastal British Columbia take on the same form as those for Alaska (for example, Masset, Rainbow Lake, and Harbledown Island; Figs. 32, 33, 36). To the south at Menzies Bay (Fig. 36) a like form is barely perceptible, however, and at Malahat (Fig. 37) at the southern end of Vancouver Island, basal predominance is the only similarity. At Malahat, lodgepole registers a fluctuating decline toward the surface. Percentages are comparatively high through most of the section and never show low values at midprofile, as is characteristic of diagrams to the north. These important differences may be caused by the strong increase of *Myrica* at upper levels and by the character of the sites, which, not being muskeg, were not subject to reinvasion by lodgepole in post-hypsithermal time.

The interpretation of the lodgepole pine profiles in this region is the same as is made for Alaskan profiles: the maximum at low levels is Early Postglacial, representing a stage in succession under a colder climate; the later minimum is mostly Hypsithermal; and the increase at upper levels is largely post-hypsithermal reinvasion, commonly following the highest prominent ligneous-peat stratum in the section.

An examination of the upper 0.5 m of the lodgepole profile almost consistently reveals a strikingly stronger representation of the species. For example, at Rainbow Lake (Fig. 33), the increase is from 21 to 70 per cent; at Summit (Fig. 33), from 14 to 53; at Pitt Island (Fig. 34), from 3 to 25; and at Susan Island (Fig. 34), from 13 to 43. Some Alaskan stations, such as Whitestone Harbor, Kendrick Bay, and Southeastern Gokachin Lakes (Figs. 25, 31), have this same trend. This change would suggest drying of the peat surface so that lodgepole might multiply, although alterations in the other profiles might possibly cause the change to be only apparent but not real. Fire, as shown by remains of charred plants in the peat, is known to have burned a number of these sites recently, and such removal of competition is also likely to have favored lodgepole.

Western White Pine (*Pinus monticola* Dougl.)

Western white pine, not noted in sections farther north than Port Hardy (Fig. 35), is only sparsely represented. There is a tendency for it to increase slightly at high levels, but the increase is almost imperceptible and is not considered to have indicator value.

Sitka Spruce (*Picea sitchensis*)

Spruce profiles are commonly weak in British Columbia, particularly those from the south-central and southern part of eastern Vancouver Island (for example, Menzies Bay and Malahat; Figs. 36, 37). Hansen (1950a) also finds this to be true in his pollen studies on Vancouver Island. Spruce is better represented, however, toward the northern part of the island and in adjacent areas (for example, Port Hardy and Harbledown Island; Figs. 35, 36), but the site of its greatest representation is at Masset on the Queen Charlotte Islands (Fig. 32). This pattern for abundance generally results from a local climatic influence. Spruce is a tree of the tidelands in proximity to the open ocean. Inland along the fiords and on the "inside" borders of the coastal islands, climate is less humid and the decrease of spruce is readily seen.

The place of Sitka spruce in succession during the early part of the Hypsithermal is much the same here as in Southeastern Alaska. Spruce succeeded alder and was succeeded, in turn, by hemlock. In the profiles, the spruce stage is usually recorded by a prominence, after which the species is most often weakly represented. This is illustrated in Summit, Rainbow Lake, Upper Hope Island, and Harbledown Island profiles (Figs. 33, 35, 36).

In some instances, spruce pollen attains significant percentages about the time of the early pine interval (11 per cent at Harbledown Island and 20 at Masset; Figs. 32, 36). Spruce in Alaska during this interval, however, never exceeded more than several per cent. A review of Hansen's (1947b) profiles for the Puget Lowland in Washington also discloses that spruce was important during the pine interval. It seems apparent from these data that the role of spruce as an invader with lodgepole pine becomes less important in the direction of Alaska.

Western Hemlock (*Tsuga heterophylla*)

Under conditions of physiographic stability and in the absence of fire, insect infestation, and other factors of disturbance, western hemlock will gain predominance over Sitka spruce. In British Columbia, as in Southeastern Alaska, this species of hemlock forms the next stage after spruce, but instead of declining subsequently, as spruce does, western hemlock increases in proportion upward in the profiles. It is generally well represented along the British Columbia coast, and in most instances, it tends to parallel the development and fluctuations of the *Sphagnum* profiles. The behavior of western hemlock here and in Alaska indicates that a gradual increase in humidity, more pronounced during late millennia, has been extensive along the North Pacific coast.

Mountain Hemlock (*Tsuga mertensiana*)

Mountain hemlock never develops strong profiles in sections from near sea level, but in those from higher elevations (for example, Rainbow Lake at 440 ft and Summit at 550; Fig. 33) a greater proportion of the tree is often evident. At Masset, Harbledown Island, Menzies Bay, and Malahat (Figs. 32, 36, 37), the species stands out, although weakly and for only a short duration, during the early part of hypsithermal deposition. In each case, it follows the appearance of spruce but precedes western hemlock. At Upper Hope Island (Fig. 35), its profile is also weak and short at the outset of the Hypsithermal but is more closely contemporaneous with western hemlock. The brief prominence of mountain hemlock presumably resulted from local plant succession during the postglacial migration of hemlock up into the mountains. The tree is at present mostly a montane-climax species growing best near timber line and for some distance below this level.

Above the prominence, mountain hemlock follows the trends of the western hemlock profiles (for example, Masset and Menzies Bay; Figs. 32, 36). During the remainder of the Hypsithermal, it was present in only meager amounts but under the cool climate of the Late Postglacial, the proportion of mountain hemlock increased.

Douglas Fir (*Pseudotsuga menziesii* [Mirb.] Franco)

The status of this conifer in plant succession during the Late Pleistocene was dependent upon climatic control and the incidence of fire. In climatically wet areas at low elevations, where western hemlock thrives in abundance, Douglas fir, because of its shade intolerance, is never able to perpetuate itself without the aid of fire and is succeeded by hemlock. Drier areas that exclude hemlock, on the other hand, permit Douglas fir to achieve an indefinite tenure, even without fire. These facts underlie the interpretation of the profiles.

At Malahat (Fig. 37), Douglas fir exhibits a stronger profile than western hemlock. In fact, the profile here is the strongest for all the sections studied in British Columbia. The Malahat area is comparatively dry, climatically, and this degree of representation is to be expected. But western hemlock rises gradually to the top of the profile under the influence of what appears to be greater humidity. In the presence of a greater abundance of hemlock, Douglas fir becomes less able to endure. This is shown particularly well in the upper part of its profile following the prominence of Douglas fir that, most likely, is the result of intense fire. The tree is unable subsequently to regain its previous position and is succeeded by hemlock, which displays a high proportion in the uppermost meter.

Harbledown Island and Menzies Bay profiles (Fig. 36) are weak, but the trend toward gradual decline from higher percentages at midsection is unmistakable. Hemlock exhibits strong profiles at both places, and humid climates that become pronounced as the proportion of hemlock increases toward the surface are indicated. Toward the northern end of Vancouver Island at Port Hardy and at the two sites on nearby Hope Island (Fig. 35), Douglas fir is barely represented. Farther north at Cape Caution, Fitzhugh Sound, and Susan Island (Fig. 34), the conifer is found only at upper levels in the profiles. There is some indication here that Douglas fir has migrated recently, and fires appear to have favored its advance. Douglas fir has not been found on the Queen Charlotte Islands; the diagrams from Masset on Graham Island in the archipelago (Fig. 32) bear this out and, in addition, present no evidence to indicate that it was present at all during the Postglacial.

Although according to Schmidt (1957) Douglas fir is found only as far as the vicinity of Kemano, located over 100 mi southeast of Prince Rupert, sections in the neighborhood of Prince Rupert record the pollen of the tree (Fig. 33). At Summit, solitary grains are recorded at three widely separated levels, including the surface, and at Rainbow Lake, grains occur at seven levels, at two of these in amounts reaching 10 and 20 per cent. The levels and the abundance of pollen at Rainbow Lake indicate that Douglas fir was a temporary, but important, member of the succession during the early-postglacial pine episode. During the latter part of the Postglacial, it again appeared, presumably as a consequence of fire. The occurrence of a single grain at the top of the Summit section suggests its source to be near the site. Douglas fir has apparently advanced and retreated in the Prince Rupert region on a number of occasions, and it is likely that the tree grows farther north than near Kemano.

Crushed and shriveled microfossils resembling Douglas fir pollen were occasionally found in the lower levels of Alaskan sections at Upper and Lower Montana Creek and as far north as Cordova. Their poor state of preservation render them unidentifiable, but fragments have the characteristic appearance of Douglas fir. It is likely that this identification is correct, but it is unlikely, in view of their fragmentary remains and location far beyond the present range of the species, that the grains became interred shortly after they were shed by the tree; it seems evident that redeposition of the microfossils has taken place from preexisting sediments. This is plausible since Hopkins and Benninghoff (1953) describe fossil material of Douglas fir, among other Pacific Coastal rainforest species, from a deposit thought to be Early Pliocene (David M. Hopkins, personal communication) on the central Seward Peninsula in northwestern Alaska. If Douglas fir has ranged to such a great extent previously, its fossil remains are likely to be found at places along the Gulf of Alaska and Bering Sea coasts.

Fir (*Abies*)

It has not been possible by any palynological method thus far developed to distinguish species of the genus, with the possible exception of *A. lasiocarpa*. Without specific knowledge of the fir profiles, environmental inferences cannot be drawn. However, from what is known of the ranges of the three species found in coastal British Columbia, amabilis fir (*A. amabilis*), lowland white fir (*A. grandis* Lindl.), and alpine fir (*A. lasiocarpa*), some tentative conclusions can be made from the pollen data.

Fir profiles are finest from Vancouver Island, where the three species range at the present time. But at Malahat (Fig. 37) on the drier southeastern side of the island, lowland white fir appears to be the exclusive species growing in the area at present. Schmidt (1957) considers lowland white fir to be restricted to areas of comparatively low summer rainfall and high summer temperature, the same areas in which Douglas fir is favored climatically; therefore, since true fir appears to increase and decrease in proportion with Douglas fir as its profile develops, it appears that lowland white fir is the species represented through most of the section. Both profiles decline through the upper levels, and a humidity increase is suggested. Where fir increases in conjunction with mountain hemlock just below 6-m depth, the presence of another species is suspected. In this case, the probable species is amabilis fir because (1) the climatic conditions prevailing at the time of deposition were more humid and unlike those over the present range of lowland white fir, (2) the natural association of amabilis fir is with mountain hemlock, and (3) the size of the grains do not suggest alpine fir, the only other species under consideration.

At Menzies Bay, Harbledown Island, and Upper Hope Island (Figs. 35, 36), the species associated with mountain hemlock at depth is more apt to be amabilis fir. The slightly greater amount of fir pollen paralleling the slight increase of Douglas fir at midprofile in all three sections has probably resulted from the temporary northward migration of lowland white fir during the comparatively warm-and-dry Hypsithermal. This weak prominence is better shown in the Menzies Bay section, which falls in the range of the species. The other two sections, which are north of its present range, disclose smaller percentages at the time. Where a high proportion of true fir and western hemlock is seen in the upper profile at Menzies Bay, southward migration of amabilis fir into the drier eastern sector of Vancouver Island is suggested during the more humid Late Postglacial. Over its range along the northern British Columbia coast, amabilis fir, the apparent species, has gained in importance recently, as indicated by Fitzhugh Sound, Susan Island, Pitt Island, Prince Rupert, Rainbow Lake, and Summit diagrams (Figs. 33, 34).

Fir has never been observed growing on the Queen Charlotte Islands; the absence of its pollen in the Masset section (Fig. 32) supports these observations and indicates that the genus has not grown there during the Postglacial.

Willow (*Salix*)

Pollen shows up almost exclusively at levels in the lower halves of almost all the sections where the position of willow in late-glacial and early-postglacial plant succession is readily apparent. The Late-glacial is found only at Menzies Bay, Upper Hope Island, and Rainbow Lake (Figs. 33, 35, 36). Here willow and alder are predominant below a maximum for lodgepole pine, and a tundra-type vegetation is reconstructed on the basis of this and other supporting evidence.

Alder is so highly predominant at the Menzies Bay site that there is some debate concerning the zonation of a late-glacial interval here. The division shown is most probably the latter part of the Late-glacial, and the large amount of alder is thought to be a consequence of the relatively dry, more continental conditions prevalent on eastern Vancouver Island at that time. It is to be noted that the profile for the moisture-loving western hemlock rises later here than at stations farther northward (for example, Upper Hope Island; Fig. 35), suggesting that drier conditions endured over a comparatively long interval of the Postglacial and during the Late-glacial as well.

Alder (*Alnus*)

The shape of the alder profile is generally consistent in the British Columbia diagrams. As it succeeds during the early part of the postglacial zone, alder contributes large quantities of pollen to the basic sum, but in the remainder of the profile, it gradually contributes less. The position of alder in succession is much the same here as it is in southeastern Alaska.

As shown by profiles from the eastern part of south-central and southern Vancouver Island (for example, Menzies Bay and Malahat; Figs. 36, 37), alder was predominant through almost all postglacial time. Less humid and warmer continental climate, to a large extent, restricted Sitka spruce and western hemlock. Ostensibly, this restriction and consequent diminution of these climatically oceanic species in the basic pollen sum has allowed alder to appear in greater numbers and to serve as a hypsithermal indicator.

Sedge (Cyperaceae)

The pollen of the sedge family is almost entirely from plants growing at the site. Limnic sediments carry far fewer grains than fibrous-sedge or bryophytic peat. At Malahat and Menzies Bay, for example, the sedge profiles build conspicuously as sedge peat follows limnic peat in the course of hydrarch succession. At the muskeg sites, the proportion of sedge peat formed at the surface and, in turn, sedge pollen shed is conditioned by available moisture and the competitive ability of the plant. Where moisture is abundant sedge is unable to compete with *Sphagnum*, and where moisture is low it cannot compete with heath and sweet gale. Its moisture requirements consequently stand somewhere between those for *Sphagnum* and for heath and sweet gale.

In British Columbia profiles, sedge is identified with late-glacial and early-postglacial sediments, as well as those laid down during various times of the Late Postglacial. The sedge profile weakens quite perceptibly through the hypsithermal zone, thus revealing the moderately high moisture requirements of the group.

Skunk Cabbage (*Lysichitum*)

As demonstrated in Southeastern Alaska, skunk cabbage is a plant that achieved its greatest supremacy during the Hypsithermal. In nonlimnic British Columbia deposits,

Lysichitum pollen is more often than not associated with ligneous peat (for example, Masset, Prince Rupert, Rainbow Lake, Summit, and Upper Hope Island; Figs. 32, 33, 35). In limnic sediments, it is only poorly represented or not represented at all (for example, Menzies Bay and Malahat; Figs. 36, 37). Skunk cabbage in muskeg sections usually follows sedge and is later followed by sphagnum, sedge, heath, and sweet gale. The sharp decline of the skunk cabbage profile at ca 3-m depth in the Masset section is one of the best examples of the change in pollen spectra associated with the prominent *Grenzhorizont* along this coast.

Sweet Gale (*Myrica*)

In nine of the 15 British Columbia sections sweet gale is found, but only in three, Susan Island, Menzies Bay, and Malahat (Figs. 34, 36, 37), are its profiles strong. Sweet gale, observed in the early-postglacial levels at Menzies Bay and in higher levels here and elsewhere, has its peak representation in late-postglacial deposits usually following the heath maximum.

Heath (Ericales)

The characteristic position of the heath prominence met with in Southeastern Alaska continues to appear in these sections. It is strongest following *Lysichitum*, but where the *Lysichitum* profile is weak or does not show up, as at Malahat (Fig. 37), heath usually rises instead in the upper part of the section. The best heath profile is at Masset (Fig. 32), while less well-developed profiles are in the Prince Rupert sector (Fig. 33) and at Hope Island (Fig. 35). South of Hope Island, heath is poorly recorded and its characteristic position is more or less obscure.

Heath is chiefly a late-postglacial group. It occurs only sparingly in early-postglacial sediments (for example, Upper Hope Island) and is rare in those of the Late-glacial (for example, Menzies Bay).

Fern (Polypodiaceae)

Late-glacial fern profiles are weak but the early-postglacial profiles show a rise in proportion. Shortly after the Hypsithermal began ferns declined and during the Late Postglacial in almost every case were present only in small numbers. The part they play in postglacial succession is apparently small and largely local.

Sphagnum

The bulk of the *Sphagnum* profiles are Post Hypsithermal in age, and in certain cases the profiles do not develop (for example, Malahat and Menzies Bay; Figs. 36, 37). In some instances, *Sphagnum* gained in numbers during the Early Postglacial (for example, Masset and Upper Hope Island; Figs. 32, 35). It was absent, or present in only meager amounts, in the Late-glacial. As in the Alaskan sections, *Sphagnum* is believed to indicate surface coolness and a high degree of moisture at the time its remains became incorporated in the peat.

Other Profiles

Additional late-glacial pollen, heretofore unmentioned for this region, are from Gramineae, *Sanguisorba*, Caryophyllaceae, *Rumex*, *Urtica*, and the Tubuliflorae. The profiles from Upper Hope Island (Fig. 35) show this assemblage particularly well.

During the early part of the Postglacial, *Sparganium* appeared at Rainbow Lake (Fig. 33) and *Potamogeton* and *Nuphar* at Masset and Cape Caution (Figs. 32, 34). *Polemonium* was also present at that time, as indicated by several grains in the Masset section (Fig. 32). *Linnaea* is represented in the lower section at Menzies Bay (Fig. 36) and in the vicinity of the striking *Grenzhorizont* at Masset.

In the lower parts of most sections, *Rubus* (probably the salmonberry, *R. spectabilis*) occurs where it has a place in succession. The species *R. chamaemorus*, which is identifiable, generally follows *Lysichitum* and tends to associate with or precede the Ericales. A species of arctic affinity, *R. chamaemorus* does not appear in profiles south of the Prince Rupert sector (Fig. 33). In the surface flora (Table 10), it was not collected south of Susan Island, which suggests that the plant migrated southward during the Late Postglacial.

Similar to *R. chamaemorus*, pollen of *Sanguisorba*, albeit meagerly represented, tends to be more numerous at upper-middle and upper levels in the sections. This pattern reflects its appearance in southeastern Alaska. The weak Umbelliferae profiles display no apparent typical form, being better developed in lower parts of some sections and in upper parts of others. Pollen of the Tubuliflorae is found at nearly all levels among the sections of this region.

Of the Lycopodiaceae, *Lycopodium inundatum*, which was rare in southeastern Alaska, is represented in six of the sections and is largely Late Postglacial in age where it occurs. *L. annotinum* is not found in sections south of the Prince Rupert sector, and in this respect it behaves like *Rubus chamaemorus*. It is found on the surface of sites as far south as Fitzhugh Sound (Table 10). Although *L. annotinum* is generally infrequent in the British Columbia sections, the species tends to occur during the early and later parts of the postglacial zones. This tendency parallels its behavior in southeastern Alaska. Like *Rubus chamaemorus*, this club moss appears to have been favored by the late-postglacial climate change. In the vicinity of Prince Rupert, *Lycopodium clavatum* is also present; in sections to the south it gains in importance.

Two broadleaf trees, maple (*Acer*) and oak (*Quercus*), not encountered heretofore, are present in Vancouver Island profiles. Maple pollen is found as far north as the Harbledown Island section (Fig. 36) whereas oak occurs no farther north than Little Qualicum Falls (Fig. 37). Hansen (1950a) records oak in sections nearly as far as the Menzies Bay site, but its greatest proportion in his Vancouver Island profiles is near Victoria, which is in proximity to Malahat. Both maple and oak are more austral and show a large degree of thermophily by the patterns of their ranges. Both are best seen in the Malahat section (Fig. 37), where they are zoned in the Hypsithermal. Although less numerous at present under a cooler and moister climate, these trees were able to prosper during the Hypsithermal.

Washington, Oregon, and California Pollen Profiles

The profiles of sections from Washington, Oregon, and California are the most complicated of the entire study. Several reasons for this are apparent. The floristic composition of the communities is more complex—for example, instead of only lodgepole pine being present, as in Alaska and northern British Columbia, four species of pine are present. The ecology of the important species and their roles in plant succession vary in a number of cases because of the different topographic conditions prevalent in the region—for example, Douglas fir may be climax where conditions are too dry for western hemlock to grow and compete, while under oceanic conditions and hemlock prevalence the tree becomes subclimax. The region is partly within a glaciated area, and the vegetation has been subject to both the direct and indirect effects of glaciation, which must be taken into account in the interpretation of the profiles. Since most sections are from unglaciated country, the inception of older deposits is not uniformly dependent upon the glaciation factor, and they have begun to accrue at different times. A greater number of the available study sites have been recently disturbed by man by way of ditching, draining, burning, and logging, with the result that basal and surficial truncation or alteration of the profiles has been effected.

Despite these handicaps, the interpretation of the profiles is favored by (1) the fact that Hansen (1947a) has diagramed arboreal pollen profiles from over 70 sections throughout the Pacific Northwest, and many of these lie within the region; (2) the number of sections taken in the present study is distributed in such a fashion so as to serve in itself as a partial control; and (3) radiocarbon dates for the Glacier Peak ash in the Puget Lowland sections (Figs. 38, 39) and for the peats at Seaview, Devils Lake, and Garrison Lake (Figs. 42, 43, 45) provide exceedingly helpful chronological bases for correlating profiles.

Lodgepole Pine (*Pinus contorta*)

Where lodgepole pine pollen is more numerous in its profiles, some change that has restricted or removed competitive species has taken place. Lodgepole is an aggressive pioneer under conditions of disturbance and will colonize as the initial arboreal invader in advance of most other conifers. In Alaska and northern British Columbia, where pine is chiefly a muskeg dweller, it performed primarily in early-postglacial succession. The species since has been relegated to muskeg because of the freedom from competition offered by such a habitat. In the remainder of the study region also, lodgepole occupied the position of early-postglacial invader. This role has been taken and is still taken, on glacial and proglacial deposits, but it is not its only role. Lodgepole pioneers following fire and is the leading invader of coastal dunes. As in Pacific Alaska and British Columbia, the species commonly becomes established on the surface of peat sites in this region.

Lodgepole at Humptulips (Fig. 41), which is well removed from the glacial border, is more abundant than any other conifer in the late-glacial zone. Its high proportion is probably a reflection of proglacial and physiographic instability created by glaciers in the Olympics and by the proglacial waterway that drained the Puget glacier lobe between what is now Puget Sound and Grays Harbor. A maximum amount of pine higher in the profile is probably indicative of the stress created by climatic conditions in the Olympics during late-Wisconsin glaciation.

In Washington profiles, as in profiles to the northwest, a pronounced lodgepole interval is taken as the basis for zoning the Early Postglacial. The Wessler section (Fig. 40), however, is the only one containing this record; those studied in the Puget Lowland are younger and begin with the Hypsithermal. Pangborn Lake (Fig. 38), for example, rests on Sumas drift, which is thought to be a late-Wisconsin (Valders substage or younger) deposit, as suggested by the age of the youngest till in the nearby lower Fraser valley (Armstrong 1956). Most Puget Lowland glacial deposits are older, dating from the Vashon, which is tentatively correlated with the Early Wisconsin (Waldron, Mullineaux, and Crandell 1957).

The weak and transitory lodgepole interval at Pangborn Lake is probably a result of regional succession by climax conifers under the rapidly mollifying climate of the Hypsithermal. Following the withdrawal of Vashon ice from the glaciated southern part of the lowland, conifers presumably had been able to migrate northward but became checked by the advance of ice from the Fraser valley. Later, when the terrain about Pangborn Lake was freed of ice, climax conifers were able to become established soon after lodgepole. In the case of the Wessler site, Sitka spruce and western white pine, enduring south of the glacier border or beyond the limit of proglacial instability, were able to participate in succession soon after lodgepole had advanced over the deglaciated terrain. Consequently, lodgepole predominance was short, but the position of the species in succession was secure for a time because of the nearby disturbances attendant with the late-Wisconsin glaciation that followed the Vashon in the Fraser valley and in the mountains.

Profiles from Whidbey Island and Seaview (Figs. 39, 42) show most strikingly the evident late-postglacial development of the species in many of the sections not only from Washington, but from Oregon and California as well. With renewed growth of the peat surfaces under a more oceanic climate, pine invasion and reproduction were enhanced at these sites. But this does not seem to be the only reason the pine profiles were favored at that time. Theoretically, the change of climate, according to Cooper (1958b), was accompanied by greater storminess and an increase in the frequency of southwest gales, presumably creating deflation basins in the dune areas, which in turn became invaded by lodgepole.

Cooper attributes dune formation chiefly to eustatic sea-level change, with climatic change as an influential factor. At Devils, Tahkenitch, and Garrison Lakes in Oregon (Figs. 43–45), previously quite brackish as a result of hypsithermal marine transgression, dune activity appears to have caused the closure of tidal connections. Pollen stratigraphy and radiocarbon dates from the bases of two of these sections suggest a synchronous interval of incursion. Lodgepole tended to be numerous but was on the decline about that time, particularly in the Tahkenitch and Garrison Lakes profiles. Spruce and western hemlock also declined as brackishness increased, and their profiles suggest the destruction of climax and subclimax forest by dunes migrating inland.

Following the closure of tidal connections, the formation of incipient freshwater lakes, and the regression of the ocean, what appears to have been the migration of dunes over stable forest communities seems to have slackened. Above the interval of incursion, the profiles again redevelop in a sequence beginning with pine, followed by spruce and, lastly, western hemlock—the order of dune invasion and stabilization by these arboreal species. Fire, from evidence contained in the peat of these sections, is undoubtedly responsible for many of the fluctuations of the profiles but is not believed to have upset the trend shown. More recently pine has increased in proportions, particularly at Devils Lake (Fig. 43). The data contained in the profiles are largely in accord with Cooper's (1958b) correlation of dune history with eustatic sea-level change and his tentative correlation with glacial and climatic changes.

The rise of lodgepole in the upper parts of profiles from sections at Garrison Lake, Lake Earl, and Capetown (Figs. 45, 46) toward the southern coastal limit of its range suggests late-postglacial migration southward. It is quite probable that at Fort Bragg (Fig. 46) lodgepole contributes a small fraction of the *Pinus bolanderi* Parl. profile. However, because of the overlap of the size-frequency ranges of the two species and because lodgepole is rare along the nearby coast and *P. bolanderi* is abundant at the sampling site, the latter is considered to be the species represented in the profile. Had lodgepole been distinguishable, additional support might have been afforded the indication that this species migrated after the Hypsithermal. The low density of lodgepole in the Fort Bragg area and south to its range limit at Point Arena suggests, in combination with the above data, recent southward movement.

Western White Pine (*Pinus monticola* Dougl.)

This species of pine is never present in amounts greater than a few per cent. Its tendency is to follow the trend of the lodgepole profile; accordingly it is encountered mainly in both the early- and late-postglacial zones. Western white pine is a subclimax species that exhibits a higher degree of shade tolerance than lodgepole and, also, exhibits greater soil requirements. Its maximum representation is found in the Washington profiles. That it does not appear in the pollen record south of Tahkenitch Lake is understandable since the tree does not reach the ocean in southwestern Oregon. Its distribution southward is largely in the Cascades and the Sierra Nevada.

Bolander Pine (*Pinus bolanderi* Parl.)

This species, recorded only from the Fort Bragg section (Fig. 46), is restricted to the Mendocino coastal plain. Bolander pine and cypress (*Cupressus pygmaea* [Lemm.] Sarg.) are the principal members of what has been called the "pygmy conifer forest," which occupies a large part of the plain (McMillan 1956).

The profile for Bolander pine indicates a history of predominance through most of the section. If, however, the striking development of the *Cupressus* profile is not real but rather a result of the decay of pollen of the genus in the peat at depth, the importance of Bolander pine would accordingly be much less. But there is some indication that the grains do preserve as witnessed by the few per cent of *Cupressus* at the base of the section. In view of this fact and the evidence of fire from a depth of 0.4 m to the bottom, it seems apparent that the predominant position of Bolander pine is a result of fire. The layers of sand and silt imbedded in the section are interpreted as having resulted from erosion following fire.

The pollen record appears not to be older than the Late Postglacial, which is unfortunate in view of the key location of the section near the ends of the ranges of several of the coastal rainforest trees.

Bishop Pine (*Pinus muricata* Don)

Bishop pine is distributed along the coasts of Mendocino and Sonoma Counties and, according to Jepson (1925), as far north as the vicinity of Trinidad, a short distance north of Eureka in Humboldt County. Its range is more to the south than to the north, however, and extends to San Luis Obispo and to Lower California (Sudworth 1908).

In Humboldt County at the Capetown site (Fig. 46), Bishop pine is recorded in the profiles north of its range. The species is rather sparsely represented at Capetown but is somewhat more prevalent in the lower section in the neighborhood of the hypsithermal and late-postglacial transition. At Fort Bragg (Fig. 46), in the continuous part of its range, Bishop pine pollen is found in greater numbers. The profile pattern appears to duplicate that at Capetown except that the section is slightly younger. These data suggest a more northerly range of the species during the Hypsithermal.

Sitka Spruce (*Picea sitchensis*)

In plant succession, on deglaciated landscape early in the Postglacial or later in the course of dune stabilization, Sitka spruce may invade with or even prior to lodgepole pine. It gains only temporary predominance, however, before being replaced by hemlock. The role of spruce in succession, particularly evident in glaciated Pacific coastal Alaska and British Columbia, continues in this region.

Spruce in the late-glacial section at Humptulips (Fig. 41) forms a weak profile. During the early part of the Postglacial, spruce follows lodgepole and becomes invaded by western hemlock as shown by the profiles from Wessler (Fig. 40). The species is not represented, however, at Pangborn Lake (Fig. 38) during that time, but conditions were almost certainly too dry to permit it to gain any major status. In fact, spruce never attains more than a few per cent throughout its profile here. Average annual precipitation at nearby Bellingham is only ca 32 in (Table 1). On the basis of this information and of the high moisture-indicator value of spruce, the conclusion is reached that the area about Pangborn Lake was comparatively dry through the duration of the Postglacial. Behavior and proportion of spruce here and at Malahat in adjacent British Columbia (Fig. 37) are very similar.

The trends of the Sitka spruce profiles in the Oregon coastal lakes appear to be tied in with the dune history as mentioned previously. Where dunes were particularly active during the interval of marine transgression, the percentage of spruce reached a minimum. When dunes are stabilized by the establishment of the conifer, the result should be a rise in the percentage of spruce pollen in the sections, and spruce does show a rise over most of the remaining postglacial time.

Presence of spruce pollen in only the late-postglacial part of the Capetown profile (Fig. 46), near the limit of its range in Mendocino County, suggests southward migration as moisture favorably increased during that time.

Western Hemlock (*Tsuga heterophylla*)

The position of western hemlock subsequent to spruce in plant succession is manifest in the district sections (for example, Wessler, Ozette Lake, Humptulips, Seaview, Devils Lake, and Tahkenitch Lake; Figs. 40–44). Western hemlock was best developed during the relatively moist Late Postglacial, when climax forest with hemlock predominating reached its greatest proportion in coastal western Washington and northwestern Oregon. The almost complete absence of change in the Pangborn Lake profile (Fig. 38) indicates only a small degree of postglacial climatic alteration. It substantiates the conclusion reached previously from the examination of the spruce profile.

If the presence of meager percentages of western hemlock as well as spruce pollen in only late-postglacial sediments of the Capetown section (Fig. 46) is any indication, migration to the limit of its range in Sonoma County occurred during that interval.

Mountain Hemlock (*Tsuga mertensiana*)

Pollen of mountain hemlock is not recorded south of the profile from Warrenton (Fig. 42) near the mouth of the Columbia River in Oregon. Here the tree is represented by only a single grain. The Seaview section (Fig. 42), located just north of the mouth, does not provide much more of a record since in all only three grains were observed at as many levels.

Mountain hemlock does not thrive at present south of the Olympic Mountains, except away from the ocean in the Cascades, Siskiyous, and Sierra Nevada. It is, therefore, understandable that the above western Oregon sections record so few grains and that farther south along the coast no grains were found. It is also understandable that sections from the vicinity of the Olympics, where the species is well established, should register large numbers.

The Humptulips late-glacial profile (Fig. 41) from a section located southwest of the Olympics has quantities of mountain hemlock reaching as high as 43 per cent. This amount is not exceeded in any other section studied in the district. The maximum occurred during the middle part (LG-2) of the Late-glacial between intervals of pine predominance (LG-1 and LG-3). Other coniferous species tended to increase in proportion during the mountain hemlock episode, but grasses and other herbs were relatively abundant before and after that time. This sequence of plant assemblages implies a colder climate at first followed by one that was relatively moderate, but still cold, and perhaps also somewhat drier as suggested by the contemporaneous ligneous horizon. But moderate climate was only temporary—conditions grew more unstable subsequently, although the environment does not seem to have been as cold as during the early part of the Late-glacial.

It is significant that a remarkable parallelism to Humptulips is evident in a section Hansen (1941b) studied from a peat deposit near Forks, northwest of the Olympics. The two sections are only 50 mi apart. In describing the mountain hemlock profile, Hansen (1947a) writes: "It reached over 20 per cent at the lowest level, slightly declined upward, and then sharply increased to 54 per cent in the middle of the profile." He goes on to state: "A marked increase of lodgepole immediately above and the occurrence of much silt at these levels in the sedimentary column suggest increased erosion."

The mountain hemlock prominence occurred during an interval (LG-2) of climatic improvement during the Late-glacial. It succeeded an early episode of climatic stress

(LG-1) that has been interpreted as representing the time of withdrawal of Vashon ice; it preceded a late episode of climatic deterioration (LG-3) considered to be identical with late-Wisconsin glaciation (Sumas glaciation of the Fraser valley). Glaciers that advanced in the Olympics during the Late Wisconsin presumably were the source of the sediments that buried the late-glacial deposit at Humptulips. The high proportion of mountain hemlock may be explained by the glacial conditions in the Olympics. The pollen record indicates a severe environment probably created by a local ice cap with peripheral valley glaciers. Mountain hemlock, unable to grow in the subalpine belt because of glacier occupancy or a restrictive arctic-alpine environment, grew instead on the western fringe of the Olympic Peninsula in a refugium between the mountain front and the ocean. During LG-1 and LG-3, mountain hemlock was presumably more abundant southward. Later, during the Early Postglacial, the probability is that mountain hemlock migrated up into the Olympics as climatic amelioration ensued. Topographic changes during late-glacial burial have affected the extent of postglacial peat formation.

A mountain hemlock prominence appears in the lower part of the Wessler diagram (Fig. 40) and northward at stratigraphically identical levels in diagrams of Malahat, Menzies Bay, Harbledown Island, Upper Hope Island, Masset, and as far as Upper Montana Creek in southeastern Alaska (Figs. 24, 32, 35–37). The prominence records mountain hemlock succession and, in addition, provides an excellent stratigraphic marker. The absence of this prominence in the Pangborn Lake section (Fig. 38), resting on Sumas drift, confirms the younger age of the deposit, which formed following the recession of the Sumas glacier. The return of mountain hemlock in late-postglacial spectra from Pangborn Lake and Whidbey Island (Figs. 38, 39) reflect trends previously noted for British Columbia and Alaska.

Douglas Fir (*Pseudotsuga menziesii* [Mirb.] Franco)

Profiles for Douglas fir are weak. The best representation is in the Pangborn Lake section (Fig. 38) whereas southward on the coast the profiles become weaker and more fragmented. Since most sections in Washington and Oregon are removed from sites where high humidity is paramount, the present successional control by western hemlock is apparent. This control generally has been manifest since the outset of the Late Postglacial. During the Hypsithermal, however, climate favored Douglas fir because of the less suitable conditions for competition by hemlock. These trends can be seen in the gradual changes in the two profiles at Pangborn Lake and Whidbey Island (Figs. 38, 39). The successional trend of Douglas fir under the somewhat more humid climate of the early part of the Hypsithermal is also portrayed at Pangborn Lake.

Fir (*Abies*)

Fir profiles at Pangborn Lake and Whidbey Island generally follow the fluctuations of Douglas fir. In this respect, the parallel behavior is much the same as in the Malahat section (Fig. 37). The fir species in these profiles appears to be lowland white fir (*A. grandis* Lindl.), assuming the reasoning applied to the upper part of the Malahat profile is correct. The slight prominence in the lower profile at Malahat, where it is associated with mountain hemlock, is absent at Pangborn Lake. The distinction between these sections is fortified if alder profiles from both are compared. It seems obvious that the younger age of the Pangborn Lake deposit results from later development following the recession of Sumas ice.

True fir developed contemporaneously with mountain hemlock during the Late-glacial at Humptulips (Fig. 41). Since the locality is in proximity to the Olympic Mountains where amabilis fir is abundant and well distributed on high forested slopes as an associate of mountain hemlock, the fir in these profiles is likely amabilis. Jones (1936) states that amabilis fir is a characteristic tree of the Olympics whereas lowland white fir is rare, and Hanzlik (1932) accords amabilis fir climax status. Glacier occupation of the Olympics undoubtedly caused fir to migrate with mountain hemlock to the coastal lowland during glacial times. This fir is probably mixed with alpine fir, another characteristic associate of mountain hemlock, but its pollen, which is often separable, is not detected. Amabilis fir also appears to be the species that was associated with mountain hemlock during the Early Postglacial at Malahat, Menzies Bay, Harbledown Island, and as far north as Upper Hope Island in British Columbia (Figs. 35–37).

In coastal southern Oregon and northern California, the species represented in the profiles seems almost certainly to be lowland white fir, at present the only fir near the coast. True fir may be considered the best portrayed of the conifers in the Capetown section (Fig. 46), where it is largely Late Postglacial in age. At Fort Bragg (Fig. 46) it is evident only in the latter part of this zone. These data suggest that fir, ostensibly lowland white fir, is a fog-belt species that migrated southward along the coast as the Hypsithermal ended.

Redwood (*Sequoia sempervirens* [Lamb.] Endl.)

Pollen of coast redwood is recorded only in the three California sections (Fig. 46). Its numbers are meager but appear to be greater in the upper parts of the profiles. The increase, although probably the result of a late-postglacial multiplication and spread of this fog-belt tree, is nevertheless quite possibly caused by decomposition of redwood pollen at depth in the sections. Because of this possibility, no climatic significance can be attached to this trend.

Cypress (*Cupressus*)

The Fort Bragg section (Fig. 46) is the only one containing pollen of cypress. The species *C. pygmaea* (Lemm.) Sarg. is one of the principal members of the dwarfed type of vegetation at the site of sampling on the central Mendocino County coastal plateau (McMillan 1956). It is the species represented at the top of the profile, and the species at depth is in all likelihood the same.

The cypress profile enlarges at upper levels but, as previously discussed under Bolander pine, the change may be the result of any or all of a number of factors, chief among which is a decrease in the incidence of fire.

Willow (*Salix*)

Pollen of the genus is found in almost all the sections. Its distribution pattern is rather sporadic. Some profiles, such as Whidbey Island, Warrenton, and Capetown

(Figs. 39, 42, 46), contain strikingly large quantities at lower levels. In none of the profiles is climatic change suggested. Local succession induced by periodic disturbances is manifestly the cause of both the major and minor profile fluctuations. The best-developed profiles are from sections taken from lakes, where willow is most prevalent.

Alder (*Alnus*)

Alder is another successional tree. In coastal southern Oregon and California, red alder (*A. oregona*) is the major, if not the only, species forming the profiles. Northward, red alder becomes mixed with Sitka alder (*A. crispa* subsp. *sinuata*), and this association is undoubtedly present in the alder profiles from northerly coastal Oregon and Washington sections.

The alder profile is often the strongest in the diagrams. The proportion of alder in different areas of the profile and at different section sites is variable, chiefly on account of fires and local climate prevailing both in the past and at present. Nevertheless, certain trends are generally discernible, although not in all profiles. In the Early Postglacial, alder was more abundant by virtue of its participation in succession on glaciated terrain, as shown by the Wessler profile (Fig. 40). Alder continues to exhibit a strong profile in the hypsithermal time zone, but with the beginning of the late-postglacial zone, the profile weakens toward the top of the section. In some sections, for example, Pangborn Lake and Capetown (Figs. 38, 46), this inclination is barely perceptible, but local climatic control, hindering chiefly western hemlock and spruce, has apparently been important in maintaining high alder percentages.

Oak (*Quercus*)

The species represented in the Washington profiles is almost surely Oregon white oak (*Q. garryana* Dougl.). Hansen (1947a) states that this oak, the only species found in western Washington, achieves its best development and is most numerous on gravelly outwash plains in the Puget Lowland south of Olympia and in the Willamette Valley of western Oregon. It is not found in northern coastal Oregon sections and is sparse in those from western coastal Washington. But in the relatively dry sector of northwestern Washington, at Pangborn Lake and Whidbey Island (Figs. 38, 39), an increase in the influx of oak is used to zone the hypsithermal interval.

The Garrison Lake profile (Fig. 45) also shows a weak tendency for oak to have occurred during the Hypsithermal. According to Peck (1941), Oregon white oak is the only oak species that reaches the coast and it does so only in this part of western Oregon.

Oak in the Capetown profile (Fig. 46) is zoned, paradoxically, in the Late Postglacial. In this region of coastal prairie, oak was presumably unable to endure under hypsithermal conditions, but it multiplied as late-postglacial climate favored invasion of the grassland. Invasion probably occurred in low places and along stream courses with alder, willow, and ash, among other arboreal species. The oak species that participated are unknown. Climate has apparently also been advantageous for the influx of closely related chinquapin (*Castanopsis*), as revealed by its late-postglacial profile.

Maple (*Acer*)

Pollen of maple is found only in Washington sections. Although it is distributed in all intervals, it is never found in quantities of more than 2 per cent. At Wessler (Fig. 40) maple is identified with the sediments laid down during the Early Postglacial; at Humptulips it occurs early in the late-glacial record. Whidbey Island and Pangborn Lake profiles (Figs. 38, 39), however, show maple largely in the hypsithermal zone, but the latter displays it to some extent in the Late Postglacial as well. The species is probably either *A. macrophyllum* Pursh or *A. circinatum* Pursh, or possibly both.

Ash (*Fraxinus*)

Oregon ash (*F. oregana* Nutt.), a species of stream courses and alluvial bottoms, is the source of ash pollen in the sections. It is present at Pangborn, Devils, and Garrison Lakes, Lake Earl, and Capetown (Figs. 38, 43, 45, 46). Never in amounts greater than 2 per cent and present only at occasional levels, the pollen of the species reveals an affinity for the Late Postglacial, except near the limit of its range at Pangborn Lake, where it occurs in hypsithermal sediments.

Ditch Grass (*Ruppia*)

Ditch grass pollen is not uncommon in these sections. It is found at numerous levels in five of the lake sites; Whidbey Island, Devils, Tahkenitch, and Garrison Lakes, and Lake Earl (Figs. 39, 43–46). The fact that ditch grass is distributed along the entire coast but only in brackish pools and estuarine environments is of value in tracing the ontogeny of coastal lakes that at one time were tidal inlets of the ocean. The pollen of *Ruppia* in the sediments is clearly related to the tidal history of the basins.

With one exception, ditch grass profiles are developed only in the lower areas of the sections. At Lake Earl (Fig. 46) the profile attains its maximum (30 per cent) near the top. This is a comparatively young section, and the brackish environment from which the *Ruppia* sediments were derived appears to have been altered quite recently. Of the remaining sections, Devils and Garrison Lakes contain relatively high percentages (respectively, maxima of 38 and 28 per cent). Zonation is distinct, usually set off in addition by pollen of halophytic species of *Potamogeton* and Chenopodiaceae and silty and sandy sediments imbedded in the section.

Grass (Gramineae)

Pollen of this family is scattered through the sections, but in all but two no significance can be attached to the distribution. The exceptions are the sections from Humptulips and Capetown (Figs. 41, 46).

The Humptulips late-glacial sediments contain as much as 34 per cent grass in the lower part and 5 in the upper. The higher proportion of grass pollen is associated with Cyperaceae, *Sanguisorba*, Liguliflorae, Tubuliflorae, and several other herbaceous plants. These plants and their proportionate numbers seem to warrant the conclusion that climate was cooler early and late during the Late-glacial than during the intervening subdivision predominated by mountain hemlock.

At Capetown, the grass profile attains significant form. The vegetation of the area at present is dominated by coastal scrub or prairie. Through the Late Postglacial as well, grassland appears to have been the major type, and during the Hypsithermal, it gained an even greater proportion. Basal weakening of the grass profile is probably no indication of regional trends but has been effected by the temporary predominance caused by overrepresentation of local plants.

Sedge (Cyperaceae)

Sedge was more prevalent during the Late Postglacial under the cooler, more humid climate. In the coastal-lake sections, where *Ruppia* delimits intervals of marine transgression, sedge profiles strengthen above and/or below the *Ruppia*.

Skunk Cabbage (*Lysichitum*)

As in the coastal region northwestward, skunk cabbage profiles are best developed in hypsithermal sediments, with the exception of Wessler and Ozette Lake (Figs. 40, 41) in Washington. Although both of these show the species prominently in the hypsithermal zone, the early-postglacial and late-postglacial deposits contain strong representation. Certain factors have presumably exerted a local control, but these are unknown.

Sweet Gale-Wax Myrtle (*Myrica*)

Sweet gale (*M. gale*) is a northerly ranging coastal species growing from Alaska to northern Lincoln County, Oregon (Peck 1941). California wax myrtle (*M. californica* Cham.), conversely, is a southerly ranging species, extending on the coast from the vicinity of Grays Harbor, Washington (Jones 1936), to the Santa Monica Mountains in California near Los Angeles (Jepson 1925). In view of this distribution pattern, which presumably is climatically controlled, it might be supposed that with a change of climate, the species favored would accordingly advance while the other would retreat. This advance and retreat is likely to have occurred, although without specific identification of the pollen constituting the profiles, conclusions are not possible.

At Pangborn Lake (Fig. 38), in the sweet gale range but beyond that of wax myrtle, the strengthening of the *Myrica* profile in the late-postglacial zone is undoubtedly caused by sweet gale; the strengthening in the hypsithermal zone is, plausibly, the result of wax myrtle migration northward. Along the Oregon coast at Devils Lake (Fig. 43), just north of the southern limit of sweet gale, the late-postglacial rise of *Myrica* seems certain to have been due to migration southward. Late development is not manifest at Tahkenitch Lake (Fig. 44) farther south and beyond the range; however, the genus was clearly more abundant during the Hypsithermal, probably attributable to northern migration of wax myrtle. At Garrison Lake, Lake Earl, and Capetown (Figs. 45, 46), the *Myrica* profile, largely if not entirely wax myrtle, declines in the late-postglacial sediments, in keeping with the prevailing climatic trend. The predominance of wax myrtle at Fort Bragg (Fig. 46) was gained following fire, but under the present warmer and drier climate within the central part of the range of this species, such abundance is to be expected.

Heath (Ericales)

Pollen of heath is in part zoned in the Late Postglacial. Largely a northerly group, a number of plants have an austral affinity. Like sweet gale, heath shows a preference for the change toward the cool and moist climate that occurred during the Late Postglacial. The family is also zoned in the Late-glacial and the early part of the Postglacial.

Fern (Polypodiaceae)

Profiles for Polypodiaceae do not develop consistently. Lake profiles, such as those from Pangborn and Devils and Tahkenitch Lakes (Figs. 38, 43, 44), diminish upward from an abundance during the early part of the hypsithermal zone. Bog profiles from Wessler and Seaview (Figs. 40, 42) are strongest, respectively, during the Hypsithermal and Late Postglacial. Fern spores were found in abundance in the early part of the Late-glacial (LG-1) but in subsequent divisions of this interval (LG-2 and 3), their numbers were few. The inconsistent trends of the fern profiles appear to be of little or no value for reconstructing climatic relationships.

Sphagnum

This bryophyte genus behaves rather harmoniously in its profiles. The plant is not in evidence at every site, and some profiles are quite weak, but the tendency to have developed during the Late Postglacial is well illustrated. Profiles are mostly undeveloped through hypsithermal sediments, but in a single case, the Wessler profile (Fig. 40), a distinct prominence of short duration appears in the early part of the hypsithermal sediments. The behavior of the Wessler profile is like that at Masset in northern British Columbia (Fig. 32). The late-glacial profile at Humptulips (Fig. 41) contains only small numbers of *Sphagnum*. Trends in this region are generally consistent with those in the regions to the northwest.

Other Profiles

Pollen of *Rubus*, though sparse, is found most closely related to the Late Postglacial, particularly southward, and the Late-glacial. Species of the genus occurring along the coast are largely salmonberry (*R. spectabilis*) and thimbleberry (*R. parviflorus*) and probably comprise most, if not all, of the profiles. The two species are rainforest plants and range only as far south in California as the fog belt extends. At Capetown (Fig. 46), the *Rubus* profile is clearly Late Postglacial. This lends support to the thesis that the above representatives are late-postglacial migrants, although there is some likelihood that the pollen may be from *R. vitifolius* C. & S.

Pollen of *Sanguisorba*, not evident south of the Garrison Lake section (Fig. 45), is found northward at Wessler, Ozette Lake, and Humptulips (Figs. 40, 41). The plant was Late Postglacial but was also a member of the early, and particularly the late, Late-glacial (LG-1 and 3). The Umbelliferae are also Late-glacial but were most prominent during the Hypsithermal (for example, Wessler and Capetown; Figs. 40, 46).

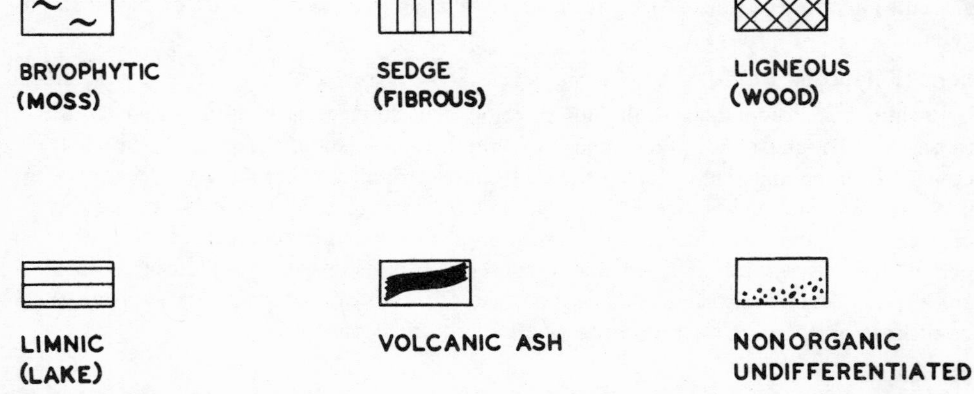

FIG. 12. Symbols used for the sedimentary types appearing in sections shown in Figures 13–46.

In postglacial deposits, the Liguliflorae is only occasionally recorded whereas the Tubuliflorae is generally common, though not in amounts of more than a few per cent. The Capetown profile (Fig. 46) contains perhaps the best representation. In the late-glacial zone of the Humptulips section (LG-1 and 3) both groups are well represented. The club moss *Lycopodium clavatum* is mostly Late Postglacial in age and is not in the diagrams south of Humptulips, where it is only rare in late-glacial sediments.

Two genera heretofore not mentioned for the late-glacial assemblage at Humptulips should be noted. In the early part of the interval (LG-1) *Polygonum*, only rarely encountered in the sections studied, occurs at a number of levels; in the late subdivision (LG-3), *Polemonium* is represented by single grains at only two levels.

Finally, since most of the sections are from lakes, where hydrarch succession is in progress, profiles are included for a number of aquatic or semiaquatic plants: *Typha*, *Sparganium*, *Potamogeton*, *Nuphar*, and *Myriophyllum*.

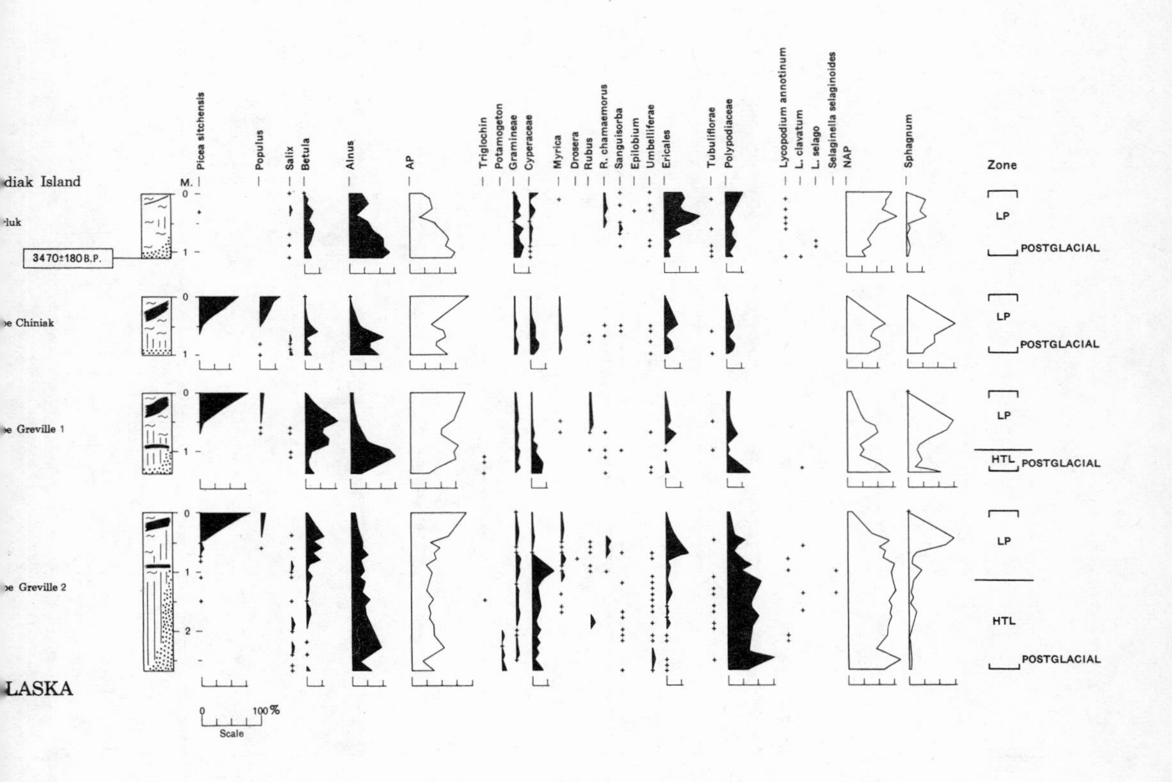

FIG. 13. Peat and pollen stratigraphy and zonation for sections from Karluk (1), Cape Chiniak (2), Cape Greville 1 (3), and Cape Greville 2 (4).

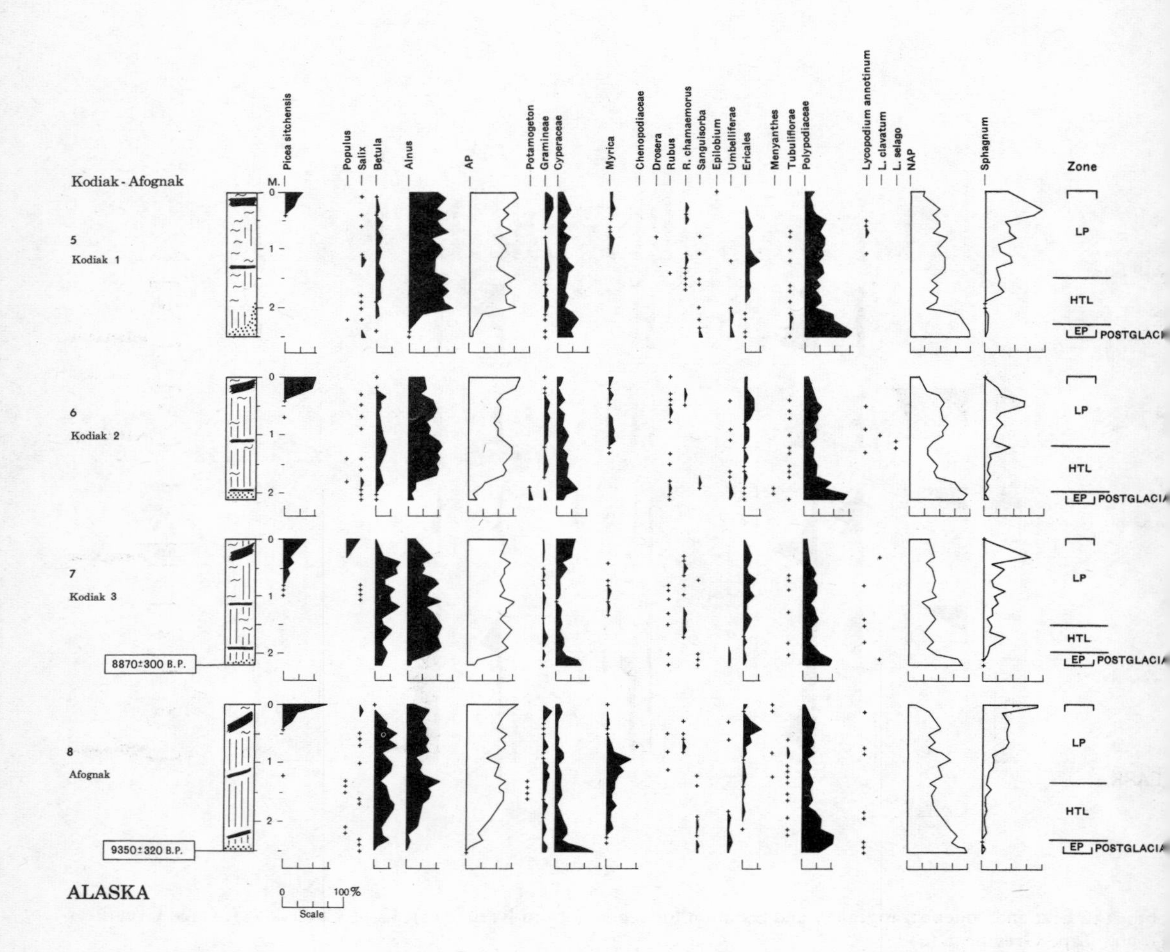

FIG. 14. Peat and pollen stratigraphy and zonation for sections from Kodiak 1 (5), Kodiak 2 (6), Kodiak 3 (7), and Afognak (8).

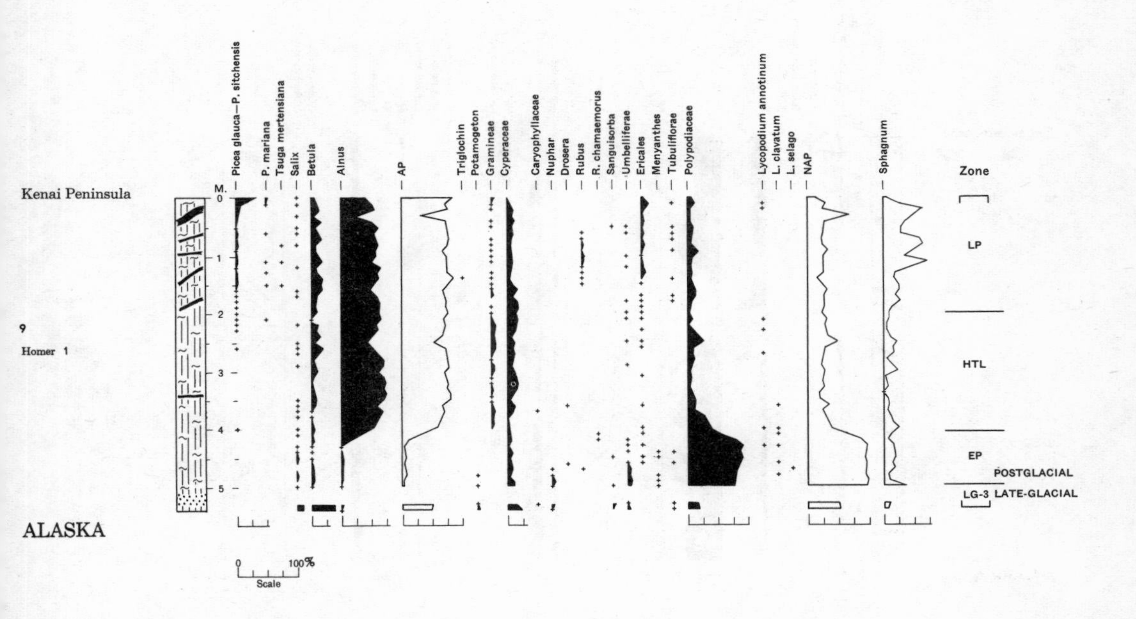

FIG. 15. Peat and pollen stratigraphy and zonation for the section from Homer 1 (9).

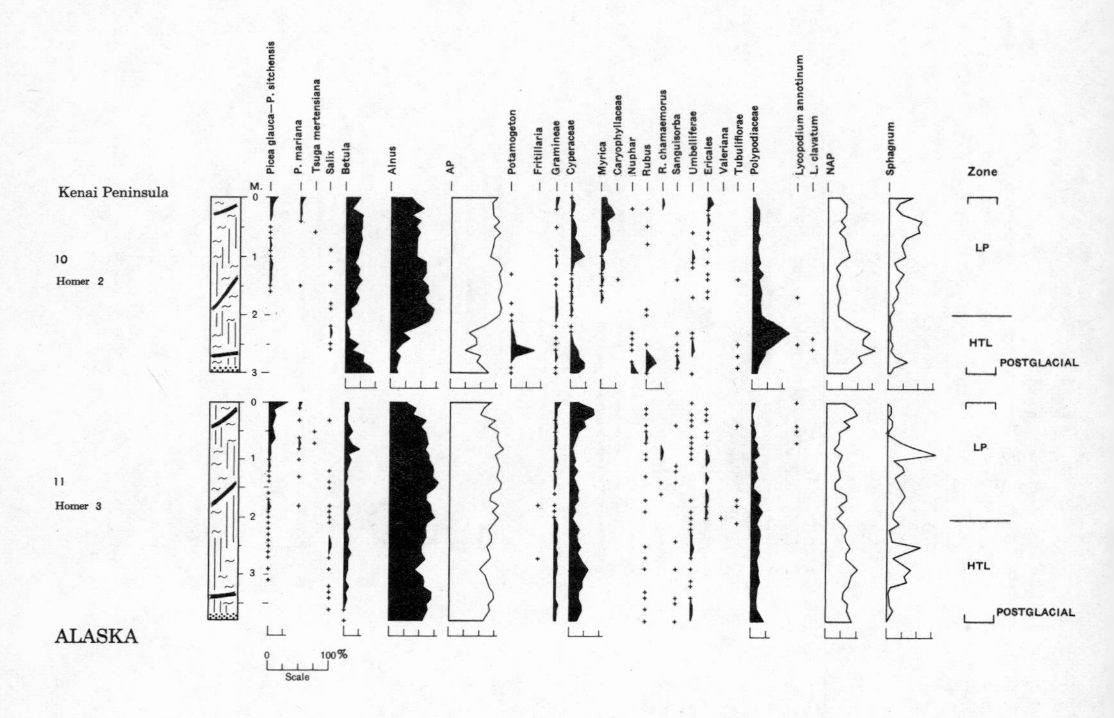

FIG. 16. Peat and pollen stratigraphy and zonation for sections from Homer 2 (10) and Homer 3 (11).

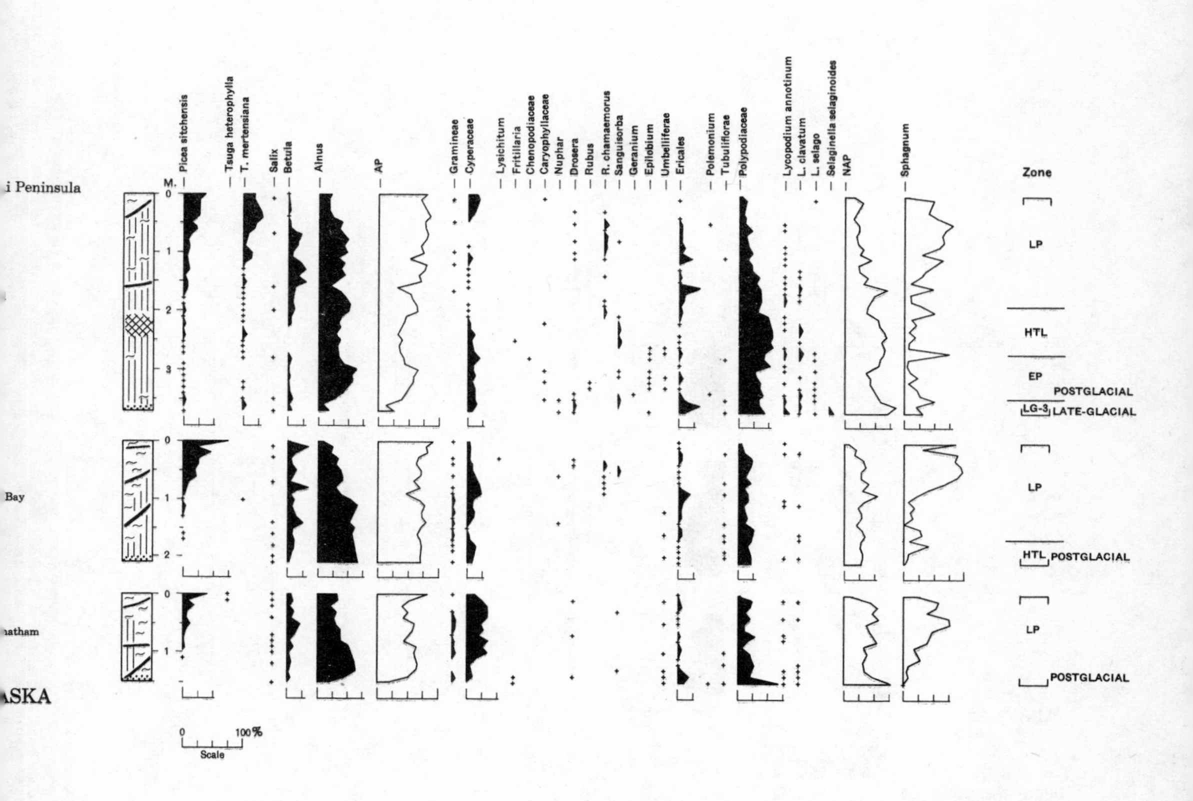

FIG. 17. Peat and pollen stratigraphy and zonation for sections from Seward (12), Windy Bay (13), and Port Chatham 14).

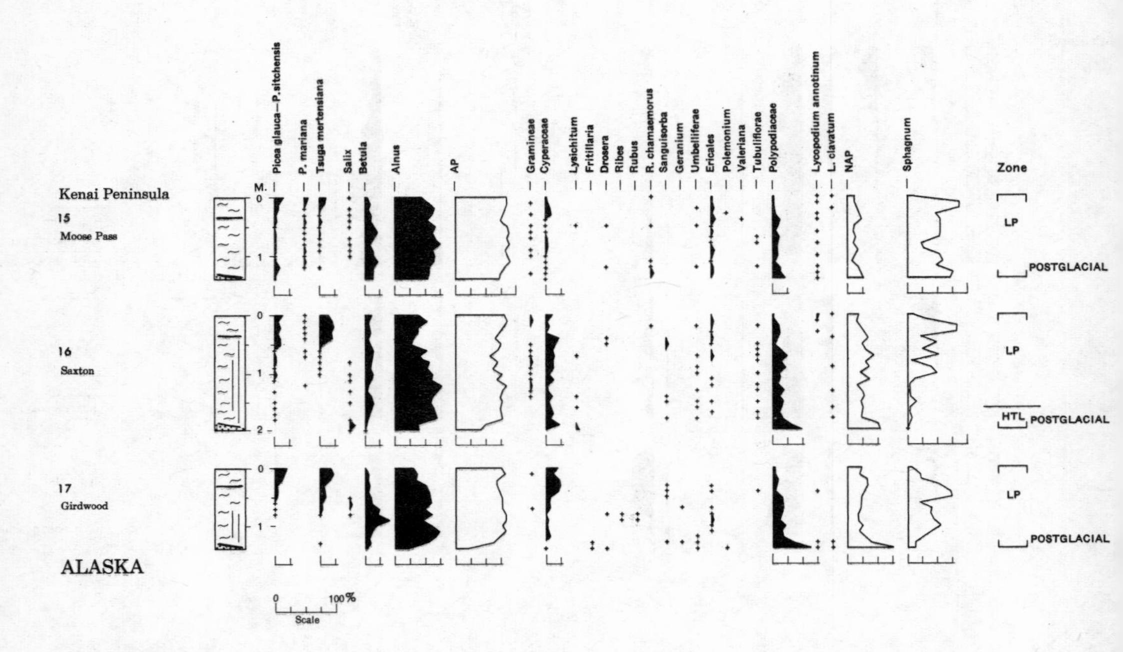

FIG. 18. Peat and pollen stratigraphy and zonation for sections from Moose Pass (15), Saxton (16), and Girdw (17).

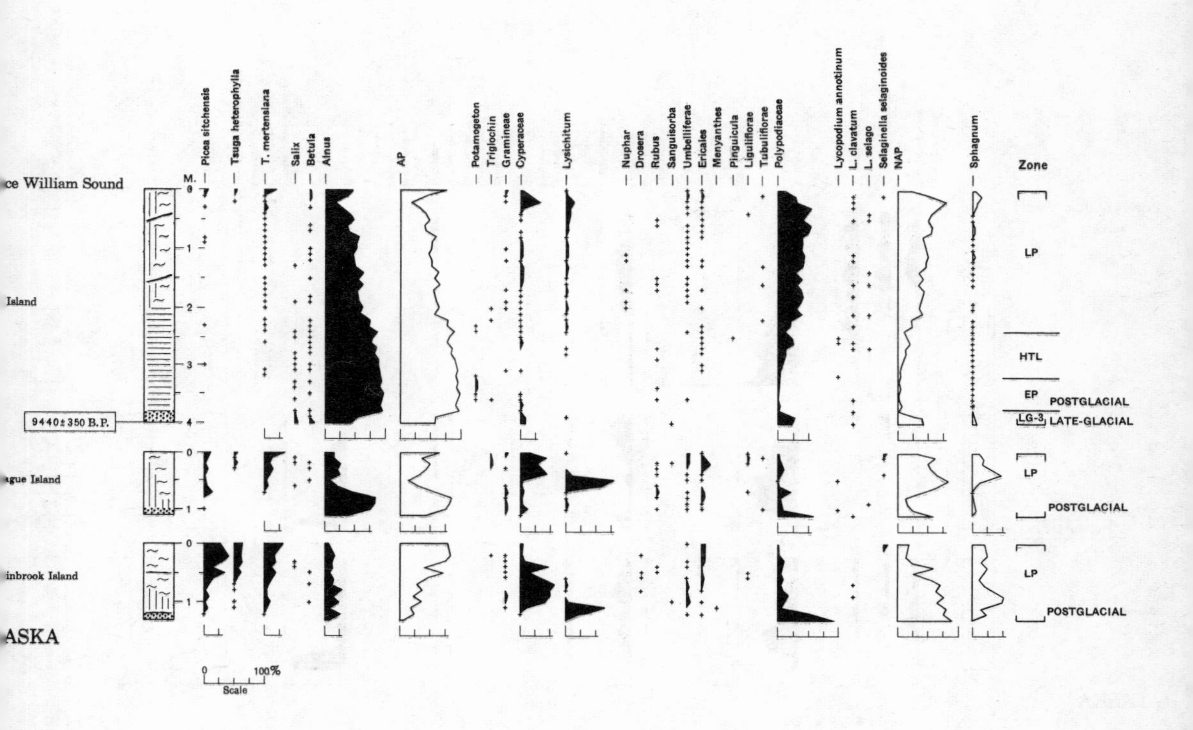

FIG. 19. Peat and pollen stratigraphy and zonation for sections from Perry Island (18), Montague Island (19), and Hinchinbrook Island (20).

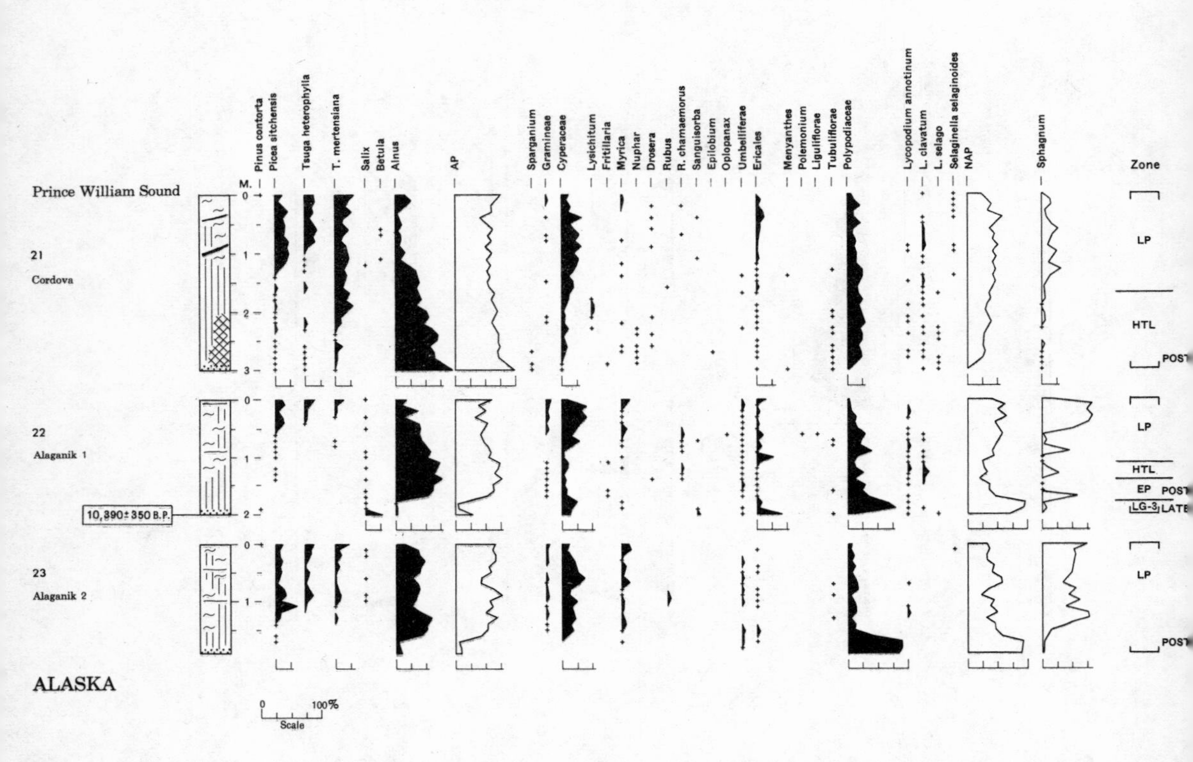

FIG. 20. Peat and pollen stratigraphy and zonation for sections from Cordova (21), Alaganik 1 (22), and Alaganik 2 (23).

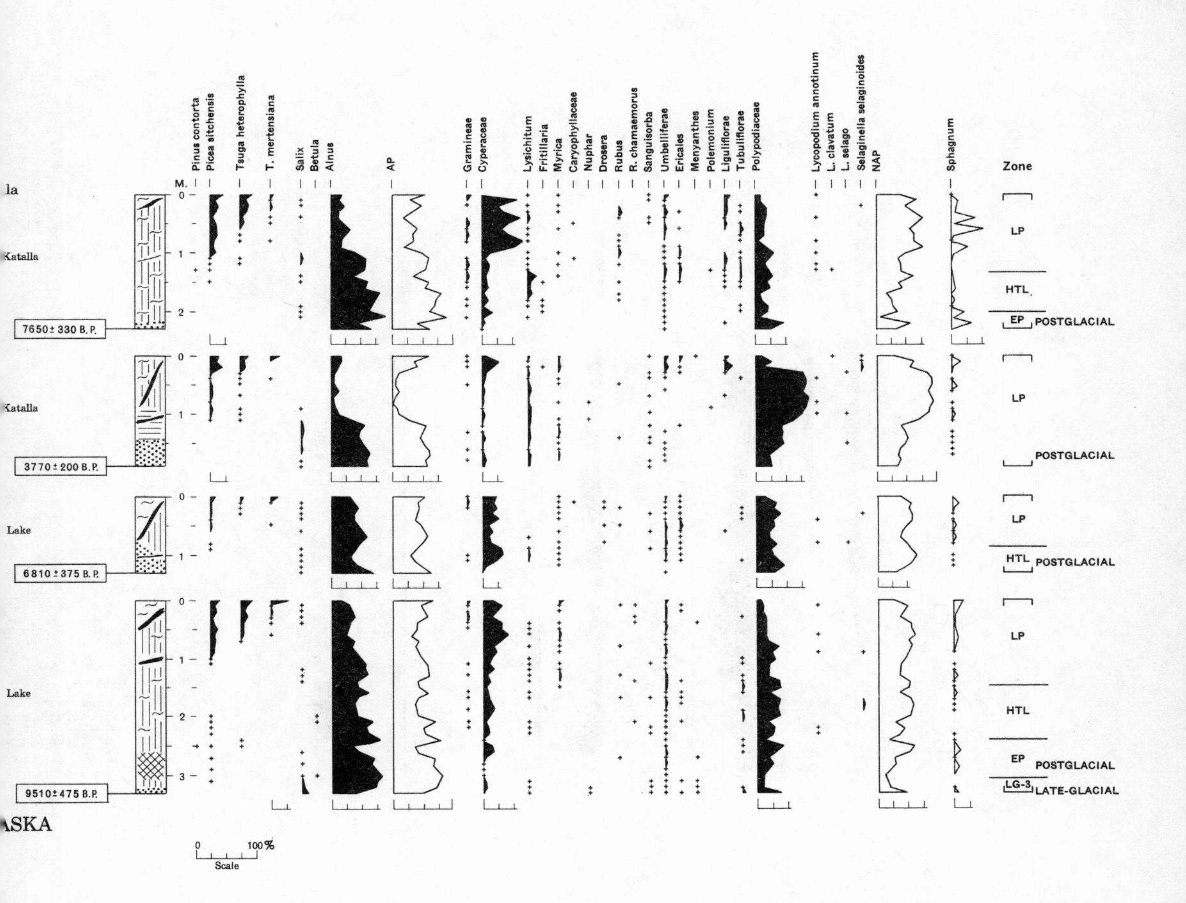

FIG. 21. Peat and pollen stratigraphy and zonation for sections from Upper Katalla (24), Lower Katalla (25), [M]artin Lake (26), and Bering Lake (27).

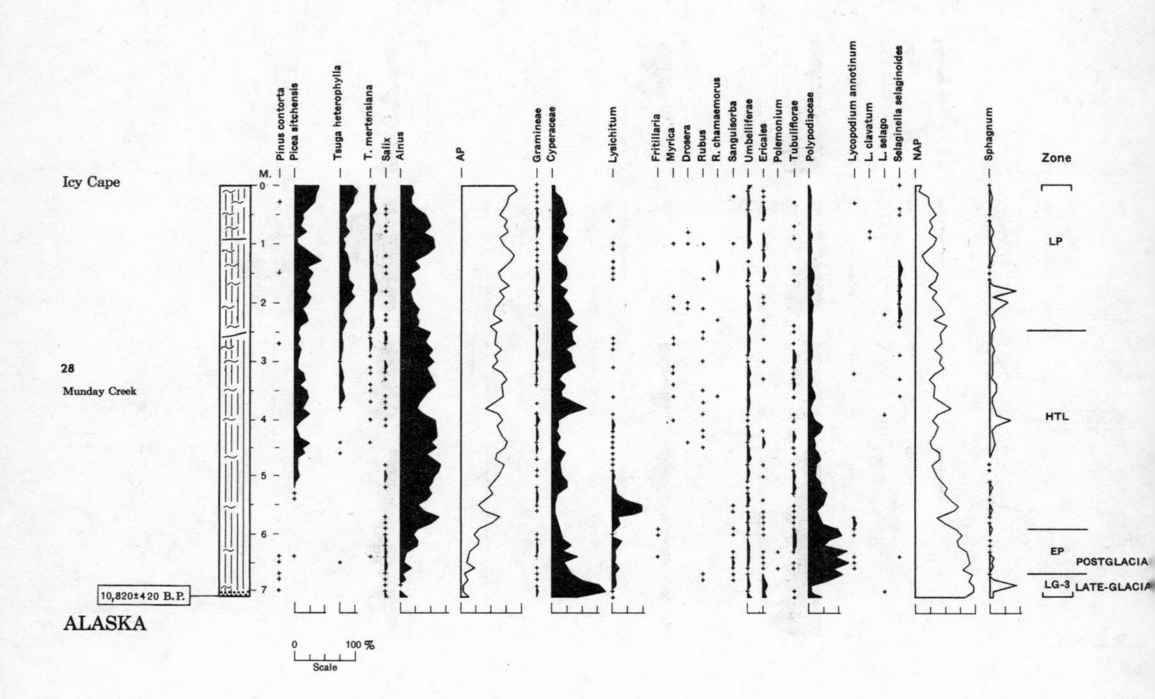

FIG. 22. Peat and pollen stratigraphy and zonation for the section from Munday Creek (28).

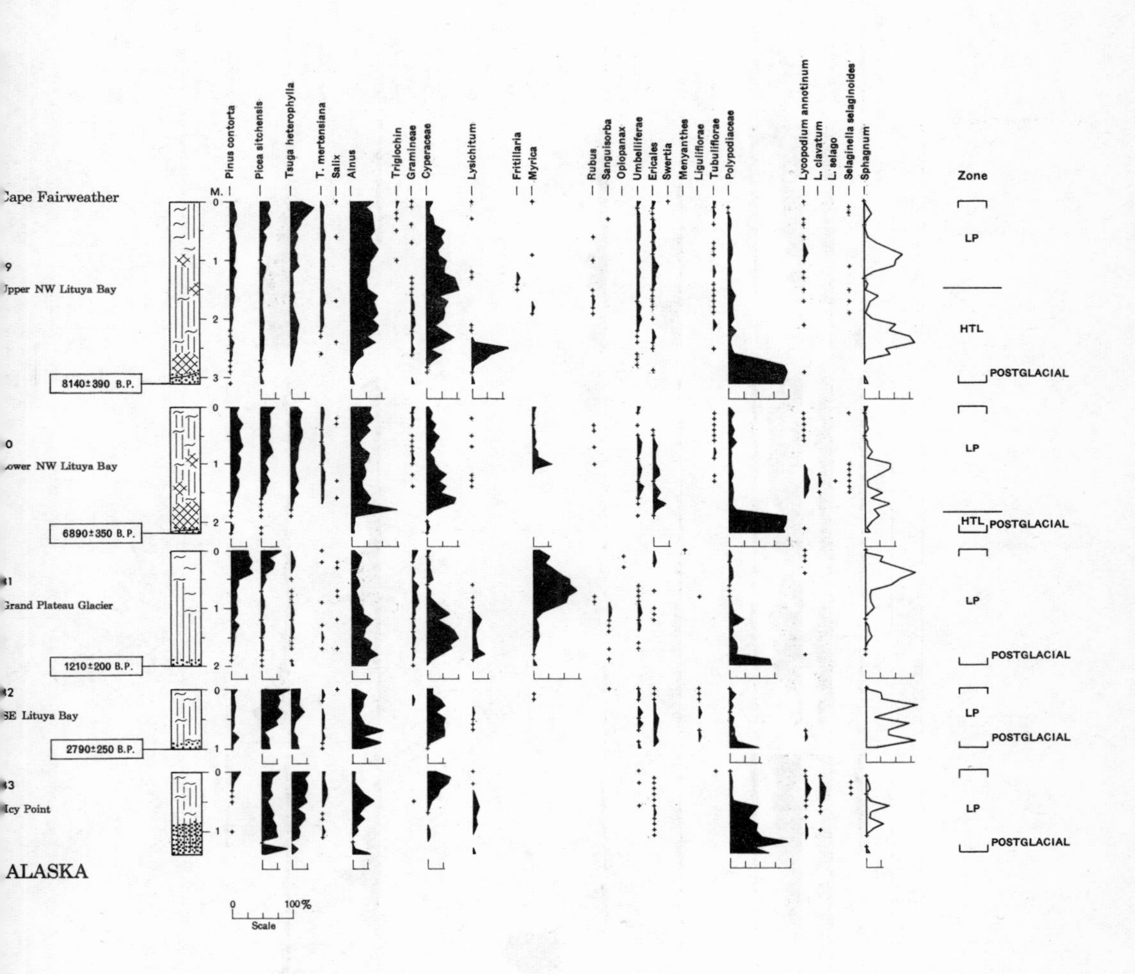

FIG. 23. Peat and pollen stratigraphy and zonation for sections from Upper NW Lituya Bay (29), Lower NW [Li]tuya Bay (30), Grand Plateau Glacier (31), SE Lituya Bay (32), and Icy Point (33).

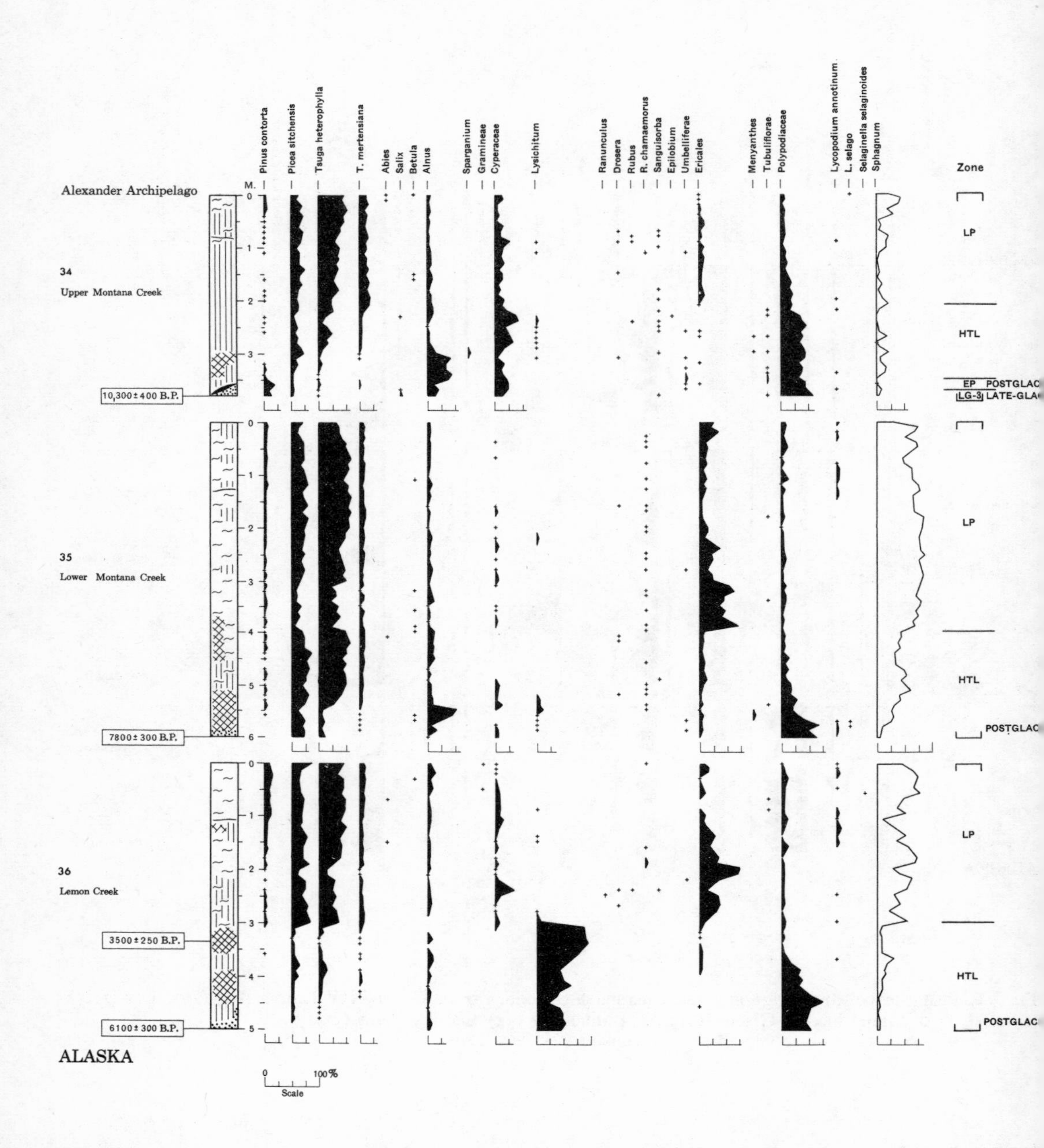

FIG. 24. Peat and pollen stratigraphy and zonation for sections from Upper Montana Creek (34), Lower Monta Creek (35), and Lemon Creek (36).

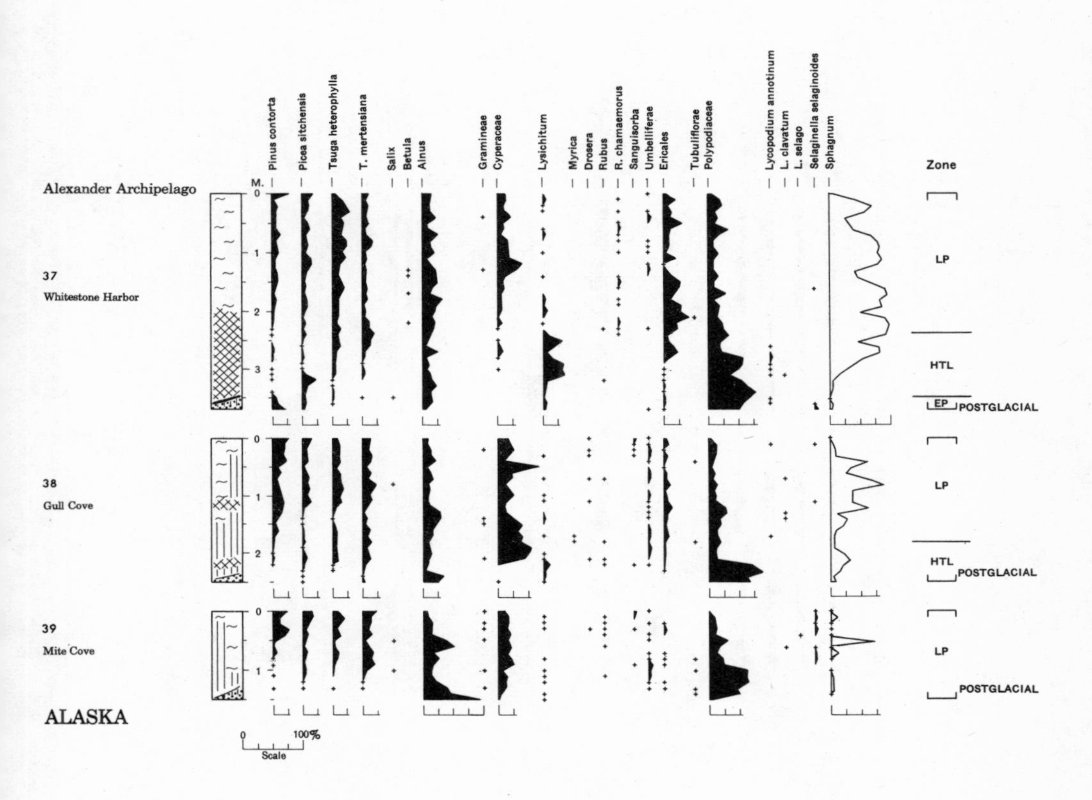

FIG. 25. Peat and pollen stratigraphy and zonation for sections from Whitestone Harbor (37), Gull Cove (38), d Mite Cove (39).

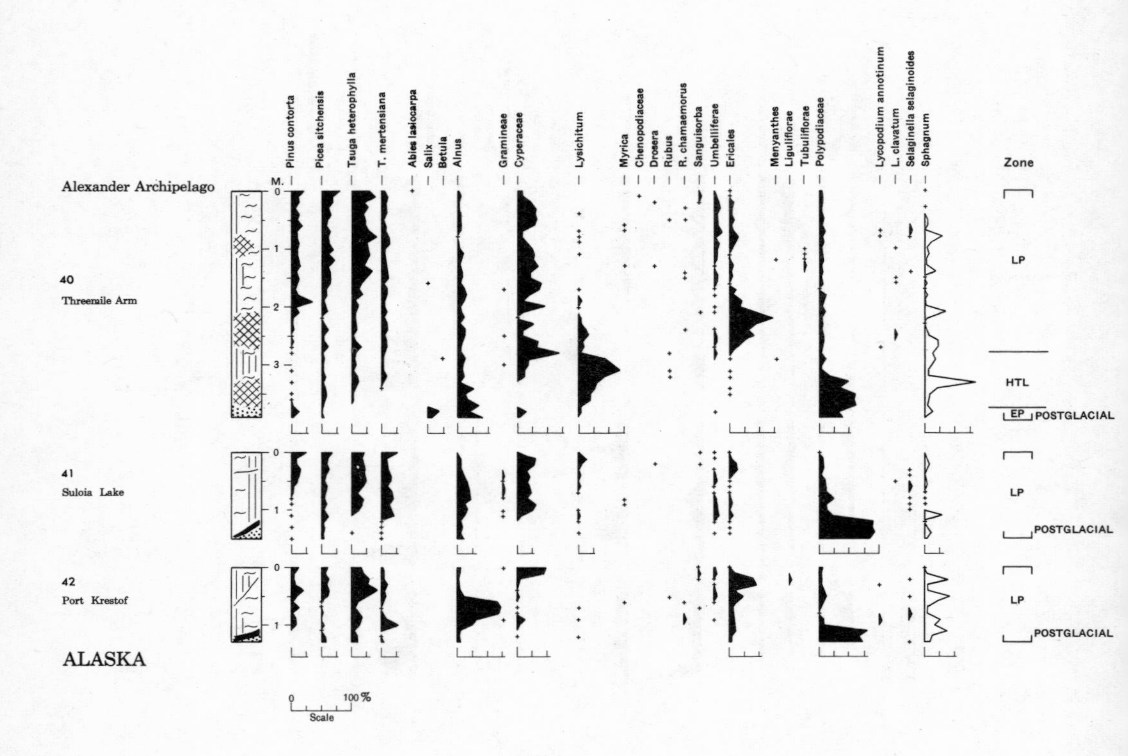

FIG. 26. Peat and pollen stratigraphy and zonation for sections from Threemile Arm (40), Suloia Lake (41), and Port Krestof (42).

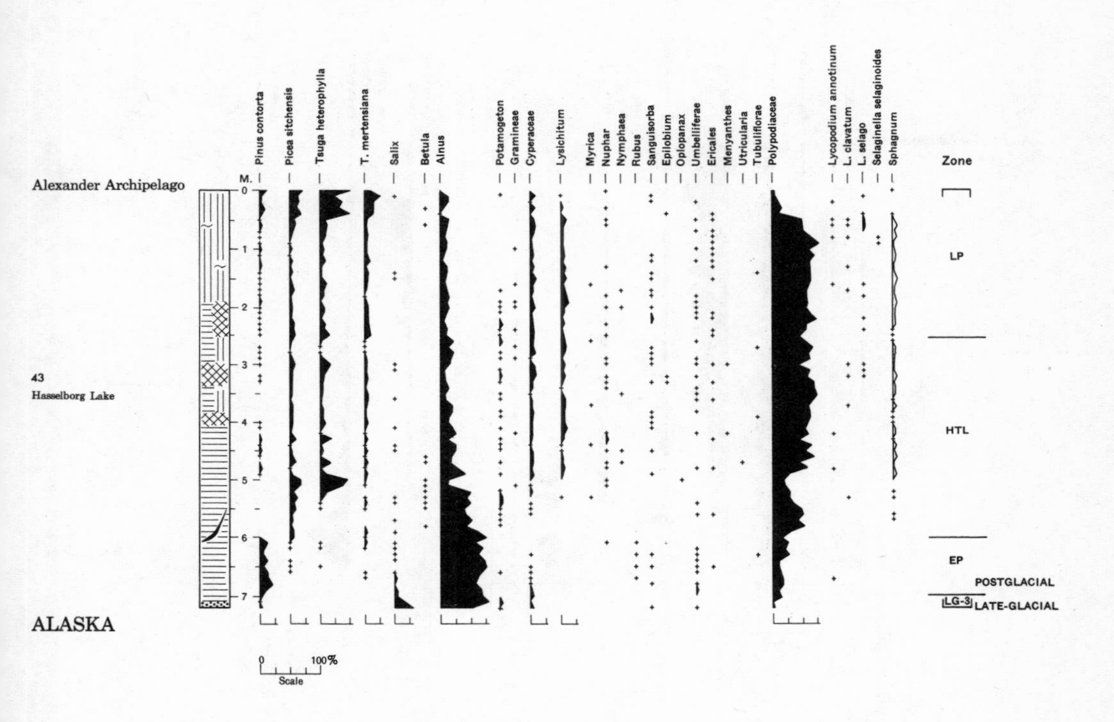

FIG. 27. Peat and pollen stratigraphy and zonation for the section from Hasselborg Lake (43).

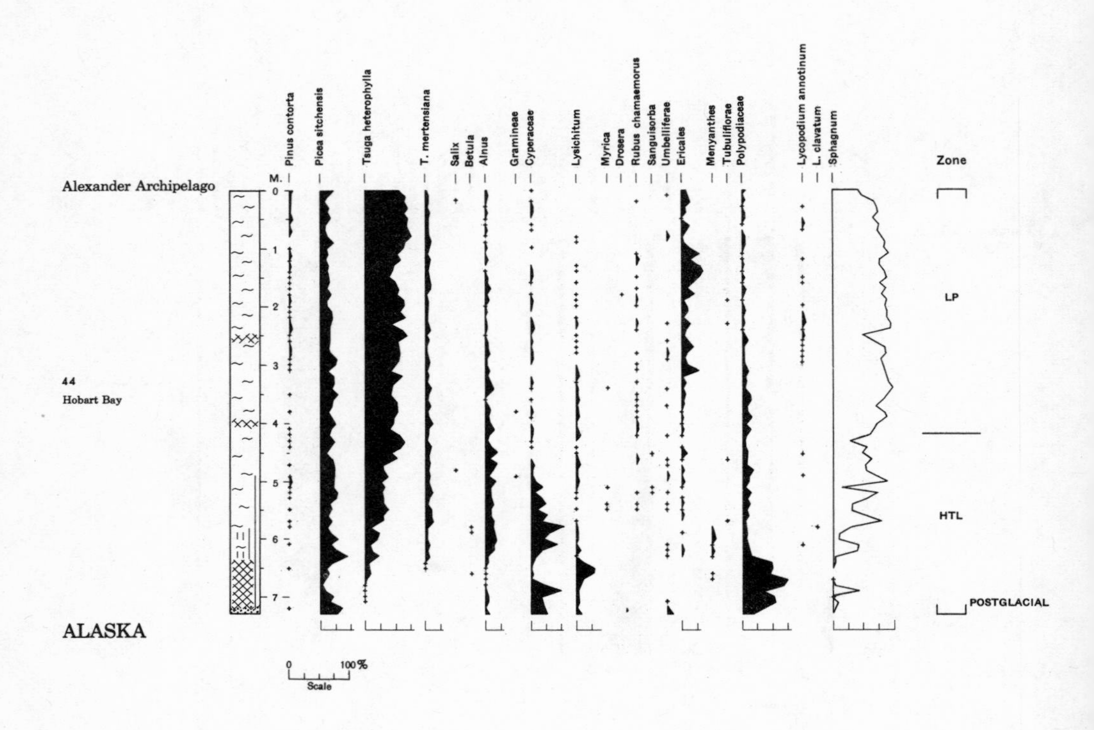

FIG. 28. Peat and pollen stratigraphy and zonation for the section from Hobart Bay (44).

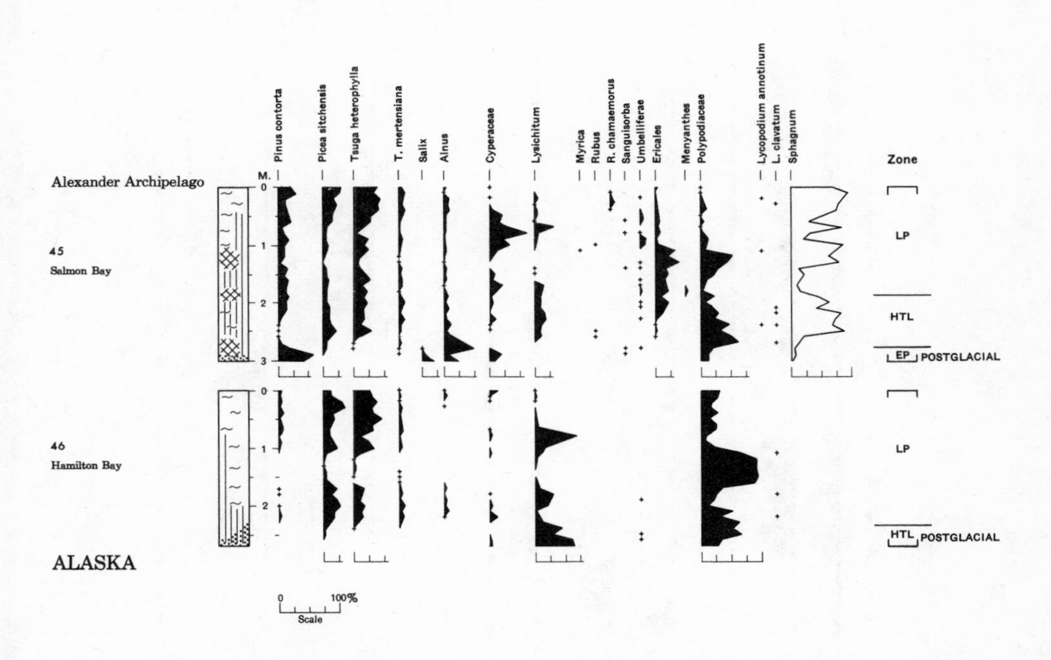

FIG. 29. Peat and pollen stratigraphy and zonation for sections from Salmon Bay (45) and Hamilton Bay (46).

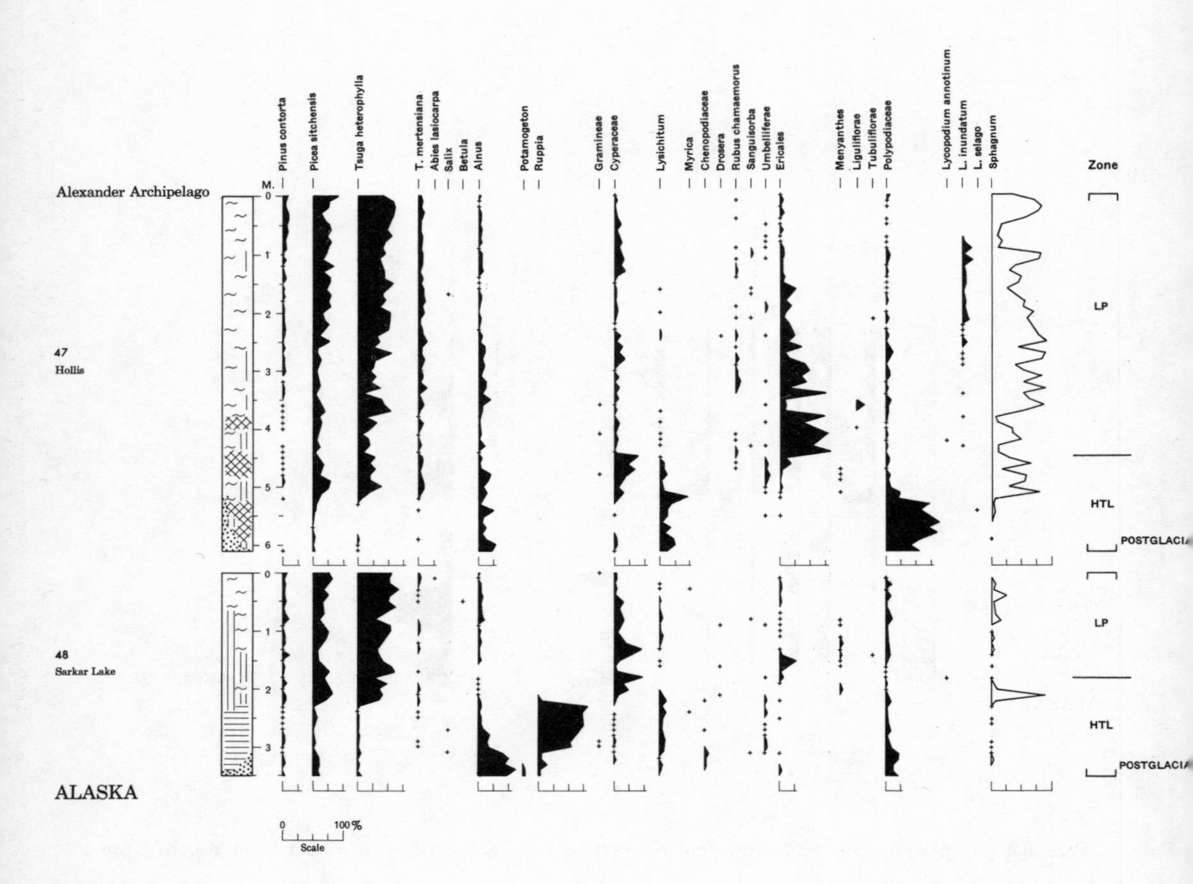

FIG. 30. Peat and pollen stratigraphy and zonation for sections from Hollis (47) and Sarkar Lake (48).

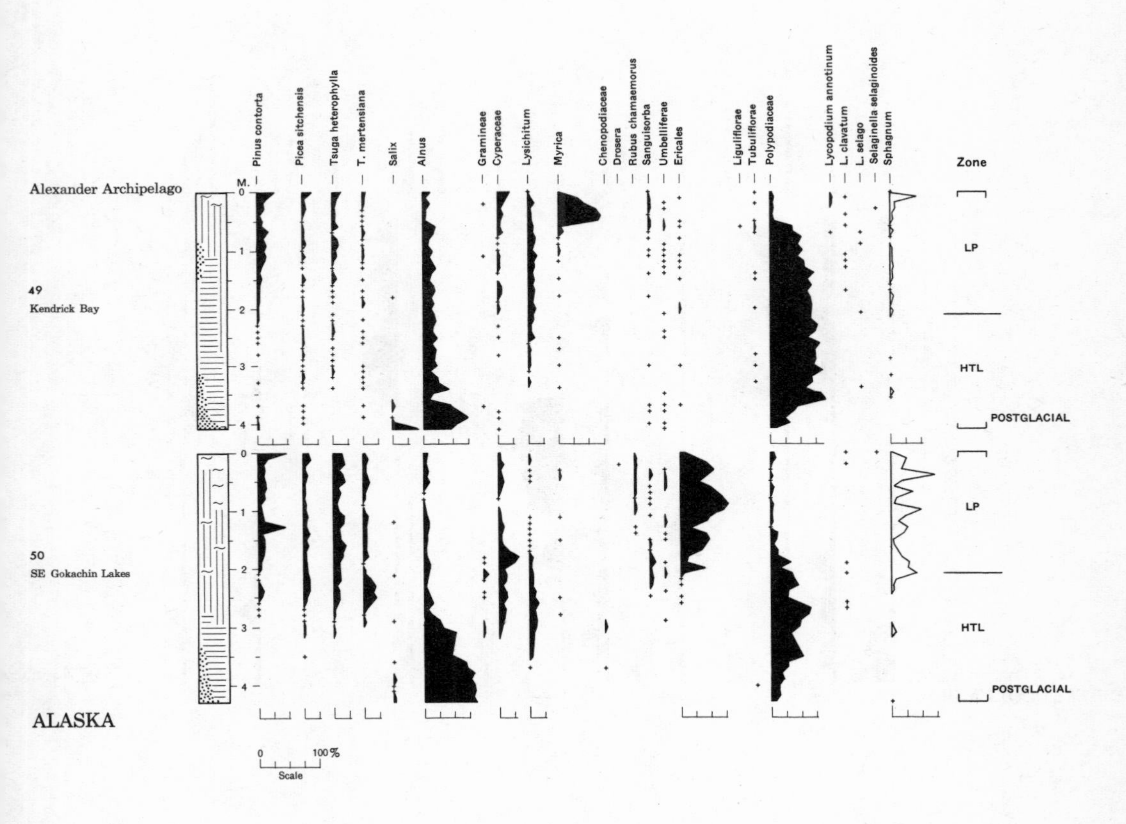

FIG. 31. Peat and pollen stratigraphy and zonation for sections from Kendrick Bay (49) and SE Gokachin Lakes (50).

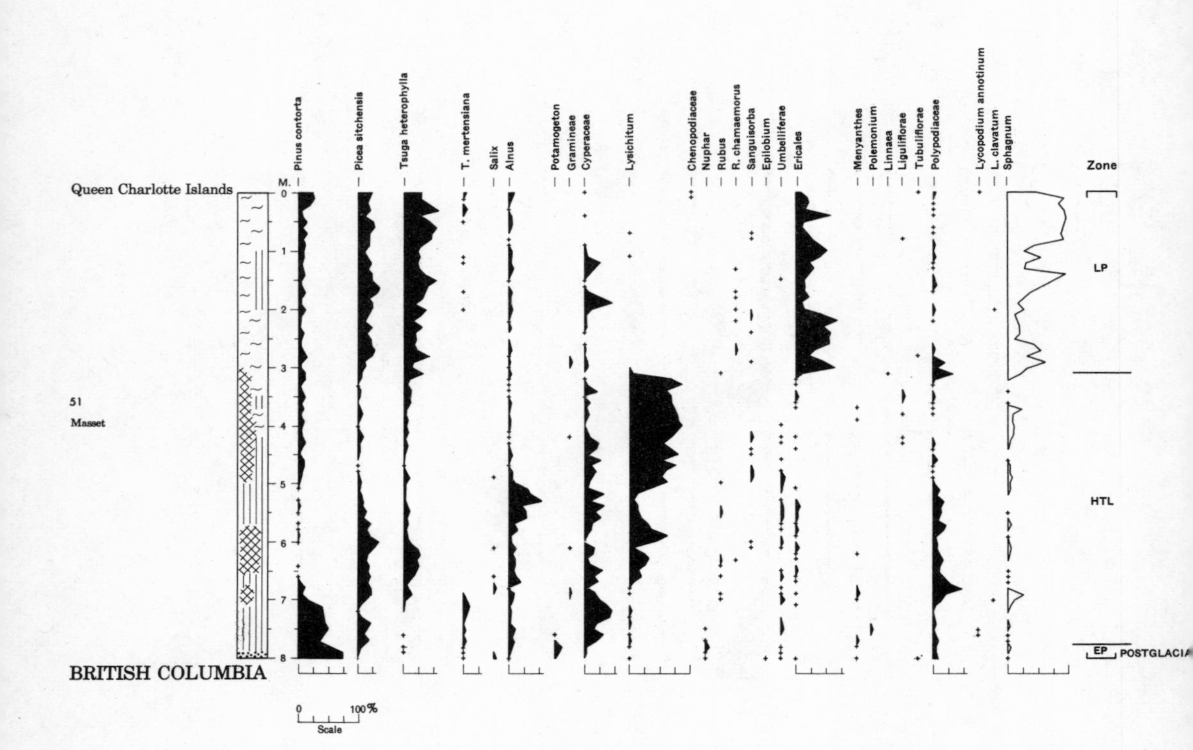

FIG. 32. Peat and pollen stratigraphy and zonation for the section from Masset (51).

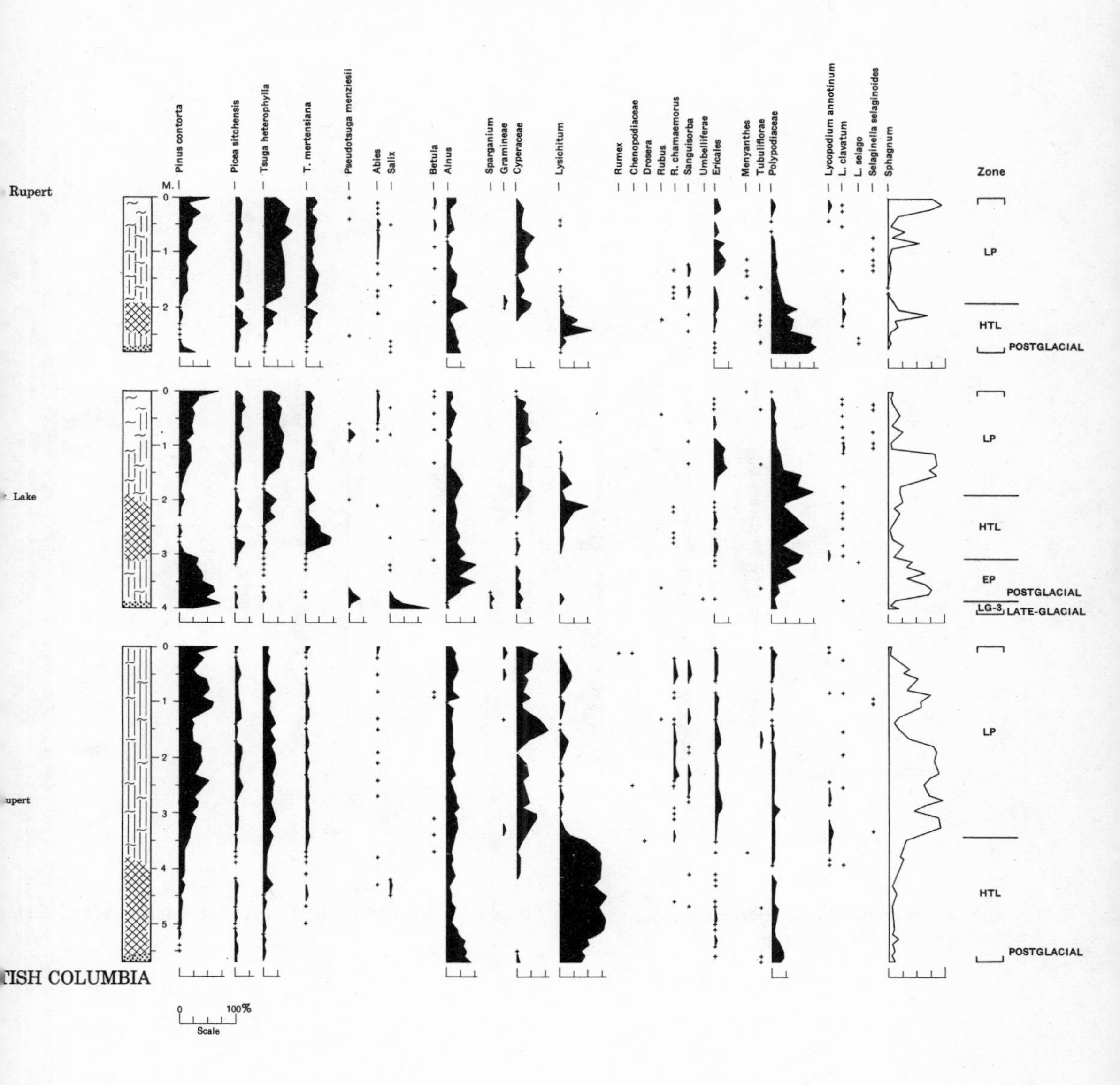

FIG. 33. Peat and pollen stratigraphy and zonation for sections from Summit (52), Rainbow Lake (53), and Prince Rupert (54).

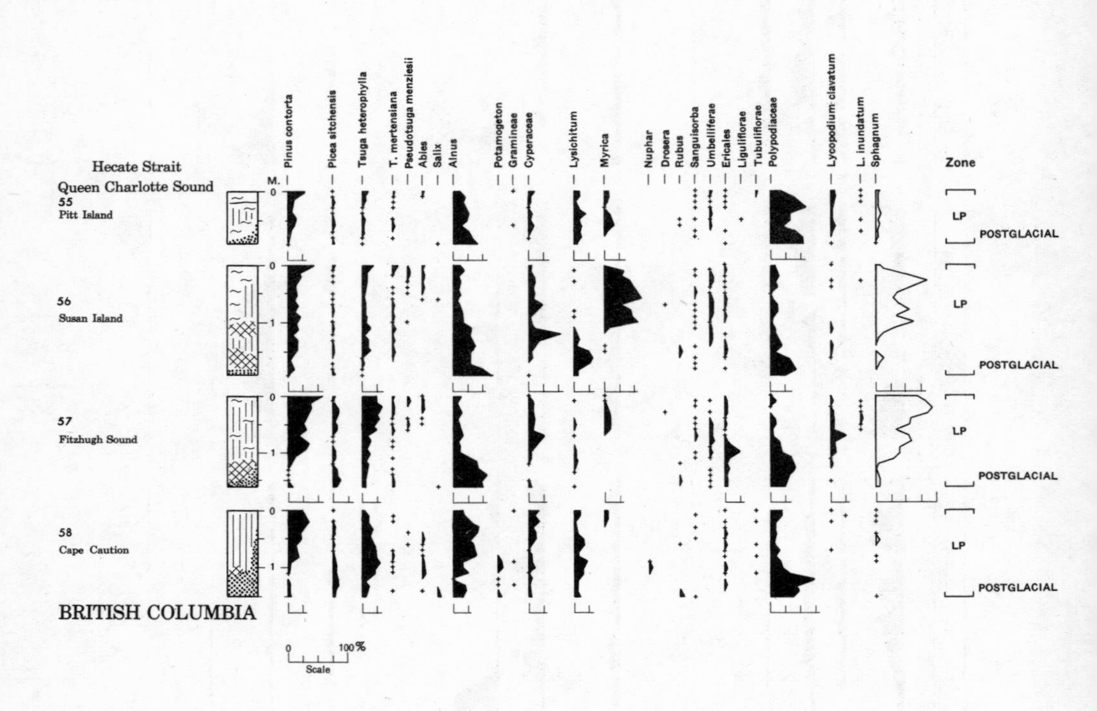

FIG. 34. Peat and pollen stratigraphy and zonation for sections from Pitt Island (55), Susan Island (56), Fitzhu Sound (57), and Cape Caution (58).

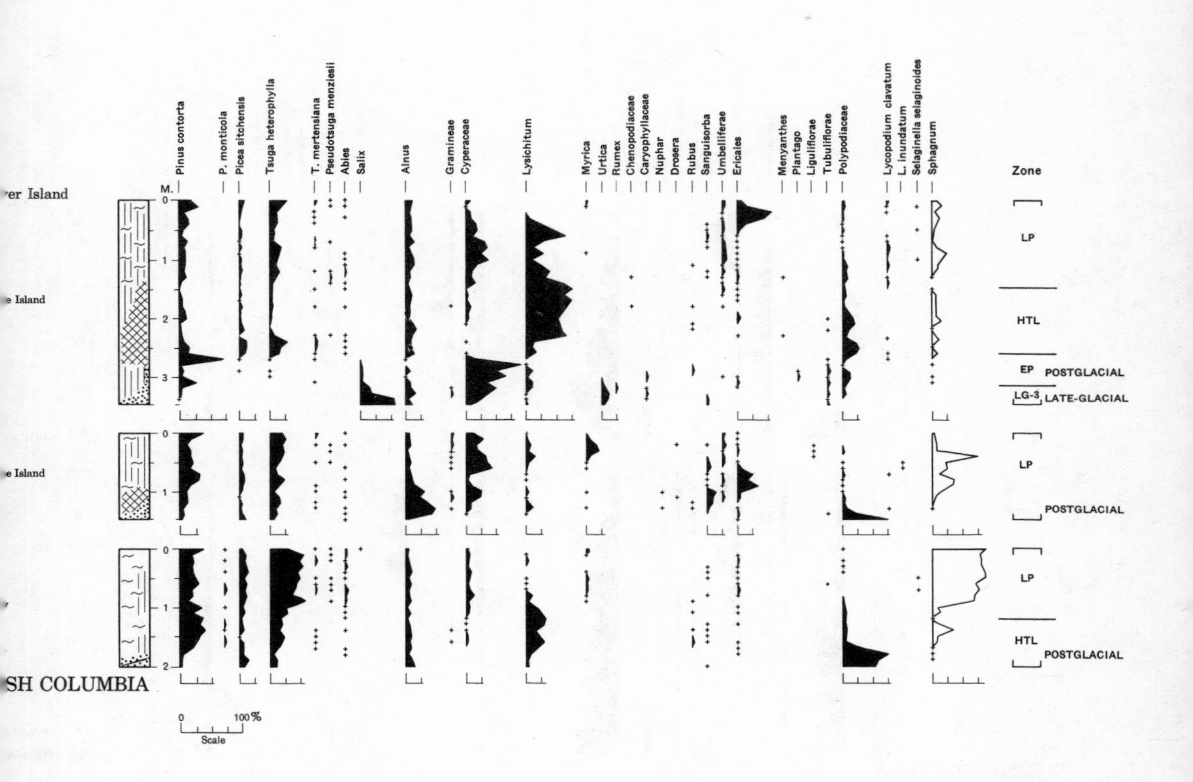

SH COLUMBIA

FIG. 35. Peat and pollen stratigraphy and zonation for sections from Upper Hope Island (59), Lower Hope Island), and Port Hardy (61).

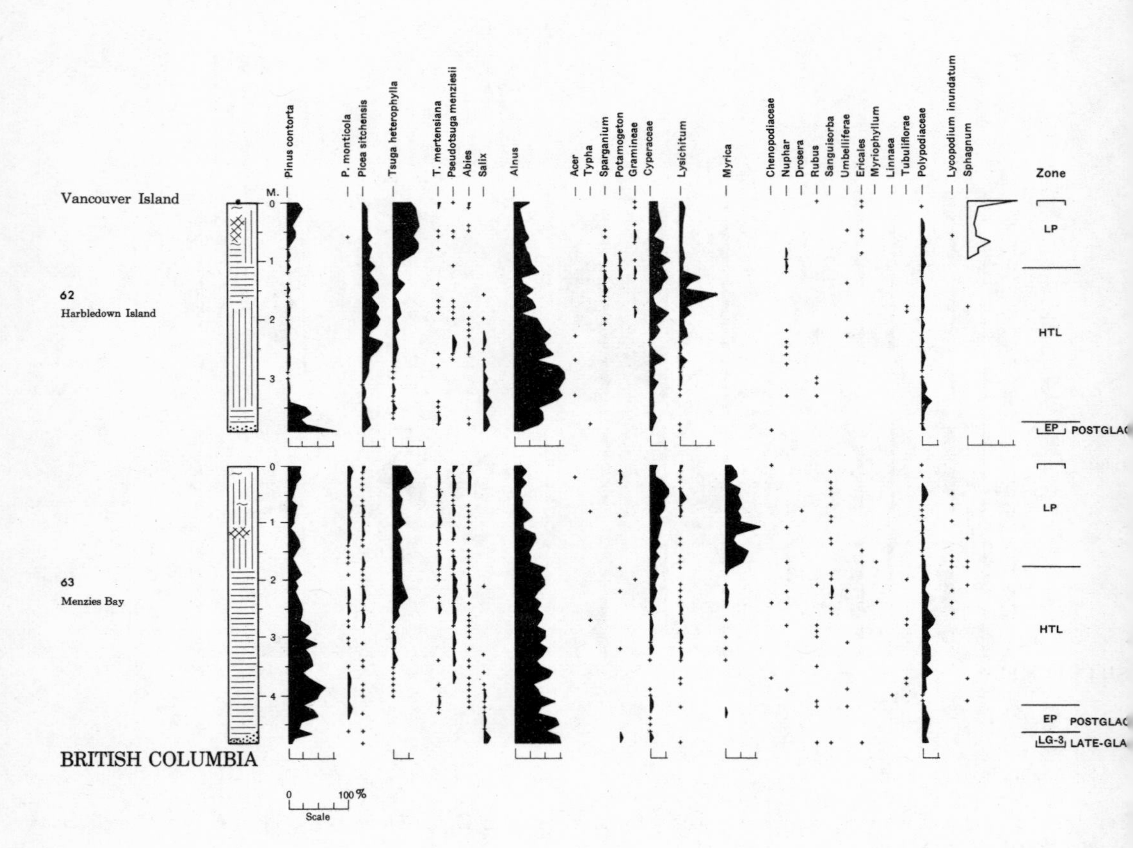

FIG. 36. Peat and pollen stratigraphy and zonation for sections from Harbledown Island (62) and Menzies Bay (6

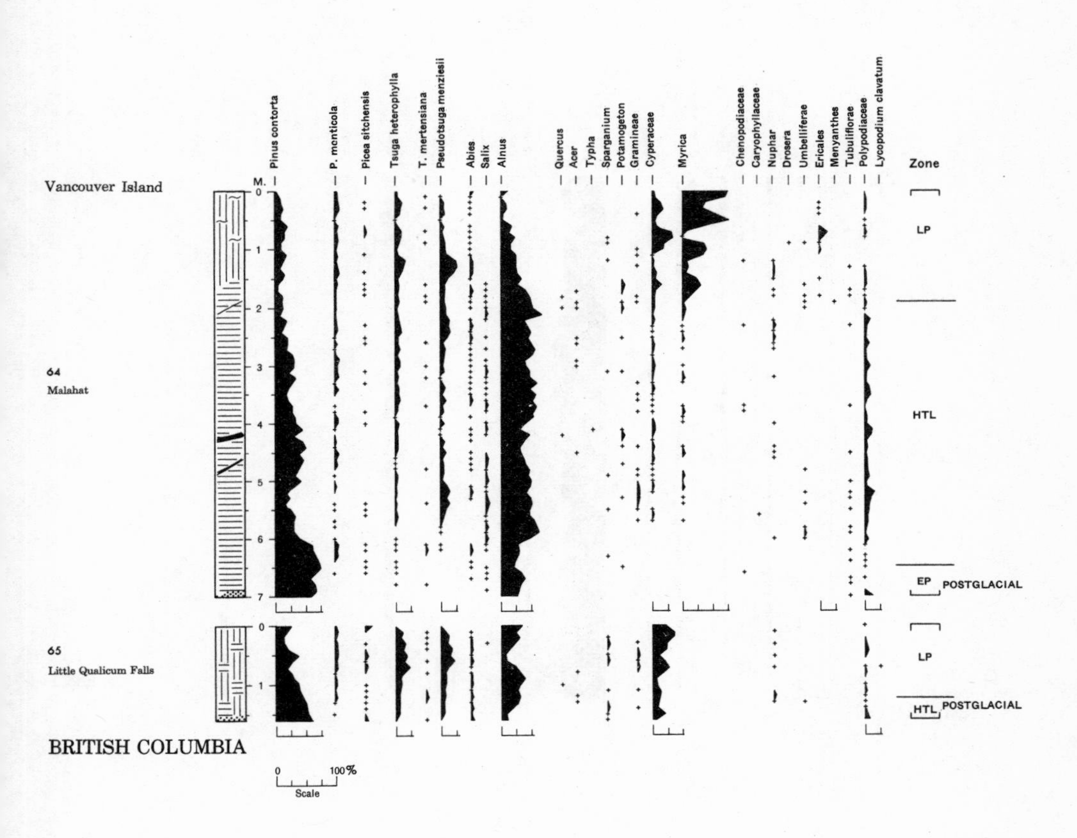

G. 37. Peat and pollen stratigraphy and zonation for sections from Malahat (64) and Little Qualicum Falls (65).

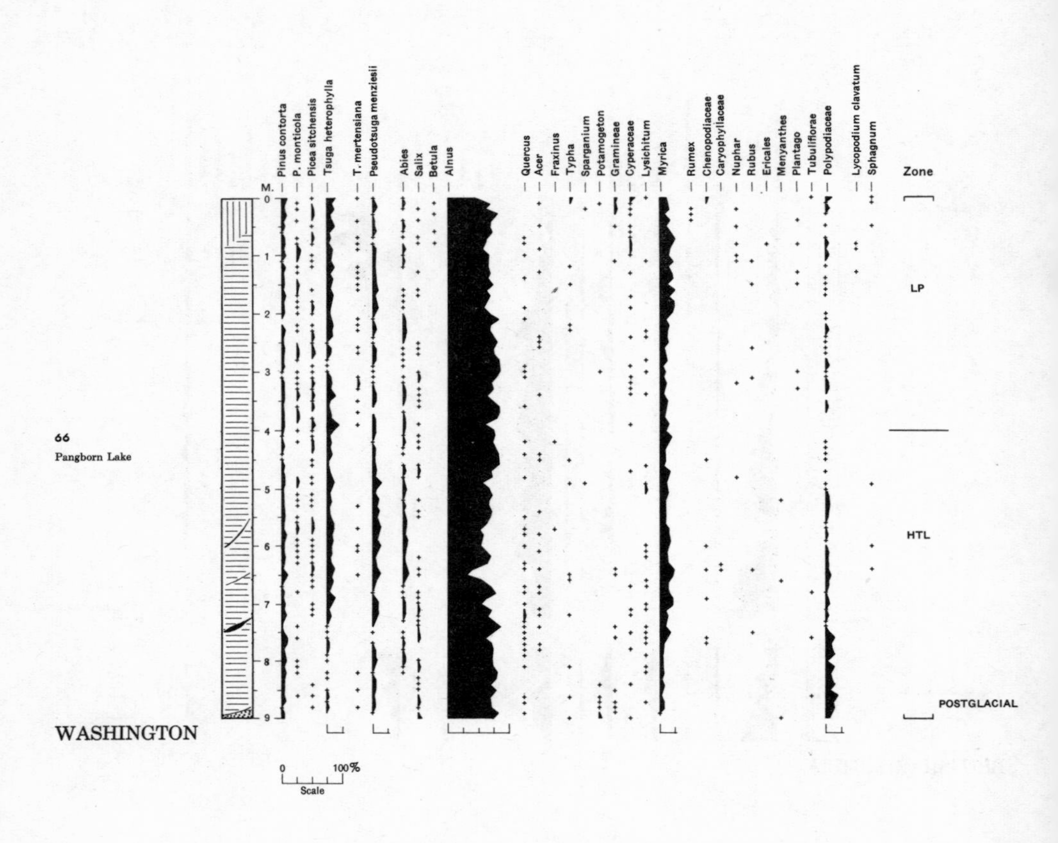

FIG. 38. Peat and pollen stratigraphy and zonation for the section from Pangborn Lake (66).

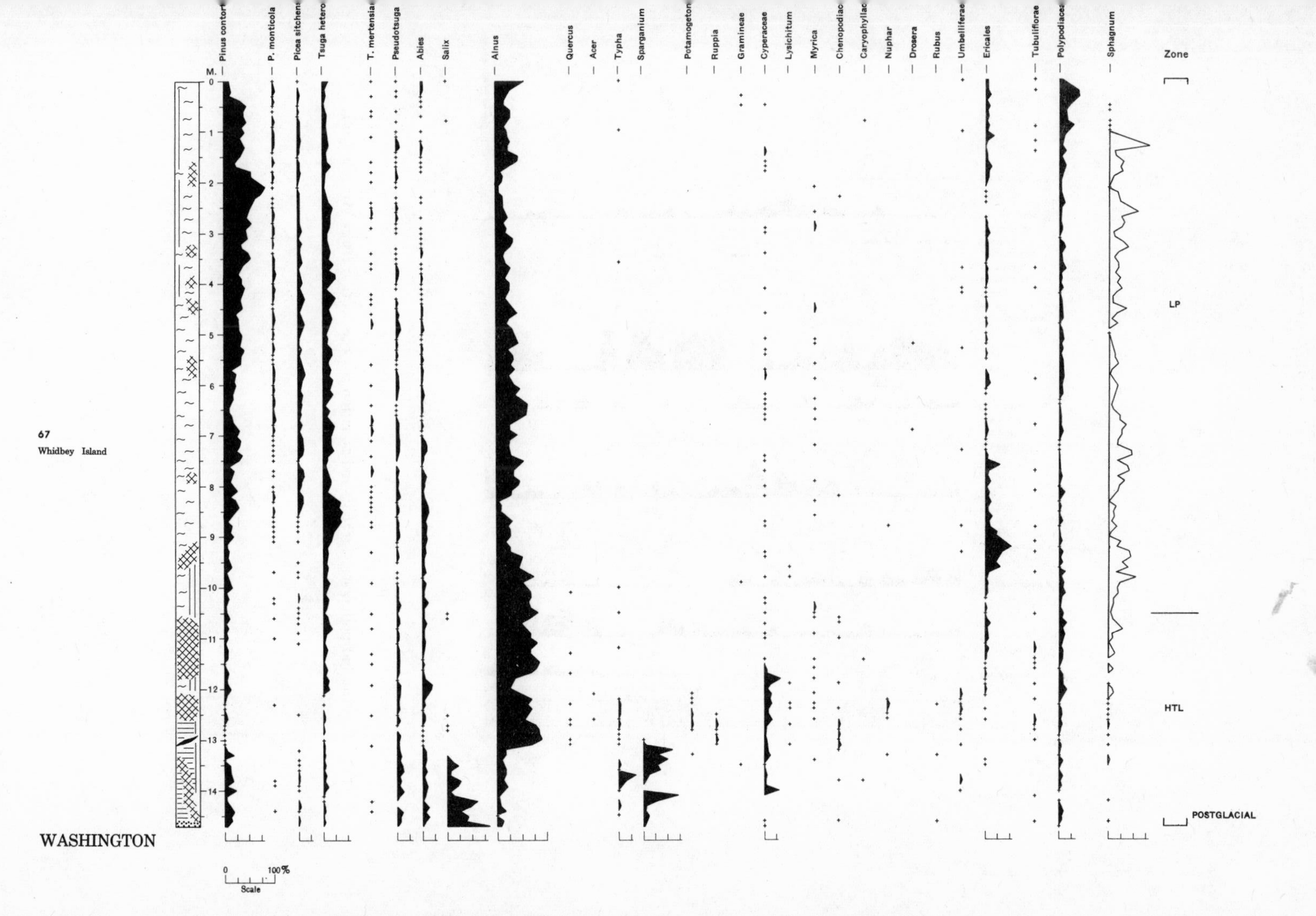

FIG. 39. Peat and pollen stratigraphy and zonation for the section from Whidbey Island (67).

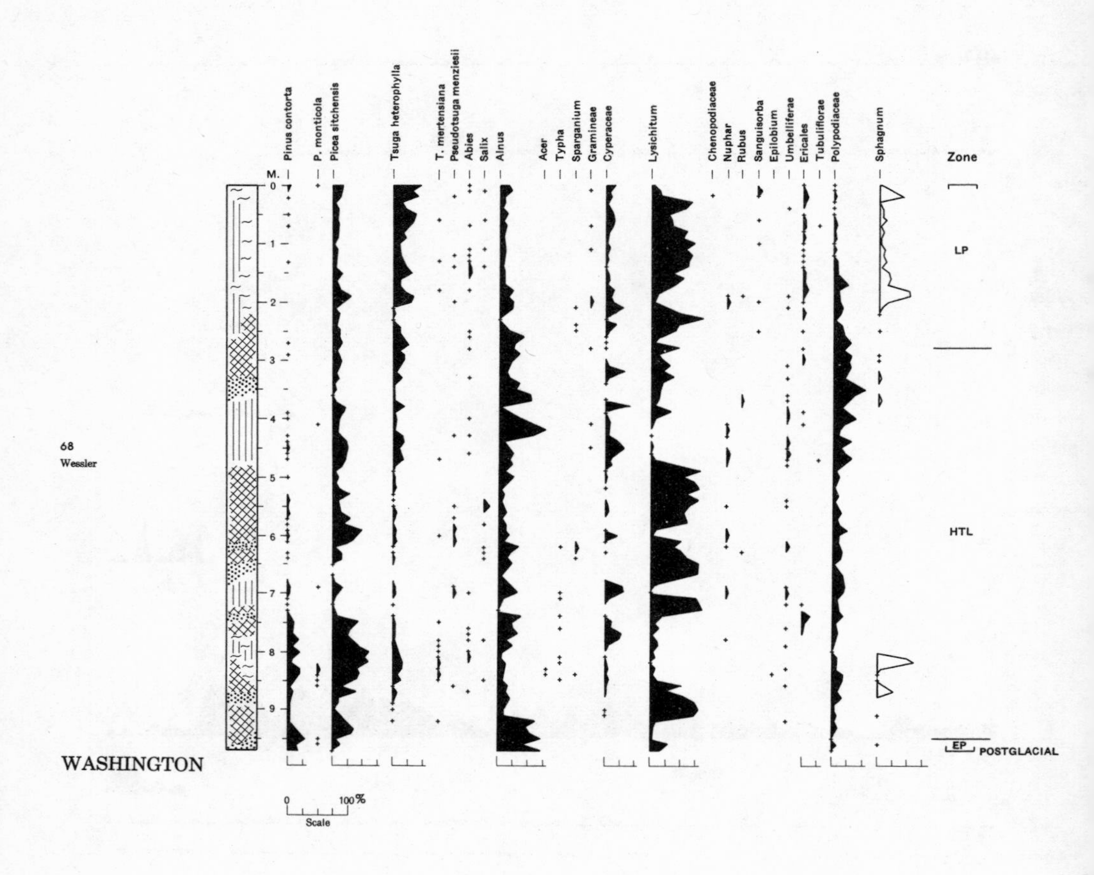

FIG. 40. Peat and pollen stratigraphy and zonation for the section from Wessler (68).

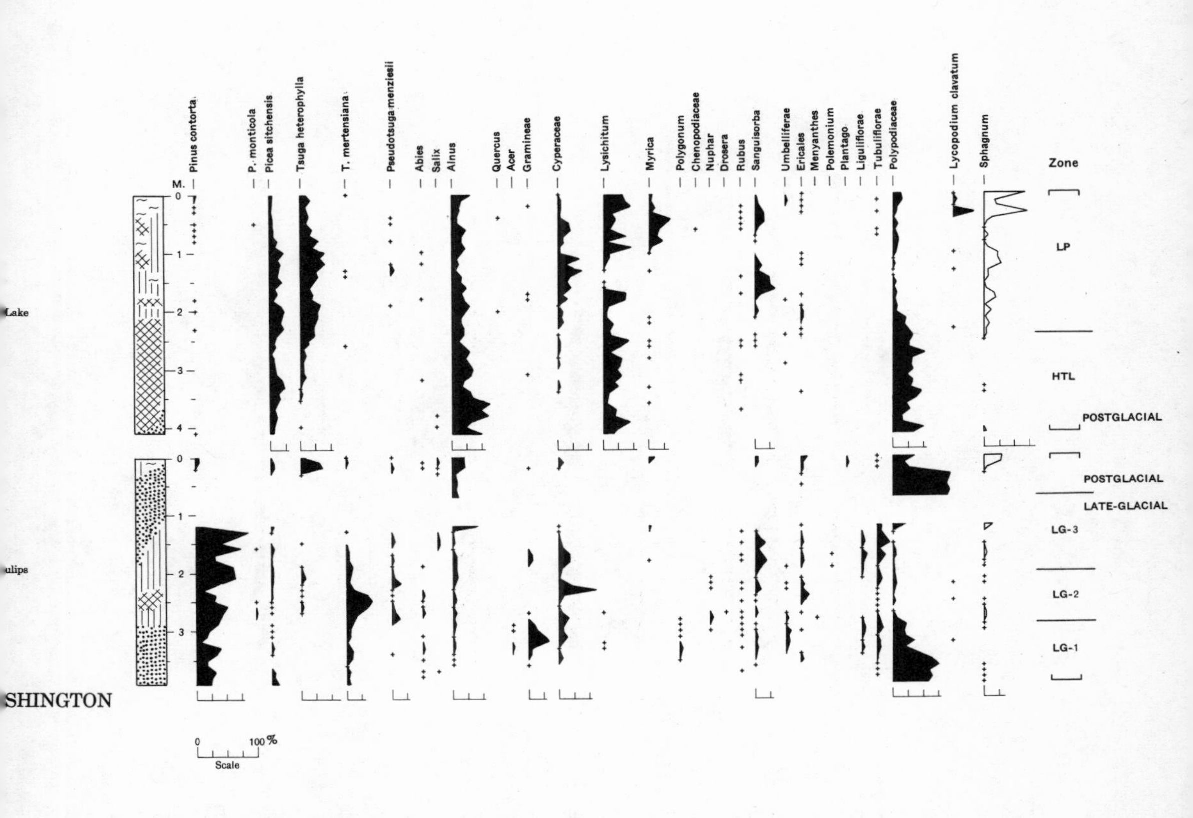

Fig. 41. Peat and pollen stratigraphy and zonation for sections from Ozette Lake (69) and Humptulips (70).

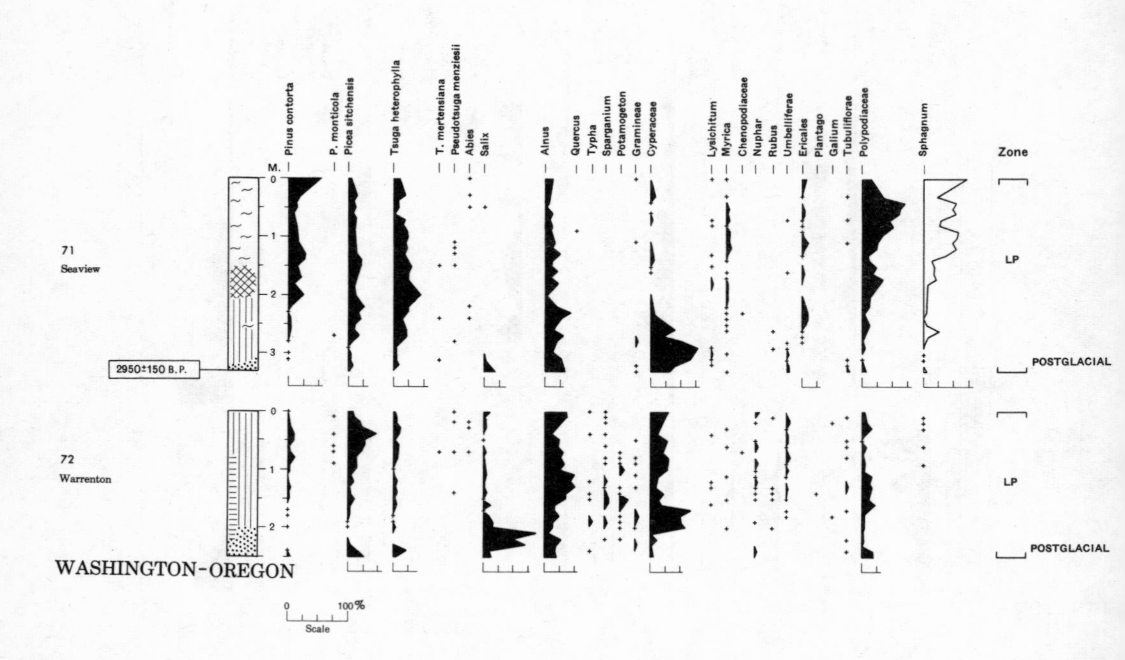

FIG. 42. Peat and pollen stratigraphy and zonation for sections from Seaview (71) and Warrenton (72).

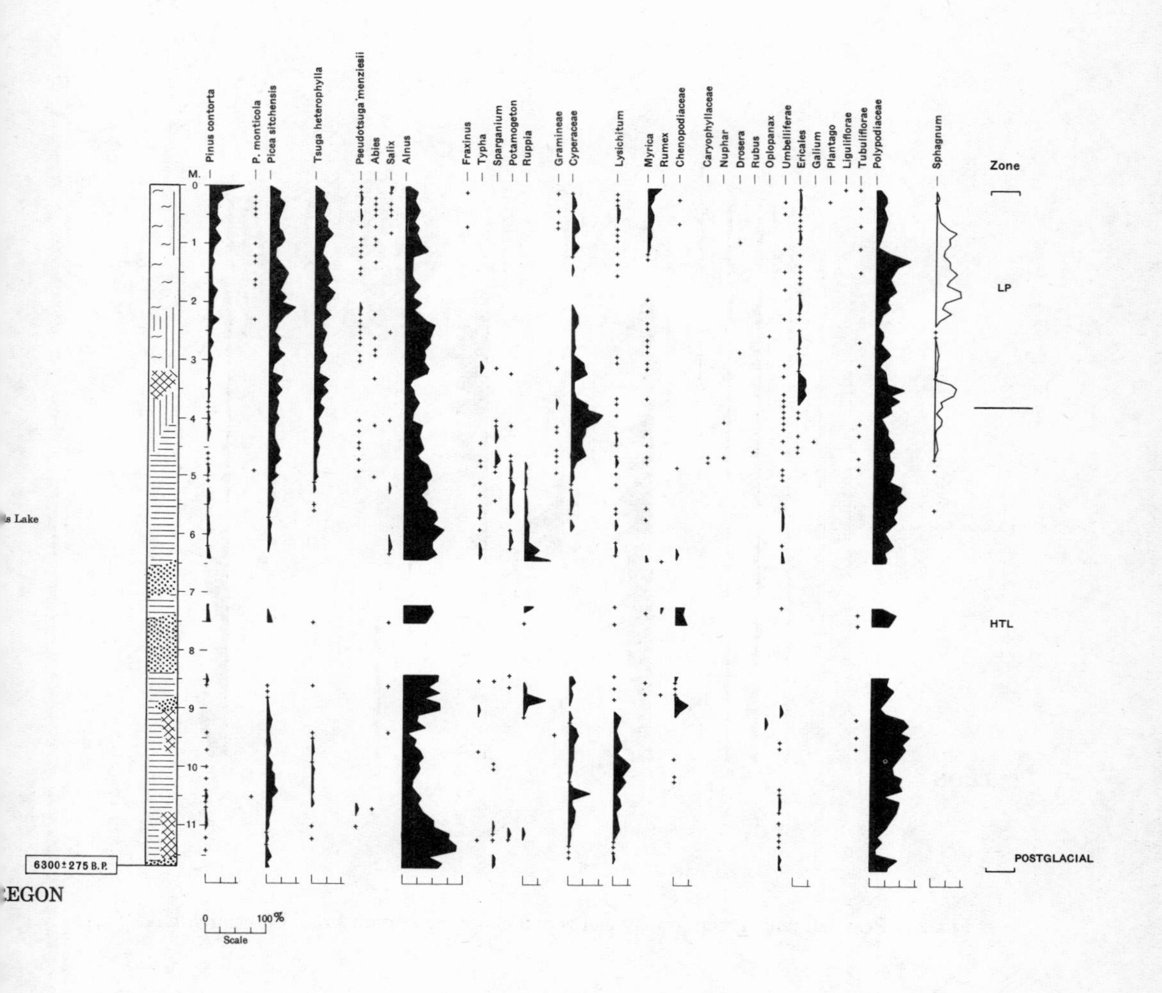

FIG. 43. Peat and pollen stratigraphy and zonation for the section from Devils Lake (73).

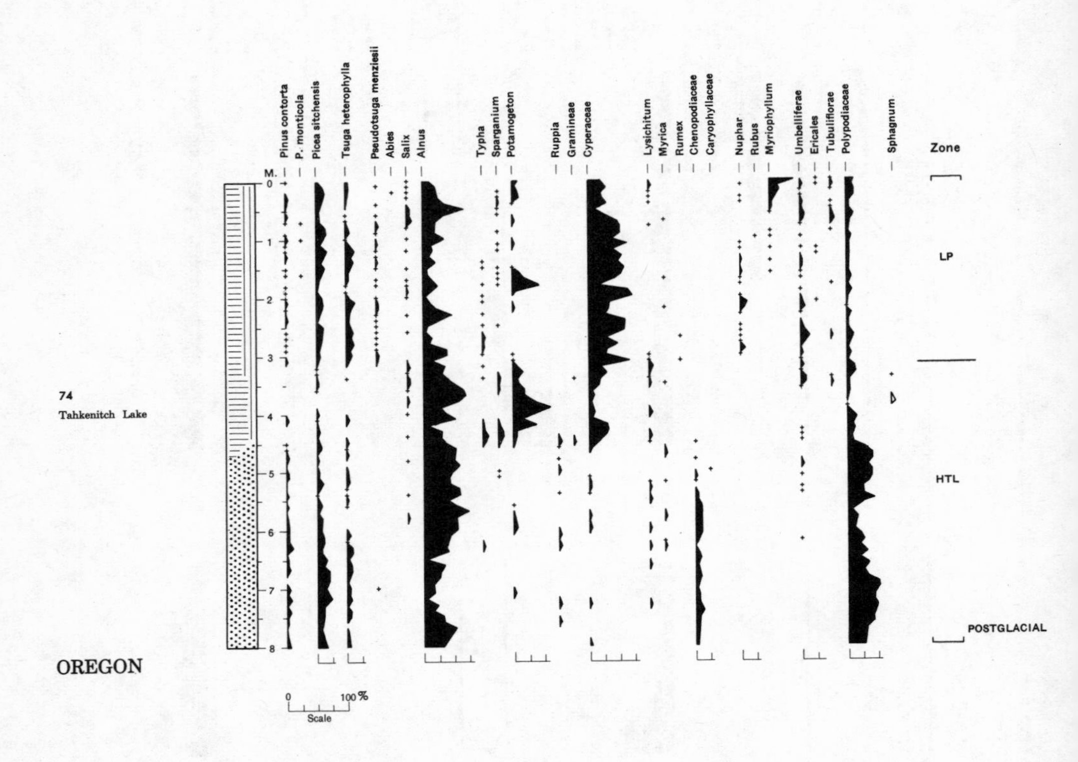

FIG. 44. Peat and pollen stratigraphy and zonation for the section from Tahkenitch Lake (74).

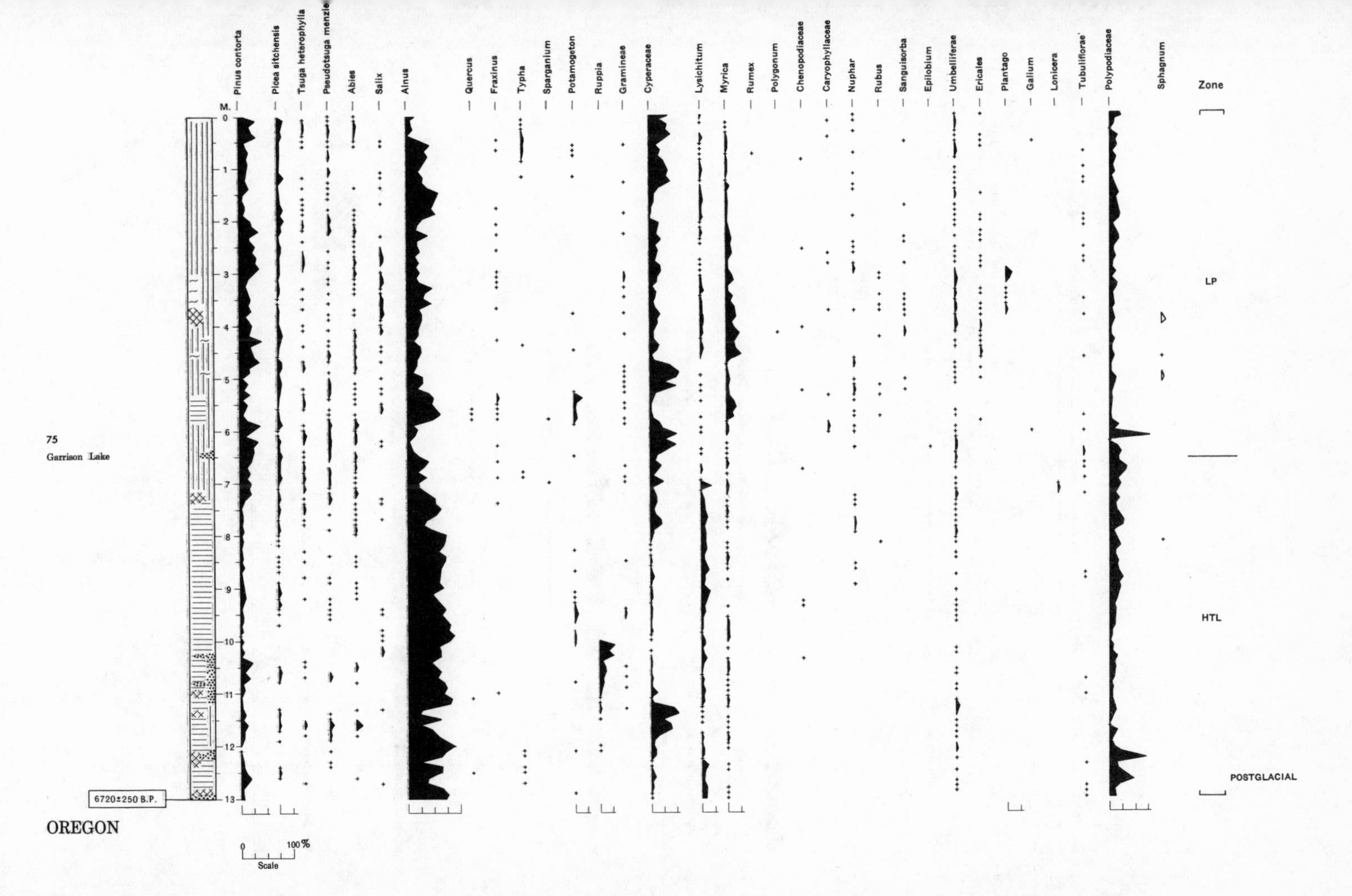

FIG. 45. Peat and pollen stratigraphy and zonation for the section from Garrison Lake (75).

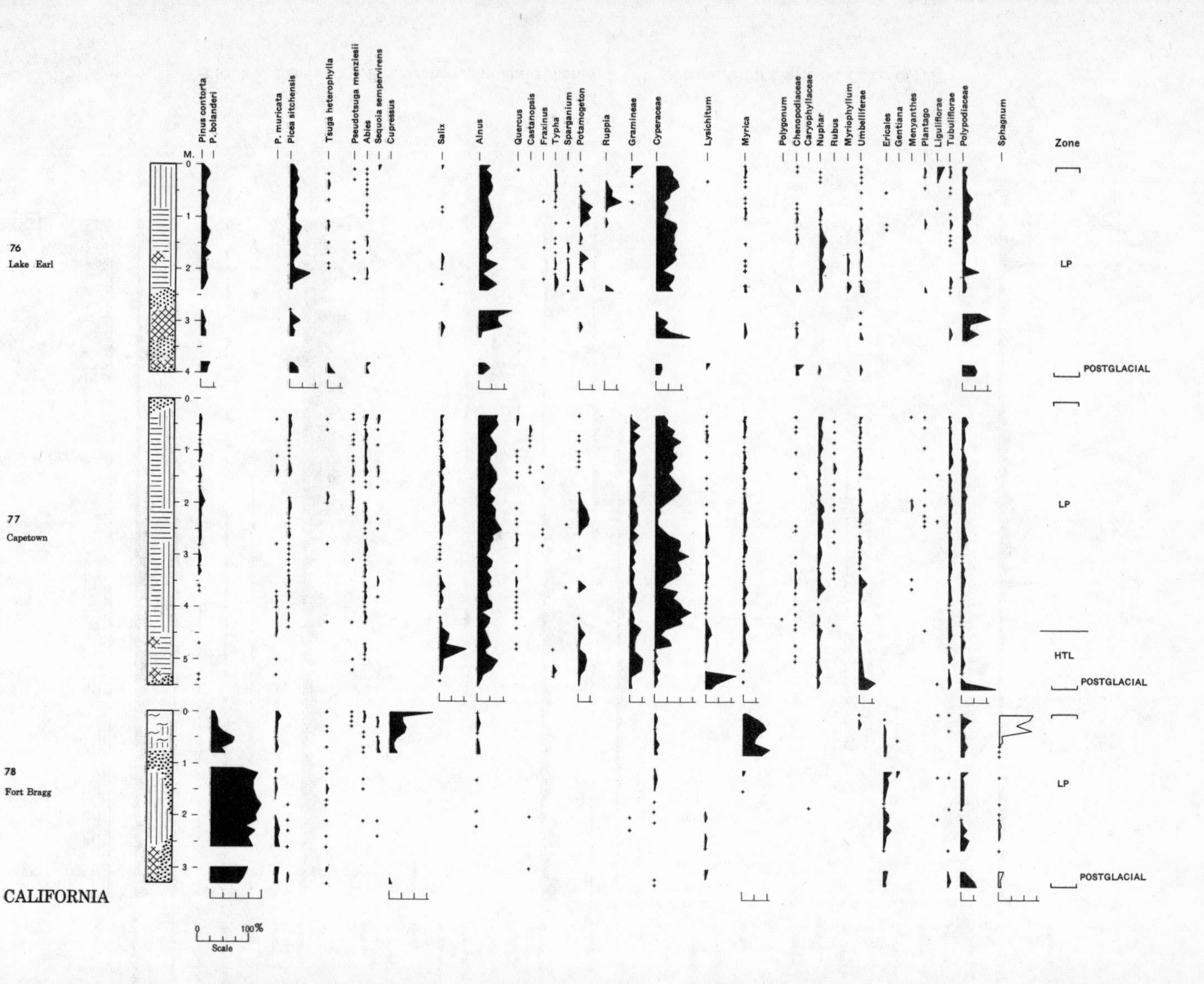

FIG. 46. Peat and pollen stratigraphy and zonation for sections from Lake Earl (76), Capetown (77), and Fort

Chapter VIII

LATE-PLEISTOCENE VEGETATION, ENVIRONMENTS, AND CHRONOLOGY

The distribution of plants and of the vegetational units they comprise is the sum effect of the forces constituting the environment. This existing relationship is the key to the reconstruction of past environments from fossil evidence—the basis for the principle of uniformitarianism. Daubenmire (1947) writes that environment "etymologically implies surroundings." He goes on to state, "In fact, any force, substance, or condition which affects organisms in any way becomes a factor of their environment, and the sum of all such factors constitutes environment." He groups the environment into the major categories: climatic, edaphic, biotic, and pyric. Some authors (for example, Oosting 1948) classify the edaphic factor as physiographic. Cain (1944b) sets down certain principles concerning the environment based on the works of Good (1931) and Mason (1936). He states that climate is a primary control and has varied in the past; the relations of land and sea have varied in the past; edaphic control is secondary; biotic factors are also of importance; and the environment is holocoenotic, or in other words, all the factors act in unison and interdependently. The present work takes into account these plant-environment relationships in interpreting the late-Pleistocene milieu. In the absence of comprehensive autecological data on the major pollen contributors, however, many approximations are necessarily made of the meaning of the pollen profiles.

The modern pollen stratigrapher should have at his disposal a vast array of radiocarbon-dated horizons to aid him in his interpretations. Short of this information, he must depend upon his judgment and experience in making correlations. The pollen-stratigraphic correlations at hand (for example, Tables 5, 6) form a case in point. Available chronological control is far insufficient for a refined radiocarbon-based chronology in most instances. In certain areas, particularly southeastern Alaska, more refinement is achieved for the entire stratigraphic column. In others, such as the Puget Lowland in Washington, considerable data are available on the ages of the Late-glacial and Postglacial, as well as the interbedded Glacier Peak volcanic ash. California sections have no dated levels, and most of the remaining coastal sections are delimited by only late-glacial or postglacial dates. It is essential that greater control be developed in the future in order to place the pollen and peat stratigraphy in its exact chronological setting. For the time being, provisional dates for many of the zonal boundaries must be used.

The North Pacific North American pollen-stratigraphic columns (Tables 5, 6) show parallelism, but only in closely related districts are they considered synchronous as well. Columns at low latitudes generally begin earlier than those at higher, and intervals of coolness are interpreted to be longer (intervals of warmth interpreted to be shorter) at higher latitudes. Only the major fluctuations of temperature are recorded. Minor fluctuations presumably do not exceed environmental threshold

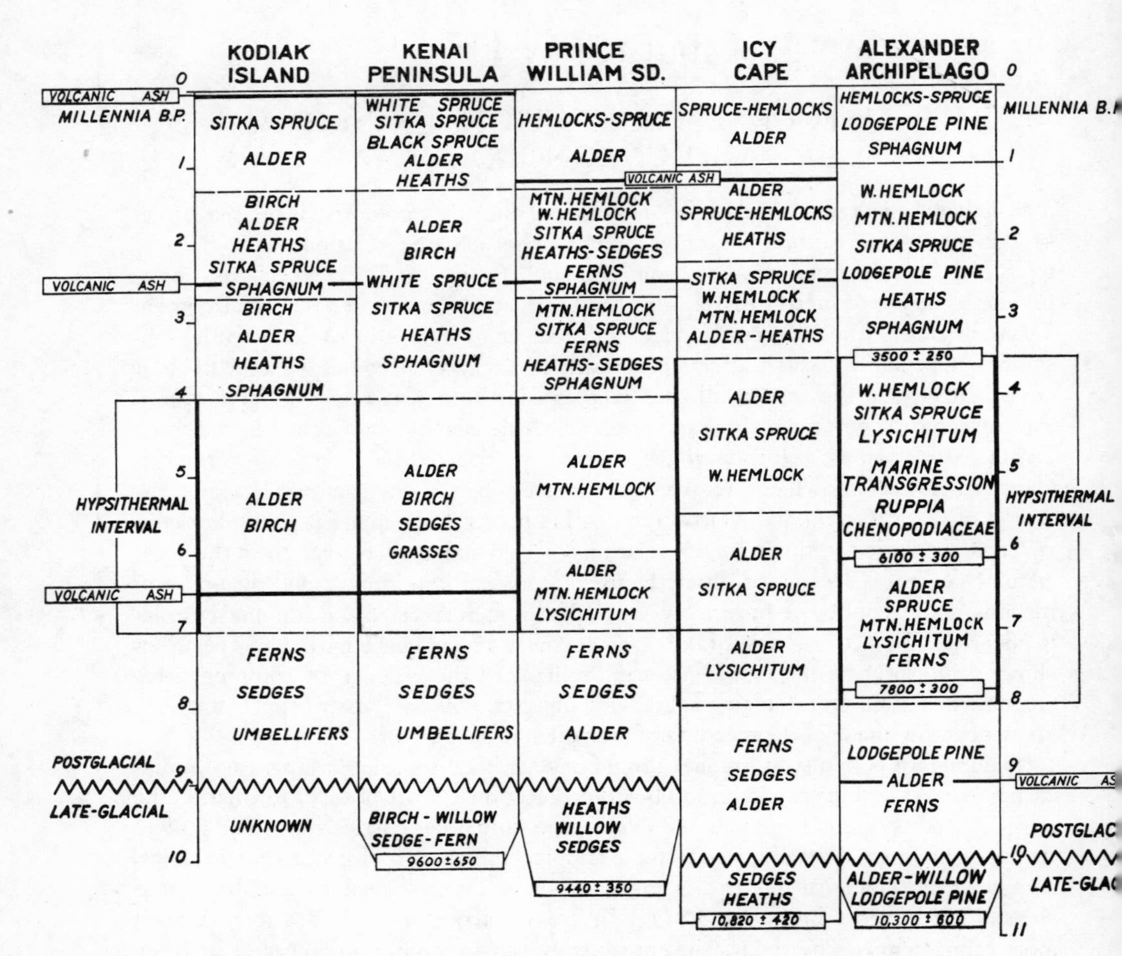

TABLE 5. Late-Pleistocene vegetation, environments, and chronologies for representative Alaskan areas.

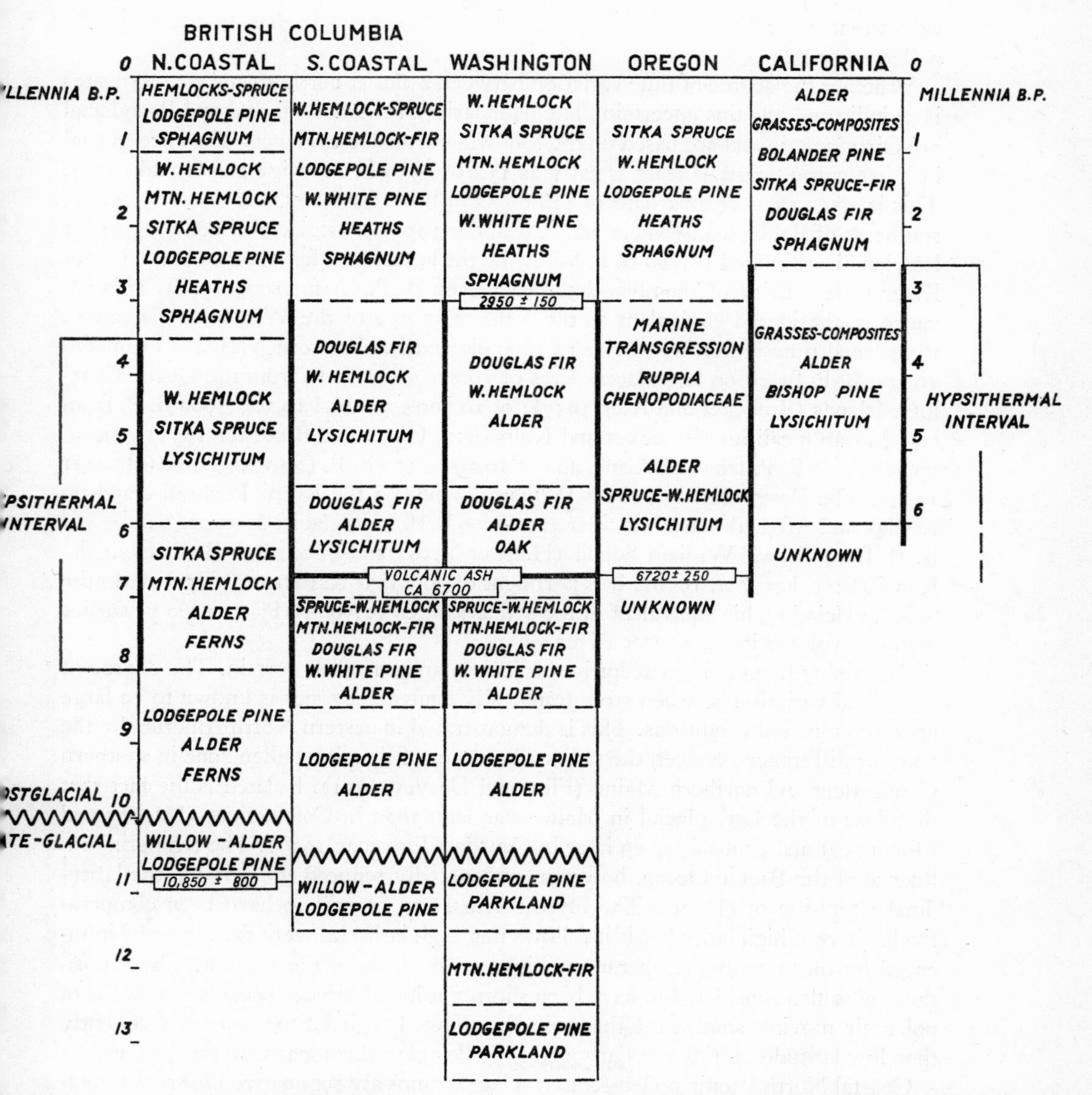

TABLE 6. Late-Pleistocene vegetation, environments, and chronologies for representative areas in British Columbia, ashington, Oregon, and California.

values that control the autecology of the species components that contribute to the pollen records.

Whether the degree of time variation between zones at northern and southern sites is as indicated remains uncertain. The boundaries of the Late-glacial and Postglacial are fairly certain and are based on the following available evidence. The Late-glacial in Washington began at least as early as 13,650 ± 550 B. P. (Rigg and Gould 1957). This is given support by a date of 12,900 ± 330 B. P. for a bog near Sedro Woolley, southeast of Bellingham (Rubin and Alexander 1958). Postglacial time in the Puget Lowland is estimated 10,500 B. P. following the late-glacial ice advance in the Fraser River valley, British Columbia, dated ca 11,300 B. P. (Armstrong 1956). This advance is considered equivalent to the Valders subage of the Wisconsin glaciation. Postglacial time in northern British Columbia and southeastern Alaska is estimated 10,000 B. P. based on late-glacial dates of 10,850 ± 800 B. P. from the Queen Charlotte Islands (Broecker and Kulp 1957); of 10,300 ± 400 and 10,300 ± 600 B. P. from two Juneau localities (Broecker and Kulp 1957, Olson and Broecker 1959); and of 10,820 ± 420 B. P. from Icy Cape, and of 10,390 ± 350 B. P. from Alaganik (Heusser 1959). The Postglacial in Prince William Sound, on the Kenai Peninsula, and on Kodiak and Afognak Islands is figured ca 9000 B. P. Late-glacial dates are 9440 ± 350 B. P. from Prince William Sound (Heusser 1959) and 9600 ± 650 B. P. from the Kenai (Broecker *et al.* 1956). It is pertinent to note that Karlstrom (1957) dates the Skilak glaciation, his equivalent of the Valders, at ca 12,500 B. P., ca 1200 yr earlier than the Valders in the Fraser River valley.

Remaining boundaries, except in the Juneau area, are less certain. The degree of latitudinal variation between stratigraphically equivalent zones is known to be large under continental conditions. This is demonstrated in eastern North America by the 3000-yr difference between the radiocarbon ages of the pine-pollen zone in southern Connecticut and northern Maine (Flint and Deevey 1951). Related is the fact that the close of the Late-glacial in Maine was later than in Connecticut (Deevey and Flint 1957) and probably even later in Canada (Terasmae 1959). The tempering influence of the Pacific Ocean, however, undoubtedly reduced the delay in the latitudinal alteration of climate. The Hypsithermal can be said to have been comparatively short at high latitudes, if it follows that high latitudes were the last to be influenced by mean annual temperatures higher than those of the present. The Hypsithermal is also considered to have been shorter at high latitudes because outbreaks of polar air moving southward theoretically affected high latitudes more frequently than low latitudes during the Early and Late Postglacial compared to the present.

Coastal North Pacific pollen-stratigraphic columns are summarized for representative areas. Those from Alaska appear in Table 5: Kenai Peninsula, Prince William Sound, and Icy Cape represent the South-Central District; Kodiak Island, the Southwestern District; and Alexander Archipelago, the Southeastern District. Table 6 contains British Columbia, Washington, Oregon, and California columns. It is emphasized that all columns are strictly representative and do not purport to include all fluctuations in pollen spectra. They are discussed by pollen-stratigraphic zones beginning with the Late-glacial.

THE LATE-GLACIAL

The longest late-glacial record is interpreted at Humptulips in Washington (Fig. 41), an unglaciated site that appears to have begun to accrue peat after the cessation of proglacial disturbance, as Vashon ice retreated in the Puget Lowland, the Strait of Juan de Fuca, and the Olympic Mountains. No radiocarbon dates are available to support the claim of a late-glacial age for the deposit, but its location and peculiar pollen-stratigraphic record favor the current interpretation. Dates are in accord with the late-glacial radiocarbon chronology for the nearby Puget Lowland and related areas. The early zone (LG-1) begins at an age of ca 13,500 B. P., based on the age of Lake Washington at Seattle (13,650±330 B. P.; Rigg and Gould 1957), but it is probably older. The middle zone (LG-2) lies between an estimated 12,500 and 11,500 B. P. The close of this interval appears related to the ice advance in the Fraser River valley at ca 11,300 B. P. (Armstrong 1956). The late zone (LG-3) closes ca 10,500 B. P.

The earliest record (LG-1) suggests a lodgepole pine parkland and a colder climate, perhaps somewhat warmer initially. The Polypodiaceae were abundant locally at first but later gave way to an assemblage of nonarboreal plants dominated by grass and sedge and including *Polygonum*, *Rubus*, *Sanguisorba*, Umbelliferae, Ericales, Liguliflorae, and Tubuliflorae, among others, all characteristic of northern tundra. Along with lodgepole pine, and to some extent Sitka spruce, mountain hemlock, fir, and alder, the boreal plants point toward parkland-type vegetation.

The successive zone (LG-2) records an interval of mountain hemlock-fir occupancy, although Douglas fir, western hemlock, Sitka spruce, western white pine, and lodgepole appear together with this association. Climate had warmed and had also become less humid as shown by the contemporaneous ligneous layer interbedded in the sedge peat. Nonarboreal pollen are fewer in the interval with the exception of the Ericales, which appear to have been favored by this climatic change.

The late zone (LG-3) marks a return of lodgepole predominance in even greater proportion than previously, and a parkland under a colder climate is again suggested. Douglas fir, mountain hemlock, Sitka spruce, willow, and alder occurred in small amounts, though alder gained predominance at the close of the interval. More prominent nonarboreal entities were sedge, Tubuliflorae, and *Sanguisorba*. Grass, Umbelliferae, and the Polypodiaceae were less abundant than in LG-1, but sedge, *Sanguisorba*, Ericales, Tubuliflorae, and Liguliflorae rose in proportion. The burial of the section during the most recent episode of the Late-glacial is thought to have been caused by proglacial disturbance resulting from renewed glaciation in the Olympics, equivalent in age to the Fraser River valley advance.

No late-glacial evidence was located in Oregon and California. In northern and southern British Columbia, the most recent zone (LG-3) of cold climate is recognized. Discovered at Rainbow Lake, Upper Hope Island, and Menzies Bay (Figs. 33, 35, 36), it was dominated by willow, alder, and lodgepole pine. Sedges and the Polypodiaceae were also present in variable numbers, the ferns in only small amounts. Of all the pollen records, that at Upper Hope Island contains the most varied group of plants, composed of grass, sedge, *Lysichitum*, *Urtica*, *Rumex*, Caryophyllaceae,

Sanguisorba, and Tubuliflorae; the collection is very similar to a late-glacial record from Langara Island in the Queen Charlotte Islands (Heusser 1955b). Nonarboreal plants on Langara included several species of Polypodiaceae, *Lycopodium*, *Sparganium*, grass, sedge, *Lysichitum*, Chenopodiaceae, Caryophyllaceae, *Rumex*, *Nuphar*, Ericales, *Epilobium*, *Polemonium*, *Plantago*, and Tubuliflorae. Arboreal types are lodgepole, Sitka spruce, western and mountain hemlocks, *Alnus*, and two species of *Salix*. In all 23 pollen types were counted.

The Alaska Late-glacial is also limited to the LG-3 zone. Alder pollen is generally more abundant in the Southeastern District than in British Columbia and, accordingly, the vegetation is named alder-willow-lodgepole pine in the order of dominance shown in the pollen profiles. The interval is found in the Alexander Archipelago area at Upper Montana Creek and Hasselborg Lake (Figs. 24, 27). Some Sitka spruce and western hemlock are in evidence, and nonarboreal pollen are largely Polypodiaceae with sedge, *Potamogeton*, *Sanguisorba*, Umbelliferae, and Tubuliflorae. Late-glacial pollen in the Southeastern District appears less varied than in the columns previously discussed.

In the South-Central District, sedge and heath comprise zone LG-3 at Icy Cape whereas heath, willow, and sedge are the principal vegetation components in Prince William Sound. On the southeastern Kenai about Seward (Fig. 17), the pollen record shows a strong similarity to Prince William Sound, but on the southwestern Kenai about Homer (Fig. 15), the record is distinctive and consists of birch, willow, sedge, and fern. Columns in the district containing late-glacial pollen are Homer 1, Seward, Perry Island, Alaganik 1, Bering Lake, and Munday Creek (Figs. 15, 17, 19–22). A survey shows the following consistently present at the above sites, though in varying amounts: *Salix*, *Alnus*, sedge, *Sanguisorba*, and *Polypodiaceae*. Birch occurs at only the first three sites, which is indicative of its continental affinity. By contrast, the Ericales occur only in more oceanic localities, being absent at Homer 1 and Perry Island. At half or more of the sites, *Lysichitum*, Umbelliferae, Tubuliflorae, and *Lycopodium*, largely *L. clavatum*, are present.

These records have two especially significant features. The first concerns the Late-glacial at Seward (Fig. 17) where a particularly varied group of plants is in evidence. A total of 19 entities is diagramed, among which are the arboreal Sitka spruce and mountain hemlock. Such a large group containing pollen of arboreal plants is unprecedented in the South-Central District and supplies strong evidence for at least a local refugium. The second feature is the hiatus in the pollen stratigraphy at Homer 1 (Fig. 15), where an interval of nondeposition of pollen is represented by gray silt between ca 5.1 and 5.2 m. This silt may be loess, as Krinsley (1953) finds in the Anchor Point-Homer area, or glaciofluvial sediments from the advance of the Tanya (Cochrane) glacier (Karlstrom 1957), or both. The glacier-site relationship here is quite similar to that at Humptulips, but the events that effected silt deposition were not contemporaneous. The late-glacial zone at Homer 1 is short by comparison and may indicate an interstadial of curtailed duration, which Karlstrom (1957) dates ca 9000 B. P., between the Skilak and the Tanya glaciations.

No evidence for late-glacial conditions on Kodiak and Afognak Islands was discovered, and the sections collected here begin with the Early Postglacial. A likely reason for this is the fact that the localities of the sections are marine terraces that were being formed as a consequence of a higher stand of the ocean in relation to the land at this time.

THE EARLY POSTGLACIAL

The Early Postglacial lasted an estimated two millennia, and evidence of it is found in all sectors of the study region with the exception of Oregon and California. It is considered to have been in effect between 10,500 and 8500 B. P. in Washington and southern British Columbia; between 10,000 and 8000 B. P. in northern British Columbia and from the vicinity of Icy Cape southeastward through the Alexander Archipelago; and between 9000 and 7000 B. P. in Prince William Sound, on the Kenai Peninsula, and on Kodiak and Afognak Islands.

Lodgepole pine was the principal member of the vegetation between Washington and the Alexander Archipelago. Its major associate was alder, and in northern British Columbia and the Alexander Archipelago, fern was an additional noteworthy member of this affiliation. At Icy Cape, Prince William Sound, Kenai Peninsula, and Kodiak Island, fern was predominant, associated with sedge and alder at the first two sites and with sedge and umbellifer at the last two. The Early Postglacial contains the pioneer stages of plant succession that gave rise to the climax communities evident later during the Postglacial. The climate was generally cool and moist but warmer than that which dominated the final interval of the Late-glacial. At some time during the Early Postglacial, theoretically prior to the Hypsithermal when mean annual temperatures had not yet begun to exceed those of the present, climate was much the same as it is today.

A cold, humid climate sustained lodgepole where it grew but the maintenance of the tree was made possible by continuing disturbances that prevented the subclimax- and climax-forest arboreal components from gaining more than local representation. Sitka spruce, western and mountain hemlocks, and fir, although evidently established in limited numbers, never gained areal proportions exceeding local enclaves in extent. Physiographic unrest coupled with climatic adversity favored lodgepole predominance for ca 2000 yr. Only with subsidence of physical stress on the landscape at the outset of the Hypsithermal were forest species able to gain an increasingly secure foothold.

Besides glaciation, with its direct consequences, changes between land and sea and, in one instance, vulcanism were also in effect during the Early Postglacial. By the close of the interval, radiocarbon dates indicate that in Alaska the land was at least 150 ft lower than at present in the Juneau area, 300 lower northwest of Lituya Bay, and 180 lower about Katalla. At many other Alaskan localities and in British Columbia and Washington, changes in land–sea-level relations were undoubtedly taking place, mainly as a result of differential uplift but also due to other tectonic movements and eustatic rise of sea level. The only volcanic eruption discovered on the basis of interbedded ash in the early-postglacial sections was that of Mt. Edgecumbe or its complex in the Alexander Archipelago. Ash ostensibly from this eruption, estimated to be 9000 B. P. in age, covers at least the northern half of Baranof Island, all of Kruzof and Chichagof Islands, most if not all of Admiralty Island, the Juneau area, the vicinity of Icy Strait, and extends as far to the northwest as the neighborhood of Lituya Bay, and possibly even farther. Winds at the time of the eruption were blowing somewhat to the northeast but mainly to the northwest.

THE HYPSITHERMAL

The Hypsithermal is placed between ca 8000 and 3500 B. P. in the Alexander Archipelago and is set off by the most reliable set of time brackets for the interval along the North Pacific coast. Between Icy Cape and northern British Columbia, the duration of the Hypsithermal is considered to have been the same. Westward along the Gulf of Alaska, because of a greater influence of polar air breaking southward, the interval is shortened to between ca 7000 and 4000 B. P. Southward, on the other hand it is lengthened to between ca 8500 and 3000 B. P. in southern British Columbia, Washington, and Oregon. In California, the Hypsithermal may have closed as recently as ca 2500 B. P.; its beginning date is not yet figured, though presumably it is earlier than the date set for its onset in Oregon, Washington, and southwestern Canada.

Successional subdivisions are recognized in most of the columns. In the Alexander Archipelago column, alder, Sitka spruce, and mountain hemlock succeeded first with a ground cover dominated by *Lysichitum* and fern. A radiocarbon date of ca 6000 B. P. marks the close of the episode. Later, western hemlock became predominant and Sitka spruce was relegated to a secondary position among the conifers; *Lysichitum* remained prominent. This coniferous sequence is being reenacted at the present time on the moraines and outwash of southeastern Alaskan glaciers. Northwestward at Icy Cape, three hypsithermal subdivisions show an alder-*Lysichitum* interval at first, subsequently alder-Sitka spruce, and, lastly, an alder-Sitka spruce-western hemlock interval. In Prince William Sound, alder was also dominant in association with mountain hemlock, and with *Lysichitum* evident initially. Coniferous species during the Hypsithermal are poorly represented on the Kenai and appear to have been absent on Kodiak Island. Alder primarily and birch secondarily succeeded the early-postglacial group of fern-sedge-umbellifer. Sedge and grass, in addition to alder and birch, were affiliated on the Kenai.

Vegetation in northern British Columbia developed in much the same sequence as in the Alexander Archipelago. Sitka spruce, however, was more important at the beginning and alder less important, while *Lysichitum* occurred mainly during the upper subdivision. The successive order of plants was more complex in the southern part of British Columbia. The first of three subdivisions had a coniferous assemblage principally of Sitka spruce-western hemlock, and including mountain hemlock, fir, Douglas fir, western white pine, and the nonconiferous alder. This was followed next by Douglas fir, alder, and *Lysichitum* and ultimately by western hemlock becoming mixed with Douglas fir but with alder and *Lysichitum* remaining. In Washington the sequence was almost unchanged. Differences lie in the replacement of *Lysichitum* by Oregon white oak in the middle subdivision and the exclusion of this araceous plant in the upper subdivision.

The Oregon column begins no earlier than ca 6700 B. P. A marine transgression obscures the record of upland vegetation, but alder was evidently most abundant. The conifer forest was an association of Sitka spruce and western hemlock with *Lysichitum* present locally. The abundance of alder was presumably chiefly a result of fires in the Coast Range. The California column shows a prevalence of grass and composites but with alder, Bishop pine, and *Lysichitum* in significant percentages. The age of the column is unknown.

The Hypsithermal by definition (Deevey and Flint 1957) opened and closed with mean annual temperature higher than at present. Temperature is known to have fluctuated during the interval, and superimposed on the temperature curve were fluctuations of moisture. Along certain sectors of the coast, two episodes of humidity increase and two of decrease are recorded. Alexander Archipelago and British Columbia muskeg sites disclose these changes by a succession of peat types: two horizons of ligneous peat separated and underlain by sedge peat. The order of events is well illustrated by the Upper Montana Creek and Masset sections (Figs. 24, 32). Many of the sections exhibit only a solitary ligneous deposit, apparently representing continuity of the lower and upper horizons. In addition, several contain a prominence of *Sphagnum* at the start of the hypsithermal deposits (Masset, Rainbow Lake, and Wessler; Figs. 32, 33, 40), and most display *Sphagnum* in abundance following the close of the interval. It seems safe to conclude that in these British Columbia and Alaskan sectors, at least, climate of the Hypsithermal was warm and moist in the beginning, became drier later with an intervening episode during which humidity increased somewhat, and closed as strongly humid conditions coupled with cooling began to prevail.

One of the more interesting discoveries of the radiocarbon method of dating is a series of dates for trees buried by glacial sediments in Glacier Bay ca 60 mi northwest of Juneau (Preston *et al.* 1955, Barendsen *et al.* 1957). The series shows glacier episodes dated at ca 7000, 4200, 2500, 1500, and 800 B. P. (Deevey and Flint 1957). One additional episode, ca 200 B. P., is dated by Cooper (1937). The first two, at ca 7000 and 4200 B. P., fall within the limits of the Hypsithermal as determined for the Alexander Archipelago in Table 5. Episodes of glaciation during a time warmer than the present would be difficult to comprehend were it not for evidence in the data of intervals of higher humidity. In a mountainous environment where summits are as much as 15,300 ft in elevation, rising humidity will undoubtedly effect glaciation, even under hypsithermal conditions. The lofty Fairweather Range is almost certain to have been instrumental in causing glacier growth as solid precipitation accumulated on slopes facing Glacier Bay. Significant in this regard is the fact that in the Coast Mountains about Juneau, where elevations do not exceed ca 8500 ft, the ca 200 B. P.-maximum of Lemon Creek Glacier has not been exceeded for at least 10,000 yr. Evidently, these mountains are of insufficient height to have accumulated enough ice to cause glacier advances in the valleys during the Hypsithermal. It appears, therefore, that where high mountains abound, glaciers were able to develop even during intervals of warmth greater than the present, if humidity had been sufficiently high to cause solid precipitation to accumulate and to exceed the influence of summer ablation at low elevations. The advances in Glacier Bay, dated ca 7000 and 4200

B. P., may be correlated in the Lemon Creek section (Fig. 24) near Juneau with the intervals of sedge peat preceding the ligneous horizons dated at ca 6000 and 3500 B. P.

By the close of the Hypsithermal, the land about Juneau stood close to its present position in relation to sea level, having changed at least 150 ft during the interval. A considerable amount of change occurred at other localities, but the greatest determined in this study, ca 260 ft, is northwest of Lituya Bay. The changes are considered to be the result of differential uplift due to isostatic readjustment. But evidence of what appear to have been changes related to eustasy are found in the hypsithermal deposits at Sarkar Lake in Alaska, at Whidbey Island in Washington, and at Devils, Tahkenitch, and Garrison Lakes in Oregon (Figs. 30, 39, 43–45). Evidence for these eustatic changes is based largely on the *Ruppia* and Chenopodiaceae profiles.

Two volcanic eruptions, perhaps contemporaneous, are evident. One is the eruption of Glacier Peak, dated ca 6700 B. P., in the northern Cascades of Washington. Rigg and Gould (1957) show that ash from this volcano covers an area eastward as far as north-central Montana and northward to west-central British Columbia and east-central Alberta. In the present study, only sections from the Puget Lowland and nearby Vancouver Island contain Glacier Peak ash. The other eruption is encountered in sections on the Kenai Peninsula and on Kodiak Island. Its ash is of limited extent on the coast, and its point of origin appears to have been a volcano in the Aleutian Range.

THE LATE POSTGLACIAL

A sharp change in the upper peat and pollen stratigraphy is conspicuous in many of the diagrams: (1) a buried horizon of humified wood peat, marking the close of the Hypsithermal, is abruptly succeeded by nonhumified sphagnum and sedge peat, and (2) the *Lysichitum* profile, so strongly developed in hypsithermal sediments, is in most cases suddenly succeeded by strong profiles of heath and *Sphagnum*. This boundary in the sections, the apparent correlative of the classic *Grenzhorizont* of European peat and pollen stratigraphers, is dated in the Juneau area at 3500±250 B. P. (Kulp *et al.* 1952, Heusser 1953) and approximates the age of the opening of the late-postglacial interval.

In accordance with the shortening of the Hypsithermal at high latitudes, the Late Postglacial became gradually longer northwestward from California, where it began ca 2500 yr ago. In Oregon, Washington, and southern British Columbia, it started ca 3000 B. P.; in northern British Columbia, the Alexander Archipelago, and Icy Cape, ca 3500 B. P.; and in Prince William Sound, on the Kenai, and on Kodiak Island, ca 4000 B. P. It is reemphasized that these changes with latitude, although reasonably certain for the beginning of the Late-glacial and Postglacial, must be considered tentative for the subdivisions of the Postglacial until additional radiocarbon dates are available. The date of 2950±150 B. P. for the close of the Hypsithermal in Washington fits this scheme of latitudinal change, in keeping with the Juneau date, ca 3500 B. P., and the date from Karluk, 3470±180 B. P. (Heusser 1959).

The Alexander Archipelago column indicates that western hemlock maintained its position of superiority in the forest during the Late Postglacial. The proportion of

Sitka spruce, on the other hand, decreased to some extent while mountain hemlock increased and lodgepole pine regained its status as arboreal dominant on muskeg. As previously noted, heath and *Sphagnum* produced major prominences in their respective profiles. Heath usually preceded *Sphagnum*, but very recently a trend developed toward a return of heath and a decline in *Sphagnum*. A present trend toward a less humid environment is indicated by the invasion of spruce and hemlock on muskeg surfaces and the drying of pit ponds by midsummer.

The vegetational changes depicted in the pollen diagrams are the result of climatic conditions generally colder than the present and at times more humid, a combination particularly conducive to glacier formation. The occurrence of four dated glacial episodes at Glacier Bay during the Late Postglacial compared with two during the Hypsithermal is proof of this. A time relationship is seen between the strong Ericales and *Sphagnum* profiles above the ca 3500 B. P. *Grenzhorizont* and the ca 2500 B. P. glacier advance in Glacier Bay. Subsequent advances, dated ca 1500, 800, and 200 B. P., are difficult to reconcile by means of the pollen record since they occur in such close succession. Under a cold climate, small changes in precipitation that may bring about glacier nourishment and advance often cannot be detected in the profile fluctuations.

The Icy Cape column also contains evidence that points toward cooling, but pronounced moisture changes may not have taken place. The arrival of heath and mountain hemlock in increased numbers substantiates the claim for lower temperature, but *Sphagnum*, the moisture indicator, never gains status equivalent in importance to most other late-postglacial sections. Sitka spruce and both hemlocks, the only coniferous trees in the forest, rose in proportion following hypsithermal time. Alder varied from a position of secondary importance at the opening of the Late Postglacial to one of predominance. Now, at the close of the interval, however, alder has reverted to a less important place in the vegetation.

The columns farther along the Gulf of Alaska manifest the same cooling and rise in humidity apparent to the southeast. Cooling is more evident at first whereas greater humidity occurred subsequently under somewhat warmer conditions, as evidenced by heath and *Sphagnum*, the respective temperature and moisture indicators; in addition, birch became more prominent, corroborating the existence of the trend toward lower temperature. The Late Postglacial was the time of greatest forest development along this coast, and the climatic change that identifies it was responsible for the enhancement of this vegetation type. In Prince William Sound mountain hemlock and Sitka spruce rose in proportion during the interval, later accompanied by western hemlock, whose influx occurred rather sharply about the middle of the interval. On the Kenai Peninsula the proportion of alder was less than during the Hypsithermal, but it still remained predominant. Birch achieved its maximum and was accompanied by the arrival of white and Sitka spruces early during the interval. Later these conifers were joined by black spruce. White and black spruces migrated to the coast from interior Alaska. On Kodiak Island, birch and alder trends progressed in the same manner as on the Kenai, though birch ultimately rose to a level of predominance. Sitka spruce is the only conifer on Kodiak. It arrived on the island sometime during the third or fourth millennium B. P., but only recently has it spread aggressively southwestward.

Late-postglacial vegetation in northern British Columbia developed in the same manner as in the Alexander Archipelago. Coniferous-forest elements are well represented here as well as in southern British Columbia, Washington, and Oregon; in addition, the climatic indicators, heath and *Sphagnum*, continue to be in evidence. In southern British Columbia and in Washington, western hemlock and Sitka spruce became predominant, and mountain hemlock, lodgepole pine, and western white pine took lesser rank. Fir (*Abies*) in southern British Columbia apparently became better represented in the forest at that time. The profiles from Oregon register a coastal forest dominated by Sitka spruce with western hemlock of secondary importance. Lodgepole pine increased here as in the columns over its northwestward range. The California column displays a record of humidity increase and some temperature decline in keeping with the changes contained in the columns from other coastal sectors. Alder rose to primary status in the vegetation and grass and composites became secondary. Bolander pine was important over much of the interval, but during the latter part rapidly lost its importance. Many of the conifers gained greater representation; Sitka spruce and fir are the best examples, although lodgepole pine, Douglas fir, redwood, and, to some extent, western hemlock deserve to be mentioned.

Land–sea-level changes were still in effect, in some places amounting to as much as 150 ft, but were generally relatively small, less than 50. Three major volcanic eruptions were detected and this number was found only in the South-Central District of Alaska. The oldest at ca 2500 B. P. is encountered in the columns from Kodiak Island to Icy Cape and, if correctly correlated, is the most widespread ash discovered along this coast. The origin of this ash bed is undoubtedly either the Aleutian Range or the Wrangell Mountains. A powerful eruption, apparently in the Wrangell Mountains, is the source of the ash described by Capps (1916) ca 2 m below the surface of peat along upper White River in the interior. Because of the corresponding position of ash in the Kodiak-Icy Cape columns, correlation is almost certain. Capps (1916), however, estimates the ash to be as much as 1400 B. P. and at least several centuries in age. This does not agree with the chronology of the columns of the present study. An upper ash layer in the Prince William Sound and Icy Cape columns may be correlated since its age is estimated as the opening of the second millennium B. P. On the other hand, the ash rests at a depth of only 1 m or less. Because the radiocarbon-based chronology of the columns seems more certain than Capps' (1916) estimate, even in the absence of a radiocarbon date for the layer, and the positions in the peat stratigraphy agree, the lower ash is tentatively correlated with the ash bed at upper White River. It seems sure that the upper ash at Icy Cape and in Prince William Sound is also derived from the Wrangells. The uppermost ash on Kodiak and the Kenai is from the 1912 eruption in the Mt. Katmai sector of the Aleutian Range. This ash was not found in Prince William Sound but may be represented by the topmost bed in the sections from the Katalla region.

In the Alaskan Southeastern District minor ash layers in late-postglacial sediments appear in the sections about Juneau and in the vicinity of the volcanic area centered at Mt. Edgecumbe (Figs. 24, 26). Two possible sources for this ash are Mt. Edgecumbe and the Iskut-Unuk Rivers area in the Coast Mountains. In previously published sections from about Wrangell, Petersburg, and Ketchikan (Heusser 1952), near the seat of vulcanism in the Coast Mountains, stratigraphically equivalent ash is found in greater amounts, and in the first two localities multiple layers occur. Although the proximity of the Mt. Edgecumbe sites strongly suggests that volcanic area as the source region, it is possible that the ash is from eruptions in the Coast Mountains. Ash in the Juneau area is tentatively correlated with the volcanic activity about the Iskut and Unuk Rivers.

LATE-PLEISTOCENE CHANGES IN LAND–SEA-LEVEL RELATIONS

The oceans of the earth are reservoirs supplying moisture for glacier nourishment during times of glaciation. Therefore, the amount of water held by the oceans will be depleted or replenished as glaciers respectively grow or melt. Moreover, the surface of the oceans will fall and rise as the cycle from glacial to interglacial ages is completed and repeated. But this relationship is complicated by interfering factors, most noteworthy of which is crustal movement. In any study that purports to show land–sea-level relations, it is necessary to attempt a distinction between (1) eustatic changes, caused by the glacial-nonglacial cycle, (2) isostatic changes, brought about by the release of glacier load from the earth's crust, and (3) remaining tectonic changes, the result of differential earth movement.

Late-Pleistocene eustatic variations are small, amounting to a hypsithermal rise of sea level in the amount of 5 to 6 ft in the Pacific, and are also recorded in more tectonically stable, unglaciated areas. Stearns (1941, 1945a and b) observes that eustatic features are at 5 ft above sea level on Espiritu Santo Island (New Hebrides group), Oahu (Hawaiian Islands), Saipan Island and Guam (Marianas group), Guadalcanal Island (Solomon group), and the Midway Islands. More recently, Doan (1957) describes a eustatic level at 6-ft elevation on Tinian in the Mariana Islands, in the Ryukyu Islands, and near Tokyo on Honshu Island.

Isostatic and other tectonic changes are usually large, measured in hundreds of feet, and often occur in series of recognizable terraces. Isostatic changes are not discernible from nonisostatic tectonic movements in glaciated country, except in the case of current observable earthquakes, but it is often possible to deduce which influence has been of greater intensity.

Eustatic Changes

Variable but significant amounts of pollen from halophytic species of *Ruppia*, *Potamogeton*, and Chenopodiaceae are contained, at different depths below present sea level, in five sections taken at low elevations near the Pacific Ocean in southeastern Alaska and in Washington and Oregon. These sections are Sarkar Lake, Whidbey Island, and Devils, Tahkenitch, and Garrison Lakes (Figs. 30, 39, 43–45). Overlying each of the levels containing these brackish-water indicators, and underlying several of them as well, are freshwater sediments. This sketchy stratigraphy shows that at one time brackish water occupied the depressions at each of the above sites, in some instances after an interval of freshwater occupancy, and later was replaced by a freshwater environment.

The order of stratigraphic events indicates that sometime in the past the ocean was able to invade these sites so that brackish-water conditions suitable for the growth of the above halophytes developed. If no vertical changes in the crustal movement of the earth have since taken place, a subsequent lowering of sea level would be implied, although other surface changes, such as might be brought about by erosion and the migration of sand dunes between the site and the ocean, could possibly have the same effect. If, moreover, this stratigraphy had a radiocarbon chronological control that showed a general correlation of the brackish-water sediments, the conclusion that postglacial eustatic sea-level rise was the principal causal factor responsible for the marine incursion would be strongly favored. The opening and the close of the episode, because of local conditions, need not be strictly contemporaneous, but certain age relationships should be evident. Stratigraphic correlations with respect to sea level need not be present and if evident would only be fortuitous; if eustatic sea-level rise is assumed, coastal lakes will record the transgression at different depths in their underlying sediments owing to (1) the depth of each at the time, (2) the local sedimentation rate, (3) the altitude of the surface, and (4) the vertical tidal range affecting each site when the rise occurred. Accordingly, it becomes apparent that the brackish-water sediments in the five coastal lakes will rest at varying depths even when the sections are adjusted for differences in elevation.

A chronological control is at hand for three of the five sections, and the remaining two show contemporaneity on the basis of their pollen stratigraphy. All sediments under discussion are Hypsithermal in age. At Devils and Garrison Lakes (Figs. 43, 45), radiocarbon dates place the brackish-water episode, as disclosed by the *Ruppia* profiles, younger than ca 6300 B. P. but probably older than 4000. At Whidbey Island (Fig. 39), the Glacier Peak volcanic ash fixes the age of the overlying *Ruppia* between ca 6500 B. P. and likely not younger than 6000. The Sarkar and Tahkenitch Lakes sections (Figs. 30, 44) appear to register the incursion until ca 4000 B. P., although the date of its onset is unknown and the closing date is estimated by pollen-stratigraphic correlation. The range of what appears to have been a eustatic sea-level fluctuation is consequently placed between ca 6500 and 4000 B. P. during the Hypsithermal.

The transgression at Devils and Garrison Lakes in Oregon (Figs. 43, 45) is tentatively correlated with the age of the Australian Older Peron Terrace, which Fairbridge (1958) dates ca 5000 B. P. At Garrison Lake the episode, placed between ca 6000 and 5000 B. P., opened and closed abruptly as indicated by the *Ruppia* profile. At Devils Lake transgression began and ended gradually between ca 6000 and 4000 B. P. In fact, two or more fluctuations may have been responsible for the changes in the peat and pollen stratigraphy. Fairbridge (1958) dates the Younger Peron Terrace at ca 3600 B. P. This episode may be recorded at Devils Lake, and perhaps also at Tahkenitch and Sarkar Lakes, but on the basis of the time estimated for the last fall of sea level on the western North American coast (4000 B. P.), the formation of the younger Australian terrace is later.

Changes Resulting from Differential Uplift

Pollen profiles and peat sections from the glaciated part of the coast corroborate the conclusions made on purely geological grounds that transgressed sea waters, at many places hundreds of feet above the present ocean stand, were spread far and wide following the recession of the Cordilleran Glacier Complex and for some time afterward. Peat deposits that accumulated as glaciers withdrew from ground above the maximum level of transgression contain late-glacial and postglacial pollen. The deposits formed at successively lower elevations below this level reveal pollen records that begin successively later during the Postglacial. Radiocarbon dating confirms this progression toward younger basal sediments (progressively greater basal truncation).

The rates of differential uplift for four major sequences over thousands of years of the Postglacial are determined along transects beginning at or near the limit of transgression inland and ending in proximity to present sea level. Three of the sequences are located in the coastal Alaska "Tertiary Province," near Katalla and Northwest and Southeast Lituya Bay (Figs. 2, 3, 21, 23); the fourth is near Juneau (Figs. 3, 24). The rates are graphed in Figure 47, and several conclusions can be reached from the data. The forms of the resulting curves distinctively categorize the Tertiary Province apart from Juneau. Whereas the Juneau sequence gives relatively high rates of uplift (9.6 and 7.3 ft/century) between 150 ft and sea level, the remaining three give high rates (10.9, 15, and 9.5 ft/century) only to ca 100-ft elevation. It appears that with the withdrawal of ice-age glaciers at Juneau, isostatic readjustment (marine regression) was rather steady and recovery was rapid and apparently complete by ca 6100 yr ago. The Juneau area is less affected by nonisostatic tectonic activity than the Tertiary Province at the present, and this condition appears to have been prevalent for at least the last ca 7800 yr of the Postglacial. Moreover, a multiplicity of marine terraces indicating still-stands of the ocean is not readily apparent in the Juneau area, although this condition might be the result of less vigorous marine erosion caused by Juneau's sheltered position. Terraces have been measured at altitudes of 500–600 ft and 200 ft on Douglas Island near Juneau (D. J. Miller, personal communication). About Lituya Bay, particularly, and in the Katalla region, marine terraces facing the open ocean are, by contrast, distinctive and numerous.

If the curve for uplift for Juneau is predominantly the result of isostatic changes in level, those from the Tertiary Province are probably isostatic for the most part to the 100-ft contour—if comparable rates can be used as criteria. Thereafter and to the present, other crustal forces have supplemented the effect of isostasy. In fact, isostatic changes may have terminated some time ago, and the forces in effect during recent millennia may be entirely those that have caused vertical movement along the Fairweather and Chugach-St. Elias fault zones. These recent forces were active as early as the close of the Early Postglacial (8000 B. P.) as evidenced by the fluctuation in uplift that presumably created the 300-ft terrace at Northwest Lituya Bay. If the terrace Don J. Miller (personal communication) describes at a general altitude of

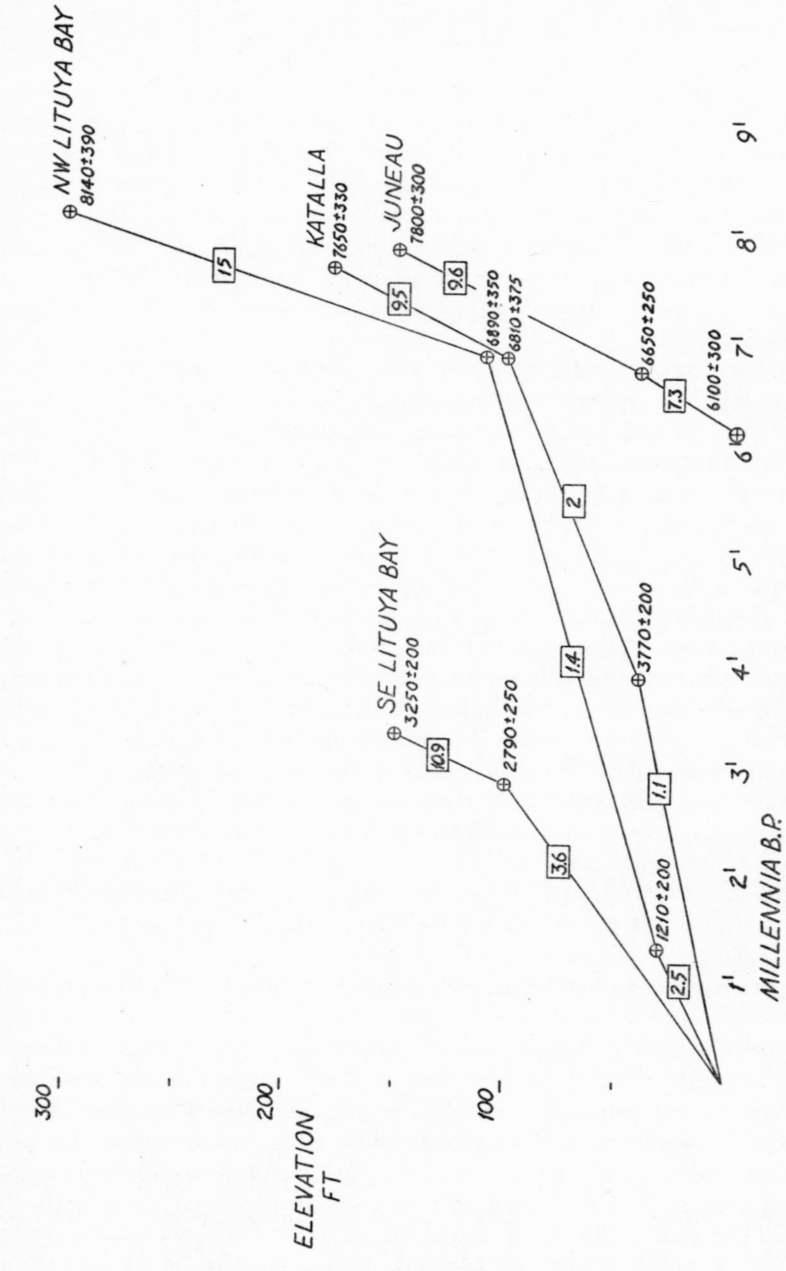

FIG. 47. Rates of late-Pleistocene differential uplift at Katalla, NW and SE Lituya Bay, and Juneau on the Alaskan coast shown by boxed numbers, which are feet per century. Numbers beside encircled crosses are radiocarbon dates in years Before Present.

1500 to 1700 ft has been wave planed, as he suspects, it would suggest pre-8000 B. P. fault movement.

The rate of uplift has generally declined for each sequence over the time represented. Rates were as high as 15 ft/century at Northwest Lituya Bay early in the Hypsithermal but subsequently during the latter part of the interval and during the Late Postglacial, the rate fell to 1.4 ft/century. The rate of change in the Juneau region during the Hypsithermal declined from 9.6 ft/century to 7.3 ft/century. The Northwest Lituya Bay and Katalla curves trend quite similarly beneath ca 100-ft altitude, the former varying between 1.4 and 2.5 ft/century and the latter between 1.1 and 2.

The Southeast Lituya Bay curve is greatly different from the others. A comparison of the ages of marine terraces at almost equal elevations at Southeast and Northwest Lituya Bay sites reveals considerable variation between their rates of uplift. A 100-ft terrace southeast of the bay is dated 2790±250 B. P., and its rate of uplift is calculated 3.6 ft/century; a 110-ft terrace to the northwest, dated 6890±350 B. P., records a rate of 1.6 ft/century. These differences indicate that (1) terraces at nearly the same altitude cannot be correlated alone on the basis of altitude, (2) terraces northwest of Lituya Bay were formed earlier than those to the southeast, and (3) uplift northwest of the bay was stronger during the Hypsithermal whereas southeast it was stronger during the Late Postglacial.

Further evidence for differential uplift in the Tertiary Province is seen in dates for levels atMunday Creek near Icy Cape (Fig. 2). A 230-ft late-glacial terrace is dated 10,820±420 B. P. (Heusser 1959), and another at ca 40-ft elevation is dated 1050±160 B. P. (Rubin and Alexander 1958). Uplift between the 230- and 40-ft levels is somewhat more than 2 ft/century, and below 40 ft, it averages 3.8 ft.century. The age of shallow-water marine mollusks at 12 ft above mean high tide in a sea cliff at Cape Suckling, ca 25 mi southeast of Katalla, is 5120±220 B. P. (Rubin and Alexander 1958). The position and age of these shells suggest formation during the episode of eustatic sea-level rise during the Hypsithermal. The age of a peat section collected near Alaganik, northwest of the Copper River mouth and the northwestern border of the Tertiary Province (Fig. 2), is significant. The section base, at ca 15-ft elevation and 10,390±350 B. P. in age, indicates that this part of the coast has been stable for at least ca 10,000 yr, and any minor changes, if they have taken place, have been less than 15 ft in magnitude.

Two sequences from British Columbia substantiate the fact, previously based alone on geological features, that marine transgression followed the recession of the last ice-age glaciers. In the Prince Rupert sector, a section from 135-ft altitude in Prince Rupert is basally truncated in contrast to a section from Rainbow Lake, ca 10 mi southeastward and 440-ft altitude (Figs. 4, 33). This stratigraphic condition is almost certain to have resulted from marine transgression and subsequent regression in the same manner as in the Juneau sector. A comparison of the pollen stratigraphy at the two sites indicates that peat deposition began ca 7500 B. P. at Prince Rupert and that the Rainbow Lake site was never covered by marine waters. An average rate of uplift at Prince Rupert between 135-ft elevation and present sea level is figured to be ca 1.8 ft/century. On Hope Island, off the northeastern end of Vancouver Island, sections from ca 100- and 15-ft elevations reveal transgression (Figs. 4, 35). The upper section was unaffected but at the lower, peat formation occurred after the regression of the ocean. Comparative pollen stratigraphy between sections enables an estimate of 3500 yr to be made of the age of the lower sections. Regression from ca 15 ft to the present ocean stand has been ca 0.43 ft/century.

Pollen stratigraphy and the radiocarbon-based chronology indicate that uplift has been greatest in proximity to the Coast Mountains in both British Columbia and Alaska. For example, if the stratigraphy for Masset (Figs. 4, 32) in the Queen Charlotte Islands, west of Prince Rupert and remote from the Coast Mountains, is examined, it can be seen that the profiles begin ca 10,000 B. P. The Masset section rests at an altitude of ca 24 ft, and it is apparent that transgression was no higher during these 10,000 yr. In Prince Rupert, on the other hand, the section at 135-ft altitude is on the western flank of the Coast Mountains and formed ca 7500 B. P. The conclusion is accordingly reached that the site of the Masset section has not been uplifted more than 24 ft, and possibly less, during the last ca 10,000 yr whereas Prince Rupert has risen as much as 135 ft in the last ca 7500 yr. In southeastern Alaska, the section at Threemile Arm on Kuiu Island at 100-ft altitude is Early Postglacial in age (Fig. 26). The Hobart Bay section (Fig. 28) at the same altitude, but nearer the Coast Mountains, does not begin until the Hypsithermal. Lower Montana Creek (Fig. 24) at 150 ft, nearer the mountains, also does not begin until the Hypsithermal. It is clear from these data and from our knowledge of the occurrence of marine features in the field that marine incursion did not affect the site at Threemile Arm, and uplift following regression was greater near the Coast Mountains than westward in the Alexander Archipelago.

LATE-PLEISTOCENE CHRONOLOGY AND POLLEN-STRATIGRAPHIC CORRELATIONS

Studies of the stratigraphy and isotopic ages of deep-sea cores disclose that temperature reached a minimum ca 15,000 B. P. (Suess 1956), at which time the ocean surface water was ca 6°C lower than at present (Emiliani 1955). In large measure based on these, but also on other studies, the beginning of the last rise of temperature is considered to lie between ca 13,000 and 15,000 B. P. (Ericson *et al.* 1956, Emiliani 1957). Major climatic change is interpreted to have occurred ca 11,000 B. P. (Ericson *et al.* 1956, Broecker 1957).

Continental studies from the midwestern United States are in general agreement with this pattern. Flint (1955) describes Wisconsin ice at its maximum ca 18,000 B. P., after which retreat occurred until ca 13,600 B. P., when readvance of Cary ice took place. Subsequent retreat followed until ca 12,000 B. P. Flint places the Mankato (Valders equivalent) readvance ca 11,400 B. P. (Two Creeks) and its maximum 10,850 B. P. He points out the close agreement between the beginning of the Cary retreat ca 12,200 B. P. and the beginning of the relatively warm Alleröd in Denmark ca 12,000 B. P., as well as the Mankato maximum ca 10,800 B. P. and the close of the Alleröd ca 10,800 B. P. (Iversen 1953). Close agreement may also be shown with the British Isles where the Alleröd is radiocarbon dated between ca 12,000 and 10,800 B. P. and the close of the Late-glacial at ca 10,300 B. P. (Godwin and Willis 1959).

Further general synchrony is seen in the West in the chronologies recently determined for pluvial lakes in the Great Basin. Broecker and Orr (1958) in their studies of the remnants of former Lakes Lahontan and Bonneville conclude that a high-water interval existed from ca 25,000 to 14,000 B. P. Lake volumes were reduced to a low-water level ca 13,000 B. P. but increased to maxima ca 11,700 B. P. Surface levels fell ca 11,000 B. P., and although some evidence suggests high water ca 10,000 B. P., the authors state that the lakes have probably remained low since ca 9000 B. P. Flint and Gale (1958), working at Searles Lake, California, place the later of two pluvial climates between ca 23,000 and 10,000 B. P. These authors emphasize the close relationship between the dates bracketing Wisconsin glaciation in the midwestern United States and this later pluvial climate. Moreover, they state: "The last glacial and the last pluvial, at least within the belt of westerly winds on the North American continent, are sensitively related to a climatic cause common to both."

In the Pacific Northwest, some uncertainty detracts from making unequivocal correlation between the youngest of Puget Sound glaciations, the Vashon, and Wisconsin-age glaciation in the central United States (Waldron, Mullineaux, and Crandell 1957; Crandell, Mullineaux, and Waldron 1958). Vashon retreat, which began some time before 14,000 B. P., appears to have begun during or prior to Cary glaciation. The minimum age of the Vashon, determined for basal limnic peat in Lake Washington, is ca 13,650 B. P. (Rigg and Gould 1957). Apparently, Cary ice was advancing ca 13,600 B. P. in the midwestern United States (Flint 1955) while Vashon ice was in a state of retreat. It is obvious that additional chronological refinement is necessary before relationships can be drawn with assured positiveness. On seemingly firm ground is the correlation of the Valders readvance in the Pacific Northwest ca 11,300 B. P. (Armstrong 1956) and in the Midwest ca 11,400 B. P. (Flint 1955).

The late-glacial pollen and peat stratigraphy beyond the limit of Vashon ice in western Washington is in accord with the sequence of Vashon retreat and Valders readvance (Tables 6–7). No radiocarbon dates have been made for this stratigraphy, and the chronology applied is founded on late-glacial radiocarbon determinations for these important events in western Washington and southwestern British Columbia. The threefold sequence represented by the pollen record is considered the equivalent of Older Dryas (Lower Dryas), Alleröd, and Younger Dryas (Upper Dryas) of European pollen stratigraphers. This climatic fluctuation is recognized in North America in the pollen studies by Deevey (1951) in Maine, S. T. Andersen (1954) in Michigan, Leopold (1956) in Connecticut, Livingstone and Livingstone (1958) in Nova Scotia, and Ogden (1959) in Massachusetts, and is suggested by Roosma (1958) at Searles Lake, California.

The results of European studies give some indication of the temperature conditions during the Late-glacial (Firbas 1949, B. G. Andersen 1954, Iversen 1954). July temperature in Denmark was below 10°C during the Older Dryas Period, above

Millennia B.P.	Southeastern Alaska	Coastal Washington	South Central British Columbia (Hansen pers. comm.)	Northern Great Basin (Hansen pers. comm.)	Oregon Cascades (Hansen pers. comm.)	Willamette Valley Oregon (Hansen pers. comm.)	Japan (Tsukada 1958)
0–3	Muskeg Regeneration and Invasion of Coast Forest Western Hemlock Maximum Lodgepole Pine	Western Hemlock Maximum Pine	Lodgepole Pine Douglas Fir Spruce	Lodgepole Pine Yellow Pine Grasses Composites	Hemlock Lodgepole Pine White Pine Yellow Pine	Douglas Fir Western Hemlock Fir	Tsuga Picea Abies
4–8 (Hypsithermal Interval)	Coast Forest Predominance Western Hemlock Sitka Spruce	Douglas Fir Maximum Western Hemlock Oak	Yellow Pine Maximum	Grasses Chenopods Composites	Yellow Pine Maximum	Oak Maximum	Quercus Fagus Ulmus Pterocarya
8–10 (Postglacial)	Lodgepole Pine	Lodgepole Pine	Lodgepole Pine White Pine Douglas Fir Spruce	Lodgepole Pine Yellow Pine White Pine	Lodgepole Pine Maximum Yellow Pine Douglas Fir	Lodgepole Pine Maximum Douglas Fir Western Hemlock Spruce Fir	Betula Picea Pinus
10–14 (Late-Glacial)	Lodgepole Pine Parkland	Lodgepole Pine Parkland NAP High Mountain Hemlock Fir Lodgepole Pine Parkland NAP High					

TABLE 7. Late-Pleistocene vegetation, environments, and chronologies for representative localities in the northern and southern hemispheres. In a few cases time-zone boundaries are not given by the above authors and have been interpreted (see text).

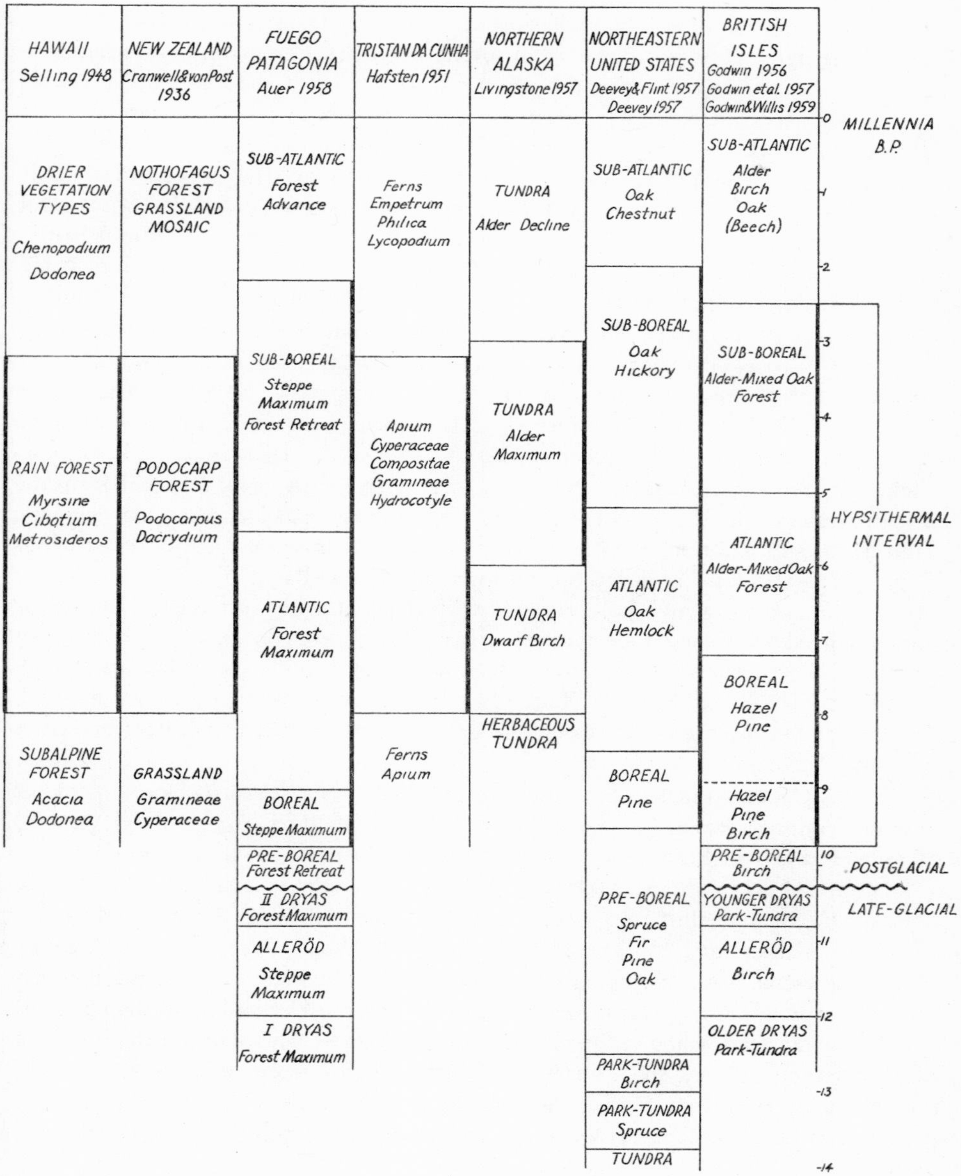

HAWAII Selling 1948	NEW ZEALAND Cranwell & von Post 1936	FUEGO PATAGONIA Auer 1958	TRISTAN DA CUNHA Hafsten 1951	NORTHERN ALASKA Livingstone 1957	NORTHEASTERN UNITED STATES Deevey & Flint 1957, Deevey 1957	BRITISH ISLES Godwin 1956, Godwin et al. 1957, Godwin & Willis 1959
DRIER VEGETATION TYPES Chenopodium Dodonea	NOTHOFAGUS FOREST GRASSLAND MOSAIC	SUB-ATLANTIC Forest Advance	Ferns Empetrum Phylica Lycopodium	TUNDRA Alder Decline	SUB-ATLANTIC Oak Chestnut	SUB-ATLANTIC Alder Birch Oak (Beech)
RAIN FOREST Myrsine Cibotium Metrosideros	PODOCARP FOREST Podocarpus Dacrydium	SUB-BOREAL Steppe Maximum Forest Retreat	Apium Cyperaceae Compositae Gramineae Hydrocotyle	TUNDRA Alder Maximum	SUB-BOREAL Oak Hickory	SUB-BOREAL Alder-Mixed Oak Forest
SUBALPINE FOREST Acacia Dodonea	GRASSLAND Gramineae Cyperaceae	ATLANTIC Forest Maximum	Ferns Apium	TUNDRA Dwarf Birch	ATLANTIC Oak Hemlock	ATLANTIC Alder-Mixed Oak Forest
		BOREAL Steppe Maximum		HERBACEOUS TUNDRA	BOREAL Pine	BOREAL Hazel Pine
		PRE-BOREAL Forest Retreat			PRE-BOREAL Spruce Fir Pine Oak	Hazel Pine Birch
		II DRYAS Forest Maximum			PARK-TUNDRA Birch	PRE-BOREAL Birch
		ALLERÖD Steppe Maximum			PARK-TUNDRA Spruce	YOUNGER DRYAS Park-Tundra
		I DRYAS Forest Maximum			TUNDRA	ALLERÖD Birch
						OLDER DRYAS Park-Tundra

MILLENNIA B.P. (scale 0–14: 0, 1, 2, 3, 4, 5, 6, 7, 8, 9, 10, 11, 12, 13, 14)

HYPSITHERMAL INTERVAL

POSTGLACIAL

LATE-GLACIAL

12 during the Alleröd, and ca 10 during the Younger Dryas Period. These conclusions are in agreement with those from southern Germany, where the July temperature was ca 2.5°C lower during the Alleröd than at present and 5.6–7 lower during Younger Dryas time than at present. Temperature during the Younger Dryas in southwestern, oceanic Norway, however, was apparently depressed only 2.8–3.9°C.

The close of the Late-glacial in Nova Scotia is placed at 10,340±220 B. P. (Livingstone and Livingstone 1958) and approximates the 10,500 B. P. estimate for the upper boundary of the Late-glacial in western Washington. In northern British Columbia and southeastern Alaska, ca 10,000 B. P. shows close correlation. Additional harmony is seen with the evidence presented by Flint (1955) for the Mankato (Valders equivalent) maximum in the United States Midwest and by Flint and Gale (1958) and Broecker and Orr (1958) in pluvial basins in the West. The tripartite zonation of the Late-glacial by Livingstone and Livingstone (1958) is paralleled in the western Washington pollen record, and the youngest partitioned zone in Nova Scotia seems evident in records from the Canadian and Alaskan coasts. Zonal parallelism is also shown between North Pacific pollen stratigraphy and that from the British Isles (Godwin 1956, Godwin and Willis 1959) and Denmark (Deevey and Flint 1957); in addition, the end of the Late-glacial is by and large synchronous (Table 7). Some zonal relationship is drawn with Fuego-Patagonia, although Auer's (1958) chronology, which he correlates with that currently in effect in Europe, is not supported by radiocarbon dating earlier than 9300±200 B. P. This date just precedes his Eruption I ash horizon, which he places roughly equivalent to the European Boreal. The Postglacial–Late-glacial boundary may therefore be approximately equal in age in southern South America, Denmark, the British Isles, and parts of North America.

The postglacial sequences presented for the Pacific Northwest (Hansen, personal communication), Japan (Tsukada 1958), Hawaii (Selling 1948), New Zealand (Cranwell and von Post 1936), Fuego-Patagonia (Auer 1958), Tristan da Cunha (Hafsten 1951), northern Alaska (Livingstone 1957), northeastern United States (Deevey and Flint 1957, Deevey 1957), and the British Isles (Godwin 1956; Godwin, Walker, and Willis 1957; Godwin and Willis 1959) are divisible into early-postglacial, hypsithermal, and late-postglacial pollen units (Table 7). Temperature in terms of annual averages was higher during the Hypsithermal than at present. In Switzerland, using temperature lapse rates and Lüdi's data on the positions of timber line, Deevey and Flint (1957) calculate that temperature was 2 to 3°C higher during the Swiss Sub-Boreal than at present. Temperature higher than at present continued in effect from the Boreal through the Sub-Boreal (hypsithermal interval).

This broad temperature fluctuation consistently shows parallelism between far-flung localities (von Post 1946). Moisture fluctuations have, on the other hand, behaved inconsistently so that correlations on the basis of the humidity factor are often impossible. European stratigraphers follow the Blytt-Sernander climatic sequence and accordingly subdivide the Hypsithermal into the Boreal (warm and dry), the Atlantic (warm and moist), and the Sub-Boreal (warm and dry). Deevey and Flint

(1957) place the European Hypsithermal between 2600 and 9500 B. P. Godwin (1956) and Godwin, Walker, and Willis (1957) are in general agreement with these dates. They place the opening of the Boreal at ca 9750 B. P. and the close of the Sub-Boreal at 2500 B. P. The classic European *Grenzhorizont*, usually dated 2500 or 2600 B. P., sets off the Sub-Boreal–Sub-Atlantic division and indicates warmth and drought during the Sub-Boreal, coolness and higher humidity during the Sub-Atlantic.

The southeastern Alaska equivalent of the classic *Grenzhorizont* (RY III) is fixed at ca 3500 B. P. This is somewhat early compared to the above chronology and the dates set by Münnich (1957). Evidently, the horizon is not consistent chronologically since de Vries, Barendsen, and Waterbolk (1958) date it between 3425±140 and 3540±140 B. P. in a large raised bog at Vriezenveen, Netherlands. Agreement between this date and the date in Alaska is remarkably close. Where two strongly developed ligneous horizons appear in the hypsithermal stratigraphy in localities such as Juneau and Masset (Figs. 24, 32), it is a temptation to correlate them with the drier Boreal and Sub-Boreal and the interbedded sedge deposits with the more humid Atlantic, particularly when the dates of the Alaskan ligneous horizons, dated ca 3500 and 7500 B. P., seem to be roughly compatible with the European chronology.

The Hypsithermal seems correlative between Japan (Tsukada 1958) and southeastern Alaska, based on dates arrived at independently. Elsewhere in the Pacific Basin, good correlation occurs with Hawaii (Selling 1948) and as far as New Zealand (Cranwell and von Post 1936). However, correlations with these places seem purely fortuitous since the dates set by these authors are based on inference alone (von Post 1946) and not radiocarbon dating. In South America Auer (1958), interpreting the fluctuations of steppe and forest pollen in his profiles as a response to respective dryness and wetness, correlated his boundaries with those in Europe, independent of radiocarbon. Subsequent radiocarbon dates are in fairly close agreement with his estimates. Auer's Boreal is interpreted to begin ca 9750 B. P. and his Sub-Atlantic ca 2200 B. P.

The Hypsithermal in the Brooks Range of northern Alaska is between 3000 and 6000 B. P.; its opening date is derived from a radiocarbon age of 5900±250 B. P. in the vicinity of the birch-alder transition; its closing date is less accurately known. In the northeastern United States, Deevey and Flint (1957) delimit hypsithermal time between 2000 and 9500 B. P., practically the same delimitation thes eauthors hold for Denmark and northern Germany, except that in the European countries, 2600 B. P. is the termination date.

Chapter IX

CERTAIN PHYTOGEOGRAPHIC CONSIDERATIONS

Hultén (1937b) in his "Outline of the History of Arctic and Boreal Biota during the Quarternary Period" postulates the existence in coastal northwestern North America of two centra or ice-free refugia, from where plants migrated as glaciers melted during the Postglacial. He places one locus in the southern Bering Sea about the Aleutian Islands and terms the biota derived from this area "Southern Beringia Radiants." He recognizes four elementary subareas spread across the North Pacific for this group of radiants; one subarea extends from southeastern Alaska to Washington and Oregon. He places the other locus in south-central Alaska, about the Alaska Peninsula, Kodiak Island, the Kenai, and the Prince William Sound region. Plants migrating from this refugium are called "Western American Coast Radiants." Hultén's method for determining these two centra is to map the concentricity of certain plant assemblages about the point from where migration has taken place; some 40 maps show centra in the higher latitudes of the Northern Hemisphere. His postulation is called the theory of equiformal progressive areas.

At the time Hultén published his treatise, knowledge of the extent of glaciation along the North Pacific coast was scanty, and Hultén apparently did not have at his disposal all the American literature containing discussions of nonglaciation in the region. He used the early glacial maps of Antevs (1929) to test certain of his ideas. Since then, significant and cogent studies have been published in support of the refugium concept. It is remarkable that Hultén, using plant-distribution patterns as his guide and without much glacial-geological data, was able to recognize coastal refugia that, as will be seen, are almost certain to have existed.

The proposition regarding persistence of plants in unglaciated lacunae or on "nunataks" advanced by Fernald (1925) has become known as the "nunatak theory." Its purpose is to explain the distribution of certain arctic and cordilleran species in eastern North America. In order to explain the occurrence of cordilleran plants in coastal northern Labrador, Abbe (1936) also resorts to this theory. Flint, Demorest, and Washburn (1942) and Odell (1938), basing their conclusions on geological evidence, disagree with this concept, and Wynne-Edwards (1937) describes the distribution in terms of postglacial migrations. In Scandinavia a similar controversy exists among biogeographers, and Dahl (1946a and b, 1955), in giving the problem considerable thoughtful attention, brings to light many interesting bits of evidence favoring the refugium concept.

Along the northwestern coast of North America, ice-free areas existed (1) in Washington south of the limit of continental glaciation and apparently northwestward (2) in the high ramparts of Vancouver Island, (3) on the Queen Charlotte Islands, (4) probably in parts of the Alexander Archipelago, (5) at places between Icy Point and the vicinity of the Copper River mouth, (6) in Prince William Sound, and (7) on the Kenai Peninsula (Fig. 48). In most cases the evidence supporting the existence of these nonglaciated land areas is both geological and biological. Certain pollen profiles of the present study are in harmony with these data, at least in some of the broader aspects, and engender the belief that glaciations were not total and that plants and animals survived episodes of glaciation in these refugia.

EVIDENCE IN SUPPORT OF GLACIAL REFUGIA

South of the ice sheet in Washington, the plant assemblage represented in the pollen record at Humptulips (Fig. 41) indicates what plant populations were present when northward migration began during the Late-glacial. Plants presumably survived ca 35 mi from the edge of the cordilleran glacier of Wisconsin age and at least 28 different entities are in evidence prior to Valders glacial readvance. Among the arboreal plants, lodgepole pine, mountain hemlock, and Douglas fir are noteworthy, and among the nonarboreals, grass, sedge, *Sanguisorba*, heath, composites, and ferns are distinctly more abundant.

Within the area occupied by the ice sheet, the southernmost refugium appears to have been on north-central Vancouver Island and perhaps oceanward on the high mountain arms between the valley glaciers. Wilson and his associates (1958) place the upper ice limit at 6300-ft elevation, which leaves almost 1000 ft of altitude remaining between this level and the summit of the highest peak, Golden Hinde, at 7219 ft. Three other peaks also lie above the 6300-ft upper ice level.

The survival of two animal species is suggested on the high alpine slopes of these mountains. McCabe and Cowan (1945) state: "The Vancouver marmot, *Marmota vancouverensis*, while a member of the *caligata* group, is specifically distinct from continental members of the species *caligata*. In this instance it seems to us that isolation for a period longer than the immediate post-Pleistocene has been necessary to foster the development of the distinguishing characters. The presence of this marmot on the high peaks of Vancouver Island suggests to us the presence, in these areas, of habitable land, during the last ice age at least, and supporting a limited residual fauna. The presence on Vancouver Island of a well differentiated race (*saxatalis* Cowan) of the implastic ptarmigan species *Lagopus leucurus* serves further to bolster this interpretation of the situation." Animal survival implies plant survival, but what the species were or what number they attained is unknown.

The major refugium was on the Queen Charlotte Islands. On southern Graham Island, where the highest summit is at 4000 ft, MacKenzie (1916) finds only partial glaciation evident above 3000-ft altitude. Preglacial Yakoun Lake at less than 500-ft elevation contains small islands that show no sign of having been overridden by ice. Glaciers that flowed oceanward from the Coast Mountains moved across the low-lying parts of the Queen Charlottes, but owing to the broad outlets provided by Dixon Entrance and Hecate Strait, could not override the high parts of the islands. It is most likely that refugia existed on the slopes between ice-occupied valleys on the ocean side of Moresby and Graham Islands. Little opportunity was afforded for ice to accumulate and spread laterally, owing to the fact that where deep ocean lies offshore the ice would become afloat. Depths of 500 ft are found almost directly off the west coast and 20 mi offshore reach 8000 to 9000 ft. Dahl (1946a and b) developed this thesis for the Norwegian coast.

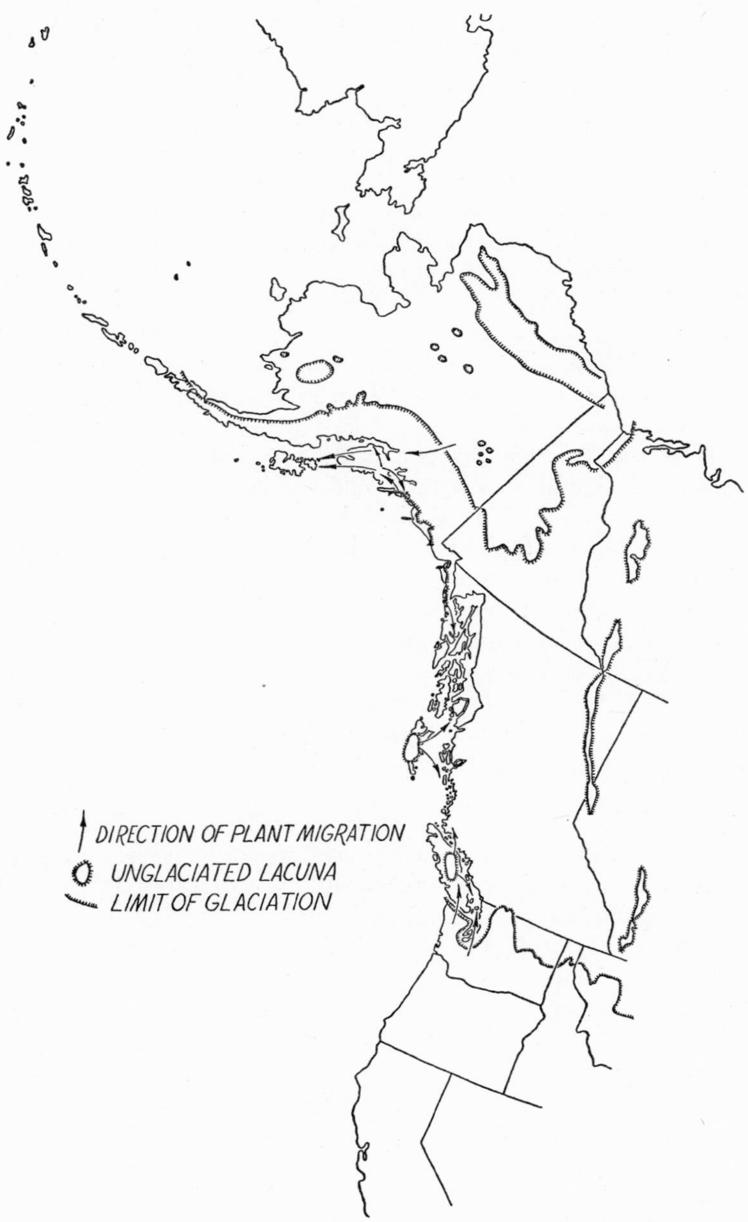

Fig. 48. Sketch map of northwestern North America and adjacent Siberia showing the extent of glaciation and the pattern of plant migration following the last ice age in the study region.

A distinctive fauna is found on the Queen Charlotte Islands. Osgood (1901b) was the first person to make a careful search of the animal populations. The land mammals he examined are distinguishable from related mainland species of the same genera. McCabe and Cowan (1945) also find this to be true and their conclusion from these data is particularly significant. They write: "While there may be room for scepticism regarding the survival on Vancouver Island of a pre-ice-age residual fauna, there can be no doubt concerning the Queen Charlotte Islands. Here there is no evidence of an overriding ice-cap and the distinctive fauna, including such unique mammal species as *Rangifer dawsonii* [caribou], *Martes nesophila* [marten], and *Mustela haidorum* [weasel], the races *Ursus americanus carlottae* [black bear], *Peromyscus sitkensis prevostensis* [white-footed mouse], and *Sorex obscurus prevostensis* [shrew] together with well characterized races of Steller Jay, Pine Grosbeak, Hairy Woodpecker and Saw-whet Owl, testifies to a long period of isolation. That part, at least, of this fauna is of preglacial or interglacial origin seems to be an inescapable conclusion."

One of the most interesting animals found on the islands is the caribou. A high-latitude, interior-continental mammal, it is not found at present in the southeastern Alaska-British Columbia coastal region. The animals that gave rise to the distinctive populations presumably arrived on the islands at the beginning of a glacial age, before glaciers moved through Dixon Entrance and Hecate Strait, when sea level was low and the islands were connected with the mainland. At these times Hecate Strait, a formidable barrier to migration at present, seems to have been crossable (Heusser 1955b).

Some of the results of a botanical survey made on the Queen Charlottes in 1957 are included in a study of British Columbia Saxifragaceae (Calder and Savile 1959a and b). *Heuchera chlorantha* Piper is recorded on the islands; the nearest other stations for this species are on southern Vancouver Island and in the Skeena River valley. Calder and Savile consider it likely that *Heuchera chlorantha* of the Skeena valley, in an area known to have been heavily glaciated, was derived from a relict population in the Queen Charlottes during postglacial time. In a personal communication (28 May 1959), Dr. Calder indicates that endemic plants (important criteria of long-term isolation) were located on southwestern Graham Island and northwestern Moresby Island. One of these, the endemic *Saxifraga taylori* Calder and Savile, he describes as "a clear cut endemic of the Queen Charlotte Ranges." Another, the umbellifer *Ligusticum calderi* Mathias and Constance, is localized in the Queen Charlottes (Mathias and Constance 1959). Dr. Calder states further: "As regards the Queen Charlotte Islands there is no doubt in my mind that there was a significant refugium in the mountainous regions in late Wisconsin at least. Only a small percentage of the Q. C. I. material has been worked over critically. The number of endemics to date are few but the proportion to the total Alpine flora is significant."

Halliday and Brown (1943), in plotting population intensity of important forest trees in Canada, lend support to Hultén's (1937b) concept of migration centra. Their findings show that Sitka spruce is most heavily concentrated on the Queen Charlotte Islands and the opposite mainland. Western hemlock is more abundant on the Queen

Charlottes and the adjacent mainland than it is along the coast southward, except for places on Vancouver Island. Postglacial migration of these two trees appears to have taken place from the Queen Charlottes.

Refugia are unknown in the southeastern Alaskan Alexander Archipelago, although the southern part of Baranof Island with elevations to 7002 ft appears not to have been completely covered by an ice sheet. Buddington and Chapin (1929) are of the opinion that glaciers reached above 2800 but under 4000 ft on eastern Chichagof Island. No biological data are available to indicate distinctive plants or animals from this district, but on the basis of what has been discovered on the British Columbia islands, the probability is large that refugia existed here as well.

Northwestward, the strip of coast between Icy Point and the Prince William Sound sector contains unglaciated country. Miller (1958b, personal communication) finds glaciation during late-Visconsin time was little if at all more extensive than at present. Unglaciated areas are notable about Bering Lake, the Suckling Hills, west of Icy Cape, along most of the foreland between Yakutat and Dry Bays, and northwest and southeast of Lituya Bay (Fig. 48). Much of this ocean border emerged from beneath sea level during postglacial time and, consequently, could not have served as an extensive refugium (or series of refugia) even if, in fact, unglaciated. Unglaciated, nonsubmarine tracts of late-Wisconsin age are apparently limited in size at present and stand hundreds of feet above sea level, inland from the existing shore line. These are the only areas that might have supported biota during glaciation, but a dearth of biological field studies along this coastal stretch is the reason for the inconclusiveness regarding the existence of refugia.

Glacial drift is neither in evidence in the vicinity of Alaganik west of the Copper River mouth, nor in Prince William Sound above 440-ft altitude on 1546-ft-high Hinchinbrook Island, nor on parts of Hawkins and Montague Islands according to Tarr and Martin (1914). It seems extremely likely that biota could survive at Alaganik and on the islands above the level of surrounding ice. It should be remembered, as pointed out previously, that changes in land–sea-level relations about Alaganik have not been greater than ca 15 ft during at least the last 10,000 yr.

Late-glacial sections on Perry Island (Fig. 19) and at Alaganik 1 (Fig. 20) do not throw much light on survival possibilities in the above areas, but the Seward late-glacial section (Fig. 17) contains strong evidence to indicate a local refugium. The Seward section is unique in its basal record of Sitka spruce and mountain hemlock pollen. No other late-glacial pollen spectra in the region contain these conifers—it seems apparent that the trees survived the last glaciation in a refugium. It is very unlikely that the pollen was blown from any great distance, since it would have been found in other late-glacial profiles; also, the pollen does not appear redeposited. These conclusions plus a rich pollen flora of 17 entities when peat began to form are compelling indications that a refugium sheltered these plants since before the last major glaciation.

The Seward refugium on the Kenai Peninsula supplies evidence that the locus propounded by Hultén (1937b) for his Western American Coast Radiants did in fact exist. The refugia recognized on the Queen Charlotte Islands, on Vancouver Island, possibly in the Alexander Archipelago, and south of the ice border in Washington are in accord with the elementary area proposed by Hultén for his Southern Beringia Radiants.

THE PROBLEM OF SURVIVAL

If the paleotemperatures of Formanifera tests in Atlantic deep-sea cores (Emiliani 1955) plotted on a radiocarbon-based chronology (Suess 1956) are true approximations of the extent of temperature drop in the North Pacific, the minimum temperature reached ca 15,000 B. P. was ca 6°C below the present, the lowest in the last ca 100,000 yr. This minimum agrees with the depression of 5.6–7°C for July temperature during the early part of the Late-glacial in Europe, as derived from the calculations of Firbas (1949) and Iversen (1954).

At representative stations along the Gulf of Alaska, where minimum temperature during the last ice age is apt to have been critical, July average values (Kincer 1941) if depressed 6°C (10.8°F) would result at Kodiak in 43.5°F, at Seward 44.5, at Cordova 44, and at Juneau 45.8. From what is known of plant growth and seed germination under relatively low temperature conditions, it seems unlikely that a 6°C depression would be critical to many of the plants now growing in unglaciated tracts representing probable refugia. The Seward refugium suggests that the plants surviving on the southeastern Kenai were, at least, Sitka spruce, mountain hemlock, willow, birch, alder, sedge, *Nuphar*, *Drosera*, *Sanguisorba*, *Epilobium*, heath, Tubuliflorae, Polypodiaceae, *Lycopodium* (three species), *Selaginella*, and *Sphagnum*.

A pertinent survival relationship can be drawn between the theoretical mean July temperature of 45.8°F at Juneau during the last ice age and the mean July temperatures of 46.3°F in 1949 and 46.0°F in 1950 recorded at 3862-ft elevation in the nearby Juneau Ice Field, where Sitka spruce was observed at its upper limit (Heusser 1954b). If a condensation level is assumed at 3500-ft altitude, and a dry adiabatic lapse rate of 2.5°F/1000 ft for this amount of rise and a wet rate of 5.5°F/1000 ft for the remaining ca 400 ft is applied, the average long-term July temperature is found to be 45.6°F, which is close to the recorded values for two field seasons in the ice field. From these data it appears very likely that Sitka spruce could have survived at Juneau during the ice age on the basis of temperature alone. That it survived at Seward at a theoretical July average of 44.5°F suggests an ability to endure under somewhat colder summer conditions. A lengthy duration of snow cover might have been critical in certain areas under ice-age conditions, but a case in point favoring survival is represented by the Sitka spruce in the Juneau Ice Field. These trees, growing low to the ground, are covered by snow for an estimated 9 months of each year and even longer during seasons of heavy accumulation. Within limits, furthermore, a heavy snow cover can afford protection against the desiccating effects of winter cold waves. Under present climatic conditions at Seward, -20°F is the minimum temperature recorded (Kincer 1941). If Sitka spruce, probably the most thermophilous of the plants in the Seward refugium survived, it is more than likely that mountain hemlock and the nonarboreal plants would survive, on the basis of temperature alone, in low-level, unglaciated coastal areas for which no data on refugia are available.

Although it appears that temperature depression did not prove detrimental to Sitka spruce, mountain hemlock, and a number of nonarboreal species confined to ice-age refugia, the effects of physiographic instability were undoubtedly influential in eliminating many of the plants in unglaciated areas recognized along this coast. That the existence of refugia has not been determined on the basis of biological evidence in the Alexander Archipelago and northwestward to Prince William Sound is more likely due to physiographic instability than to climatic restriction.

THE PATTERN OF LATE-PLEISTOCENE MIGRATIONS

Radiocarbon dates from the Puget Lowland in Washington show that the pre-Valders glacial lobe began to recede south of Seattle at some time before 14,000 B. P. (Crandell, Mullineaux, and Waldron 1958). By at least 12,900 ± 330 B. P. (Rubin and Alexander 1958), the ice had wasted away at the site of the bog at Sedro Woolley, and plants had already contributed to the peat deposit that is the basis for determining its age. A readvance in the Fraser River valley dated ca 11,300 B. P. (Armstrong 1956) is Valders in age and appears to have been restricted to the valley. Whether this ice checked for a time the progress of plant migration northwestward is not known but from the earliest late-glacial dates from the Queen Charlotte Islands (10,850 ± 800 B. P., Broecker and Kulp 1957), Juneau (10,300 ± 400 B. P., Broecker and Kulp 1957; and 10,300 ± 600 B. P., Olson and Broecker 1959), Icy Cape (10,820 ± 420 B. P., Heusser 1959), Alaganik (10,390 ± 350, Heusser 1959), Prince William Sound (9440 ± 350 B. P., Heusser 1959), and the Kenai Peninsula (9600 ± 650 B. P., Broecker *et al.* 1956), the Valders appears to have had greater coverage northwesterly, and peat deposition from immigrated plants did not begin until Valders ice had receded. Sea level was 600 ft or more higher than at present in the Fraser valley (Armstrong 1956), and it seems unlikely that land surfaces were exposed to receive the diaspores of migrating plants. On the basis of these data, plant migration did not progress far north along the British Columbia coast while Valders readvance was in effect. Following the readvance, however, deglaciation and sea regression apparently took place on a large scale and migration was rapid.

The refugium south of the ice margin in Washington was the chief source of plant migrants (Fig. 48). Diaspores, carried by wind and by water currents and on the bodies of birds and mammals, were transported progressively northwestward in post-Valders time as ice and the ocean receded from the land. Lodgepole pine was the principal conifer to move to higher latitudes along the coast. Willow, alder, and probably black cottonwood were its chief associates. These plants migrated within their limits of tolerance and in accordance with their ability to compete. As Sitka spruce, western hemlock, and mountain hemlock succeeded the early invaders, the vegetation began to adjust to the environmental requirements that fluctuated through postglacial millennia (Tables 5–6). The species characteristic of the mountains and of the lowland, of the oceanic climate of the coast and of the more continental climate of "inside" islands and fiords adjusted to the forces active in their surroundings.

Initial plant migration appears to have been extremely rapid. The radiocarbon dates for coastal localities, previously cited, reveal that plants became established on

Langara Island in the Queen Charlotte Islands simultaneously with the plants at Icy Cape. The establishment of plants ca 500 yr earlier at these places than at Alaganik or about Juneau suggests relatively greater proximity to refugia. Glaciers about Prince William Sound, on the Kenai, and on Kodiak and Afognak Islands are considered responsible for migrations having been delayed at least ca 800 yr after they were recorded near the mouth of Copper River.

Plants in refugia located northwest of unglaciated western Washington, shown in Figure 48, almost certainly contributed diaspores to contiguous deglaciated terrain. In fact, the contemporaneity of the earliest late-glacial dates for plant deposits between the Queen Charlottes and the Copper River delta provide strong evidence that these centra were major diaspore sources for repopulation as nearby land areas became subject to invasion. The distribution of *Heuchera chlorantha* Piper, *Saxifraga taylori* Calder and Savile, and *Ligusticum calderi* Mathias and Constance (Calder and Savile 1959a and b, Mathias and Constance 1959) and the concentration of Sitka spruce and western hemlock (Halliday and Brown 1943) in northern coastal British Columbia, as previously noted, are cases in point for existence of the Queen Charlotte Islands refugium.

That diaspores were capable of traveling great distances over water along the North Pacific coast during the Late Pleistocene is indicated by the floral assemblage on Middleton Island. This small oceanic land mass lies in the Gulf of Alaska, ca 50 mi from the nearest coast on Montague Island in Prince William Sound. Thomas (1957) lists 116 plants distributed among 42 families on the island. Five groups of Sitka spruce are established, but it is not known how the seeds or seedlings arrived, though man is strongly suspected as having introduced them. The other woody plants are *Salix barclayi*, *Rubus spectabilis*, and *Sambucus racemosa* subsp. *pubens*. Oddly enough, alder is not present. The principal families are Gramineae, Cyperaceae, Polygonaceae, Caryophyllaceae, Cruciferae, Rosaceae, Umbelliferae, Scrophulariaceae, and Compositae, with at least five species representing each family. Thomas believes the flora was derived from the mainland and islands to the north.

In early-postglacial time, plants that invaded newly denuded ground were subject to physiographic unrest that continued for some time during deglaciation and regression. Washouts and slides were undoubtedly fairly frequent, much more so than at present. Though these catastrophes destroyed plants and animals where they occurred, in many instances migration is likely to have resulted. McCabe and Cowan (1945) utilize slide rafts to explain the distribution of the mammal *Peromyscus* along the British Columbia coast. Slide rafts are frequently observed along the North Pacific shores, and animals have been seen among the earth, humus, branches, roots, and tree trunks that make up the rafts. There seems to be little doubt that this medium served also as a means for plant migration.

Lodgepole pine during the Postglacial migrated as far as the Yakutat flats. It appears to have been blocked from migrating farther by the piedmont foot of Malaspina Glacier. The pollen profile from the vicinity of Grand Plateau Glacier (Fig. 23) and the accompanying basal radiocarbon date indicate that the tree has been present locally for at least 1200 yr. Lodgepole has been in the area northwest of Lituya Bay, ca 18 mi southeast of Grand Plateau Glacier, for at least the last ca 8000 yr (Fig. 23). Western hemlock by contrast has been able to migrate as far as Prince William Sound, having arrived here during the Hypsithermal as indicated by the Cordova profile (Fig. 20). Not until the Late Postglacial, however, did the tree gain importance in the eastern part of the sound.

That mountain hemlock and Sitka spruce on the Kenai and about Prince William Sound originated from the Seward refugium is almost a certainty. No other late-glacial sections along the northern gulf contain pollen of these conifers. Unglaciated country about Seward has not been located, but that it existed seems assured on the basis of this pollen record. (To search for unglaciated ground in the vicinity of Seward is of phytogeographical importance.) Mountain hemlock and Sitka spruce have also moved northward along the coast, but where representatives from these separate migrations made contact or overlapped is unknown.

Sitka spruce is the only coniferous migrant to have reached Afognak and Kodiak Islands. Its arrival on these islands was not earlier than the Late Postglacial. Water barriers between the islands and the Kenai Peninsula do not seem to have impeded its progress appreciably, since the tree arrived on the southwestern Kenai about the same time as it did on the islands. The migration of Sitka spruce southwestward on the Kenai and across to the islands is attributed to the favorable cool, humid climate that prevailed during the Late Postglacial. The cold late-glacial and early-postglacial climates confined Sitka spruce to the area of the Seward refugium. During the Hypsithermal, temperature may have been suitable for migration, but moisture was apparently critical.

On the Kenai and even in Prince William Sound, pollen from elements of the Interior Spruce-Birch Forest is contained in a number of the sections. The Seward late-glacial spectrum (Fig. 17) contains birch, and it is likely that the basal spruce may in part be white spruce. The occurrence of birch, and possibly also white spruce, reveals that the Interior Forest had reached the southeastern Kenai Peninsula prior to the last major glaciation and had become mixed with the Coastal Forest elements in the Seward refugium. Profiles from the neighborhood of Homer on the southwestern, nonoceanic side of the Kenai (Fig. 15) clearly show an increase in the proportion of birch and interior white and black spruces in the late-postglacial zone. Significant is the high percentage of birch in late-glacial deposits, indicating that birch was prominent elsewhere than Seward at that time. These data show two major migrations of the Interior Forest onto the Kenai from unglaciated central Alaska, the most recent of which, as shown by the conifer profiles, appears to have taken place during the last ca 4000 yr (Fig. 48).

Chapter X

POSTSCRIPT

Any study that traces the unfolding of Pleistocene environments must, in the final perspective, consider man, for it is during the Pleistocene that his footsteps first began to appear on earth. Man, like any of his associate organisms, may be likened to a point moving in time and space. He is constantly seeking out new corners of the earth or areas beyond it on which to construct his civilizations. To follow his travels has been a real challenge to anthropologists.

In northwestern North America, the camps he made during his wanderings and during his apparent migration from Asia have been uncovered from place to place. Oddly enough, their antiquity is not as great as in the central western part of the continent. Whereas his effects date from at least 10,000 B. P., and possibly as early as 30,000 B. P. or earlier, in the Central and Far West (Libby 1952, Broecker and Kulp 1957), in Alaska the oldest artifacts found thus far are from the Denbigh Flint complex at Iyatayet on Norton Sound and are only 4658±220 yr of age (Libby 1954, Hopkins and Giddings 1953). In the Aleutian Islands, the oldest Aleut village site is on Umnak Island and is dated only 3018±230 B. P. (Arnold and Libby 1951).

Anthropologists generally agree that the route early man followed onto this continent was by way of Bering Strait (Griffin 1960). They also generally agree that his route continued southward by way of unglaciated interior Alaska and along the Rocky Mountain front. The northwestern coast is usually discounted as a route, mainly because its cultures are young. The Great Fraser midden deposit in Vancouver, British Columbia, for example, dates from only 2100±900 B. P. (Broecker and Kulp 1957). Strong geological evidence indicates that unglaciated corridors, where man may have waited for an ice age to pass during a migration, are apparent in western and central Alaska, Yukon Territory, Northwest Territories, British Columbia, and Alberta (Wilson *et al.* 1958, Fig. 48). In some of these corridors, botanical studies point toward refugia for plants at least, if not also for man and other animals (Halliday and Brown 1943, Hansen 1949a and b). But refugia and unglaciated tracts appear certain to have existed, as well, along the North Pacific coast. It would seem just as likely that early man followed this route either during or between times of glaciation. Both routes are conjectural, since conclusive evidence is still lacking.

Some favor is attached here to early coastal migration in preference to the generally accepted belief of passage through the continental interior. The coastal-migration thesis is suggested by: (1) equable oceanic climate, (2) available marine food, and (3) greater travel facility by water, particularly through coastal archipelagoes. If early man worked his way southward along the coast after having crossed Bering Strait or the Bering-Chukchi platform during the opening of the pre-Wisconsin interglacial when the platform was still exposed (Hopkins 1959), he could have reached California as early as 30,000 B. P., as some findings suggest (Broecker and Kulp

1957). However, the traces he may have left along the way have not come to light because of several possible reasons.

Glaciation and vulcanism during and since the Wisconsin ice age, both shown to have been powerful agents of destruction along the North Pacific border, would cause a dearth of proof owing to burial of the cultural remains. Equally as cogent are changes in land–sea-level relations. If man had migrated when the Pacific stood lower or the land was higher, his camps would now lie below present sea level. If his migration took place during higher levels of the ocean or lower positions of the land, hearths, middens, and cultural implements would lie tens or hundreds of feet above, and some distance inland from, the ocean stand of today. If the latter condition were to prove to have been the case, his camp grounds would probably rest either buried beneath muskeg or under thick humus of adjoining forests.

It seems plausible that man's more recent travels have taken him northwestward on the continent. Such a pattern is indicated by the postglacial age of the Denbigh Flint complex and the resemblance of its artifacts to the older Folsom culture of the United States Southwest. In this regard it is worth quoting the remarks made by A. D. Krieger (1953) prior to the radiocarbon dating of the complex. Krieger writes: "The few fluted projectile points found in Alaska . . . are held to constitute proof that Alaska was the steppingstone for the entrance of these ancient points into America from Asia, even though they have not yet been recognized in Asia. The alternative, that fluted points are an American invention, diffused northward into Alaska as game animals moved northward with retreat of the glaciers, has not received due attention."

It seems imperative in any future anthropological work done along the coast that systematic reconnaissance and excavations be carried out in regions that most likely contain unglaciated refugia. Any search must also take into account land and sea-level variations and the toxic effects of vulcanism on animals and plants. However, late-Pleistocene environments apparently did not prove to be adverse to Sitka spruce or mountain hemlock during the Wisconsin maximum in a refugium on the Kenai Peninsula. If food were not limiting, man's survival as well may have been assured. If he had been able to establish himself as part of the biota, his remains should date at least as old as 10,000 B. P.

Anthropologists, in view of the complex obstacles that have been cited, face a difficult task indeed in disinterring man's remains on the coast as well as in the interior and in discovering the routes he traveled. But to search for his remains outside likely refugia and with no regard for late-Pleistocene changes in the stands of sea and land seems certain to preclude any possiblity of determining a maximum antiquity for early man in northwestern North America.

APPENDICES

A. SAMPLING SITES: LOCATION AND DESCRIPTION

The general distribution of sites is shown in Figure 1, and more specific locations appear by name and number in Figures 2 to 5. Tables 8 to 10 contain lists of plants constituting the surface cover at each site. These tables include only the more obvious plants and do not pretend to be complete. The following descriptive sketches are numbered and named to correspond with Figures 2 to 5. They begin at Kodiak Island and progress northeastward and thence generally southeastward along the coast to northern California. The positions shown by latitude and longitude are approximate.

ALASKA

Kodiak Island and Vicinity

1. Karluk (57°34′N, 154°28′W) is a small slope-type muskeg occupying a bench just east of the village on the south side of the lagoon at the Karluk River mouth. It is the only site in this study located beyond the edge of the forest. Alder and willow thickets occur nearby in the heath-sedge tundra. Elevation ca 100 ft.

2. Cape Chiniak (57°37′N, 152°11′W) is a small, gently sloping muskeg on the east side of the Sequel Point road, 0.8 mi southeast of the fork formed by the road leading to Cape Chiniak. Sitka spruce, several feet in height, is growing on its surface and a first-generation spruce forest borders the site. Elevation ca 75 ft.

3. Cape Greville 1 (57°35′N, 152°11′W) is 3.7 mi from the aforementioned fork and is on the south side of the Sequel Point road (Plate XVIII). It is of similar type and aspect to the Cape Chiniak site. Elevation ca 100 ft.

4. Cape Greville 2 (57°35′N, 152°11′W) is 4 mi from the fork and on the northwest side of the road. The muskeg is somewhat domed because of the growth of sphagnum moss in the central part of a sedge area. Growing on the surface are Sitka spruce trees, a few feet high. Elevation ca 75 ft.

5. Kodiak 1 (57°46′N, 152°30′W) is at the Ft. Greeley military post, 4 mi along the main road southwest from Kodiak. It borders the eastern end of a small lake on the northwest side of the road. Elevation ca 150 ft.

6. Kodiak 2 (57°49′N, 152°22′W) is an elongated slope muskeg that has been drained for use as a pasture. It is 3 mi northeast of Kodiak, where the road forks, and continues to Monashka Bay and to the west side of Mill Bay. Forest in the vicinity appears to be the oldest observed on the island. Elevation ca 130 ft.

7. Kodiak 3 (57°49′N, 152°21′W), a curved elongated muskeg sloping toward either end, is ca 1 mi northeast of Kodiak 2, and is surrounded by relatively old forest. Elevation ca 100 ft.

8. Afognak (58°01′N, 152°46′W) occurs just northwest of the village. The site is a southwest-sloping muskeg, one of many at varying stages of development occupying an extensive tract between the village and Litnik Mountain. Sitka spruce, up to ca 4 ft in height, grows on the muskeg. Elevation ca 20 ft.

Kenai Peninsula and Vicinity

9. Homer 1 (59°40′N, 151°39′W), a circular peat-filled depression, is ca 4.5 mi east of Homer on the north side of the Sterling Highway and south of Diamond Creek. Forest nearby is largely Sitka spruce. Elevation ca 650 ft.

10. Homer 2 (59°39′N, 151°28′W) is a flat muskeg associated with what is locally called Nelson Lake. The site is just southeast of Beluga Lake and ca 1 mi east of Homer Airport. Sitka and black spruce grow in this vicinity. Elevation ca 75 ft.

11. Homer 3 (59°41′N, 151°28′W) is an oval muskeg located on the road to Lookout Mountain, ca 6 mi northeast of Homer and ca 1.5 south of the mountain. Groves of spruces

Table 8. Plant assemblages for sites where peat sections were taken between Kodiak Island and the mouth of Copper River, Alaska. Asterisks indicate no bryophytes were collected; plants constituting noteworthy cover are marked by circles.

	Karluk	Cape Chiniak	Cape Greville 1	Cape Greville 2	Kodiak 1	Kodiak 2*	Kodiak 3	Afognak	Windy Bay	Port Chatham	Homer 1	Homer 2	Homer 3	Seward*	Moose Pass	Saxton	Girdwood	Hinchinbrook I.	Montague I.	Perry I.	Cordova*	Alaganik 1	Alaganik 2
BRYOPHYTES																							
Antitrichia curtipendula (Hedw.) Brid.								+															
Aulacomnium palustre (Web. & Mohr) Schwaegr.		+	+	+	+		+	+	+		+								+	+			
Dicranum groenlandicum Brid.			+					+															
Drepanocladus aduncus (Hedw.) Warnst.								+															
D. uncinatus (Hedw.) Warnst.			+				+																
Hylocomium splendens (Hedw.) BSG.	+								+														
Oncophorus wahlenbergii Brid.			+																				
Pleurozium schreberi (BSG) Mitt.					+		+	+										+	+				
Pohlia nutans (Hedw.) Lindb.		+									+												
Polytrichum commune Hedw.		⊕	+																				
P. gracile Smith			+	+			⊕																
P. juniperinum var. *alpestre* (Hoppe) BSG.		+			+			+										+					
Ptilidium ciliare (L.) Nees			+																				
Rhacomitrium lanuginosum (Hedw.) Brid.									+														
Rhytidiadelphus loreus (Hedw.) Warnst.		+						⊕											+				
Sphagnum balticum Russ.									+		+												
S. fimbriatum Wils.			+																				
S. fuscum (Schimp.) Klinggr.		+			+			+					+					+					
S. girgensohnii Russ.	+																						
S. lindbergii Schimp.																			+				
S. lenense H. Lindb.																	⊕						
S. magellanicum Brid.				+																			
S. palustre L.																				⊕			
S. papillosum Lindb.									+													+	
S. recurvum P-B.										⊕													
S. tenellum Pers.																			+				
S. teres (Schimp.) Aongstr.				+	⊕																		
S. warnstorfianum du Rietz																				+		+	
PTERIDOPHYTES																							
Equisetum arvense		+		+	+			+															
Lycopodium obscurum var. *dendroideum*																				+			
L. selago							+																

SPERMATOPHYTES

GYMNOSPERMS

Picea mariana														⊕	+							
P. sitchensis		⊕	⊕	⊕	+	+	⊕	+	+		+											

ANGIOSPERMS

Monocotyledons

Triglochin maritimum																	+					
Calamagrostis canadensis ssp. *langsdorffii*	+	⊕	⊕	⊕	⊕	+	+															+
Eriophorum angustifolium ssp. *scabriusculum*		+	+	+	+	+		⊕	+	+	+	+	+		+	⊕	+	+	⊕		+	+
E. medium		+																				
E. russeolum var. *leucothrix*	+				+																	
E. scheuchzeri			+	+		+				+												
Scirpus caespitosus ssp. *austriacus*									+		+	+	+	+	+	+	+	⊕	+	⊕	⊕	
Carex pauciflora								+		+		+	+	+	⊕	⊕		⊕	⊕	⊕	⊕	
C. tenuiflora						+																
C. hindsii	+	+				⊕	⊕															
C. aquatilis						+																
C. sitchensis								⊕	⊕				+									
C. limosa	+	+	+	+	+	⊕	⊕	⊕	⊕	+	+	+				+	⊕	⊕	+	+		
C. livida																					+	
Lysichitum americanum																	+					
Juncus drummondii						+																
Tofieldia occidentalis																	+	+		+		
Iris setosa								+														
Platanthera dilatata																			+			

Dicotyledons

Salix barclayi							+															
S. arbutifolia	+						+															
Myrica gale var. *tomentosa*		+		+	+						+										+	+
Betula nana ssp. *exilis*	+				+	+		+	+	⊕	+	⊕	+	+	+	+						
Nuphar polysepalum								+	+		+								+			
Coptis trifolia									+						+		+					
Drosera anglica													+		+							
D. rotundifolia		⊕	+	+	+	+	+	+	+		+		+	+		+	+	+	+	+	+	
Spiraea beauverdiana					+																	
Rubus chamaemorus	+				⊕	+	+	+	+	+	⊕	+	+	+		+					+	
R. pedatus									+													
R. stellatus					+							+										
Potentilla palustris						+		+														

TABLE 8 (*Continued*)

ANGIOSPERMS Dicotyledons (*Continued*)	Karluk	Cape Chiniak	Cape Greville 1	Cape Greville 2	Kodiak 1	Kodiak 2*	Kodiak 3	Afognak	Windy Bay	Port Chatham	Homer 1	Homer 2	Homer 3	Seward*	Moose Pass	Saxton	Girdwood	Hinchinbrook I.	Montague I.	Perry I.	Cordova*	Alaganik 1	Alaganik 2
Geum calthifolium																		+	+	+	+	+	+
Sanguisorba sitchensis													+										
Lupinus nootkatensis	+																						
Empetrum nigrum	⊕			+	+		+	+	⊕	⊕	⊕	⊕	⊕	⊕	+	+	+	⊕	+	+	⊕		
Viola langsdorffii							+																
Cornus canadensis																		+	+	+	+	+	+
C. suecica	+																						
Moneses uniflora		+			+			+															
Ledum palustre ssp. *decumbens*	+				+		+	+	+		+	⊕		+	+		+						
Andromeda polifolia		+			+		+	+	+	+	+	+	+	+	+	+	+	+	+	+	+	+	
Arctostaphylos uva-ursi		+																					
Oxycoccus microcarpus							+		+	+	+	+	+	+	+	+	+	+	+	+	+	+	
Vaccinium ovalifolium		+																					
V. uliginosum	+			+			+	+	+	+	+	+	+	⊕	+	+	+	+	+	+	+		
V. vitis-idaea ssp. *minus*	+	+			+		+	+	+		+	+		+									
Trientalis europaea ssp. *arctica*	+				+		+	+	+	+			+			+			+	+	+		+
Gentiana douglasiana																					+		
Fauria crista-galli																		+	+	+	+		
Menyanthes trifoliata									+			+		+					+	+			
Polemonium acutiflorum													+										
Pedicularis labradorica									+		+	+	⊕	+	+	+	+	+	+			+	
P. parviflora																			+	+	+		
Pinguicula villosa									+													+	
P. vulgaris									+										+	+			
Erigeron peregrinus																			+	+			
Apargidium boreale																			+				

	Upper Katalla	Lower Katalla	Martin Lake*	Bering Lake	Munday Creek	Grand Plateau Glacier	Upper NW Lituya	Lower NW Lituya	SE Lituya	Icy Point*	Upper Montana Creek*	Lower Montana Creek*	Lemon Creek*	Whitestone Harbor	Gull Cove	Mite Cove	Suloia Lake	Port Krestof	Hasselborg Lake*	Hobart Bay	Hamilton Bay	Threemile Arm	Salmon Bay	Sarkar Lake	Hollis	Kendrick Bay	SE Gokachin Lakes
BRYOPHYTES																											
Aulacomnium palustre (Web. & Mohr) Schwaegr.																								+			
Calliergon giganteum (Schimp.) Kindb.																					+						
Campylium stellatum (Hedw.) Lange & Jens.							+																				
Dicranum groenlandicum Brid.																						+	+		+		
D. majus Smith	⊕																+										
Drepanocladus aduncus (Hedw.) Warnst.																		+									
D. bergeri Bland.																									+		
Mylia anomala (Hook.) S.F. Gray																								+			
Pleurozium schreberi (BSG) Mitt.	+													+						+			+	⊕			
Polytrichum juniperinum var. *alpestre* (Hoppe) BSG.																									+		
Rhacomitrium lanuginosum (Hedw.) Brid.							+	⊕						+								+	+				
Rhytidiadelphus loreus (Hedw.) Warnst.							+																			+	
Sphagnum fuscum (Schimp.) Klingrr.								+							⊕		+			⊕					+		
S. imbricatum Hornsch.																							+				
S. magellanicum Brid.						+																				+	+
S. palustre L.																+											
S. papillosum Lindb.		+		⊕	⊕			+	+						+			+				⊕			+		
S. recurvum P-B.																								+			
S. riparium Aongstr.	+																										
S. tenellum Pers.														⊕													
S. warnstorfianum du Rietz	+			+	+		+	+	+					+	+	+				+				+			+
Scorpidium scorpioides (Hedw.) Limpr.							+											+									
Tomenthypnum nitens (Hedw.) Loeske																					+						
PTERIDOPHYTES																											
Pteridium aquilinum ssp. *lanuginosum*																									+		
Equisetum variegatum ssp. *alaskanum*							+																				
Lycopodium annotinum							+	+				+	+										+		+		

Table 9 (*Continued*)

	Upper Katalla	Lower Katalla	Martin Lake*	Bering Lake	Munday Creek	Grand Plateau Glacier	Upper NW Lituya	Lower NW Lituya	SE Lituya	Icy Point*	Upper Montana Creek*	Lower Montana Creek*	Lemon Creek*	Whitestone Harbor	Gull Cove	Mite Cove	Suloia Lake	Port Krestof	Hasselborg Lake*	Hobart Bay	Hamilton Bay	Threemile Arm	Salmon Bay	Sarkar Lake	Hollis	Kendrick Bay	SE Gokachin Lakes
PTERIDOPHYTES (*Continued*)																											
L. selago																+	+										
Selaginella selaginoides								+																			
SPERMATOPHYTES																											
Gymnosperms																											
Pinus contorta						⊕	⊕	⊕	⊕	+		+	+	⊕	⊕		+	⊕				⊕	⊕		+		
Picea sitchensis										+		+	+														
Tsuga heterophylla										+		+	+							+					+		+
T. mertensiana										+		+	+														+
Thuja plicata																									+	+	
Chamaecyparis nootkatensis							+	+		+							+					+					+
Juniperus communis var. *montana*																		+					+				
Angiosperms																											
Monocotyledons																											
Sparganium angustifolium									+										+								
Potamogeton alpinus ssp. *tenuifolius*																			+								
Triglochin maritimum							+																				
T. palustris							+																				
Eriophorum angustifolium ssp. *scabriusculum*	+	+	+	+	+		+	+	+			+	+	+	+	+	+	+		+		+	+		+	+	+
E. russeolum						+							+											⊕			
Scirpus caespitosus ssp. *austriacus*		+	+	⊕	+		+	⊕	⊕	⊕	⊕	⊕	⊕	⊕	⊕	⊕	⊕	⊕				⊕	+		⊕	+	+
Rynchospora alba							+															⊕	+	+			
Carex pauciflora		+			+	+	+	+		+	+	+	+			+		+					+				+
C. praticola																+											
C. sitchensis	⊕	+		⊕	+	⊕	+						+		+						⊕		+	+		⊕	⊕
C. limosa				+		+	+							+		+	+					+	+	+			
C. livida		+					+							+									+			+	
C. flava							+																				
Lysichitum americanum							+			+	+	+	+		+	+											
Juncus alpinus ssp. *nodulosus*							+		+																		
J. oreganus																			+								

Maianthemum dilatatum							+			+	+		+														
Iris setosa						+																					
Platanthera dilatata					+	+	+				+				+		+				+						
Dicotyledons																											
Myrica gale var. *tomentosa*	+		+			⊕		⊕																		⊕	
Geocaulon lividum												+	+														
Polygonum bistorta ssp. *plumosum*											+	+															
Nuphar polysepalum				+	+										+			+	+	+		+					
Nymphaea tetragona Georgi ssp. *leibergi* (Morong) Pors.																			+								
Caltha palustris ssp. *asarifolia*																					⊕						
Coptis trifolia	+	+	+				+	+	+			+		+	+	+	+	+			+		+				+
Thalictrum alpinum							+																				
Drosera anglica							+								+		+										
D. rotundifolia		+	+	+		+	+	+	+	+	+	+	+	+	+	+	+	+		+		+	+	+	+	+	+
Parnassia fimbriata							+																				
Rubus chamaemorus											+	+	+	+						⊕		+	+	+	+		+
R. pedatus													+														
R. stellatus						+							+														
Geum calthifolium	+	+	+	+	+		+	+																			
Sanguisorba menziesii							+		+						+	+	+	+				+	+		+	+	+
S. sitchensis						+																					
Empetrum nigrum			+	+	+		+	+	+	+	⊕	+	+	⊕	⊕	+	+	+		⊕		+	⊕		⊕		+
Cornus canadensis	+			+	+		+		+	+	+	+	+	+		+	+	+				+	+		+		+
Ledum palustre ssp. *groenlandicum*						+		+	+		+	+	+	+	+		+	+		+		+	+	+	+		+
Kalmia polifolia							+	+	+			+	+		+	+	+			+		+	+	+	+		+
Andromeda polifolia		+	+	+			+				+	+	+	+		+	+	+		+		+	+		+	+	+
Oxycoccus microcarpus	+	+	+	+	+	+	+	+	+	+	+	+	+	+	+	+	+	+		+	+	+	+	+	+	+	+
Vaccinium uliginosum			+				+		+		+	+	+	+	⊕	+	+	+		+		+	+		+		+
V. vitis-idaea ssp. *minus*							+		+	+		+	+				+			+							
Trientalis europaea ssp. *arctica*		+		+	+		+	+	+	+			+		+	+						+			+		+
Gentiana douglasiana					+		+	+	+	+			+	+	+	+	+	+					+		+		+
Swertia perennis						+	+																				
Fauria crista-galli	⊕	+	⊕	+	+		+		+	+	+	+	+	+	+	+	+	+				+					
Menyanthes trifoliata		+		+	+	⊕	+	+	+						+					+	+					+	
Polemonium acutiflorum																					+						
Pedicularis parviflora		+			+	+	+		+							+											
Pinguicula vulgaris					+												+										
Utricularia intermedia							+																				
Erigeron peregrinus					+		+	+	+						+	+		+								+	
Apargidium boreale							+	+	+	+								+					+				

Table 10. Plant assemblages for sites where peat sections were taken in British Columbia, Washington, Oregon, and California. Asterisks indicate no bryophytes were collected; plants constituting noteworthy cover are marked by circles.

	Prince Rupert, B. C.*	Rainbow Lake, B. C.*	Summit, B. C.*	Masset, B. C.*	Pitt Island, B. C.	Susan Island, B. C.	Fitzhugh Sound, B. C.	Cape Caution, B. C.	Upper Hope Island, B. C.	Lower Hope Island, B. C.	Port Hardy, B. C.*	Harbledown Island, B. C.	Menzies Bay, B. C.	Little Qualicum Falls, B. C.	Malahat, B. C.	Pangborn Lake, Wash.	Whidbey Island, Wash.	Ozette Lake, Wash.	Wessler, Wash.	Humptulips, Wash.	Seaview, Wash.	Warrenton, Ore.	Devils Lake, Ore.	Tahkenitch Lake, Ore.	Garrison Lake, Ore.	Lake Earl, Calif.	Capetown, Calif.	Fort Bragg, Calif.
BRYOPHYTES																												
Aulacomnium palustre (Web. & Mohr) Schwaegr.																	+			+								
Dicranum majus Smith																		+			+							
Rhacomitrium lanuginosum (Hedw.) Brid.						+			+																			
Sphagnum capillaceum (Weiss) Schrank.																	⊕											
S. fuscum (Schimp.) Klinggr.										⊕																		
S. imbricatum Hornsch.						+																						
S. mendocinum Sull. & Lesq.												+																
S. palustre L.																					+		⊕					+
S. papillosum Lindb.					+		+		+	+								+	⊕	+								
S. recurvum P-B.																		+			+							
S. subsecundum Nees					+									+		+												
S. warnstorfianum du Rietz					+	+	⊕		+	+											⊕		+					
PTERIDOPHYTES																												
Cystopteris fragilis																+												
Blechnum spicant							+					+						+			+		+					+
Pteridium aquilinum ssp. *lanuginosum*																	+	+			⊕							
Lycopodium annotinum						+																						
L. clavatum							+											+										
L. obscurum var. *dendroideum*							+																					

SPERMATOPHYTES																												
GYMNOSPERMS																												
Pinus contorta	+	+	+	+	+	+	+		⊕	⊕	⊕	+					+				⊕		⊕					
P. bolanderi Parl.																												⊕
P. muricata Don																												+
Picea sitchensis																		+	+				+					
Tsuga heterophylla	+			+														+	+		+		+					
T. mertensiana					+	+																						
Thuja plicata	+			+	+	+												+	+		+		⊕					
Cupressus pygmaea (Lemm.) Sarg.																												⊕
Chamaecyparis nootkatensis	+	+	+	+	⊕	+			⊕																			
Juniperus communis var. *montana*	+	+		+	+	+	+			⊕	+																	
ANGIOSPERMS																												
Monocotyledons																												
Typha latifolia													+	+		+	+					+				⊕	+	
Sparganium eurycarpum Engelm.													⊕														+	
Potamogeton amplifolius Tuckerm.																											+	
Scheuchzeria palustris ssp. *americana*						+																						
Alisma plantago-aquatica L.																+												
Phragmites communis Trin.																+												
Eriophorum angustifolium ssp. *scabriusculum*	+	⊕	⊕	+	+		+	+	+		+																	
Eleocharis palustris (L.) R.&S.														+										+			+	
Scirpus caespitosus ssp. *austriacus*	⊕	+	+	+	⊕	⊕	+		⊕	+	+																	
S. subterminalis Torr.															+													
S. validus															+	⊕								⊕	⊕	⊕		
Dulichium arundinaceum (L.) Britton								+					⊕	⊕		+												
Rynchospora alba		⊕	⊕		+	⊕	+	+	+	⊕	+		+			+			+									
Carex arcta Boott.																			+									
C. lasiocarpa														⊕	+													
C. leptalea												⊕																
C. limosa				⊕	+		+	+		+								+										
C. livida					+	+	+	+							+			+										
C. obnupta Bailey																	+	⊕							+	+		+
C. pauciflora		+	+		+	+																						
C. phyllomanica							+																					
C. physocarpa								+																				
C. retrorsa Schw.																+												
C. rostrata						+									+													

Table 10 (*Continued*)

	Prince Rupert, B. C.*	Rainbow Lake, B. C.*	Summit, B. C.*	Masset, B. C.*	Pitt Island, B. C.	Susan Island, B. C.	Fitzhugh Sound, B. C.	Cape Caution, B. C.	Upper Hope Island, B. C.	Lower Hope Island, B. C.	Port Hardy, B. C.*	Harbledown Island, B. C.	Menzies Bay, B. C.	Little Qualicum Falls, B. C.	Malahat, B. C.	Pangborn Lake, Wash.	Whidbey Island, Wash.	Ozette Lake, Wash.	Wessler, Wash.	Humptulips, Wash.	Seaview, Wash.	Warrenton, Ore.	Devils Lake, Ore.	Tahkenitch Lake, Ore.	Garrison Lake, Ore.	Lake Earl, Calif.	Capetown, Calif.	Fort Bragg, Calif.
Angiosperms																												
Monocotyledons (*Continued*)																												
C. sitchensis					+	+						+		+					+			+						
C. vesicaria L.										+				+														
C. viridula Michx.													+			+												
Lysichitum americanum					+	+				+		+						+	+		+		+					
Juncus alpinus ssp. *nodulosus*					+																							
J. covillei Piper								+								+												
J. effusus																+	+											
J. nodosus							+																					
Tofieldia occidentalis	+	+	+	+	+	+	+				+																	
Maianthemum dilatatum				+			+					+									+		+					
Dicotyledons																												
Myrica gale var. *tomentosa*					⊕	⊕	+	+		⊕	+				⊕	+		+		+								
M. californica Cham. & Sch.																					+		⊕					+
Betula glandulosa Michx.																+												
Brasenia schreberi																									+			
Nuphar polysepalum				+									+		+	+	+					+		⊕			⊕	
Coptis asplenifolia							+																					
C. trifolia	+	+	+			+	+		+																			
Drosera anglica		+	+			+	+				+																	
D. rotundifolia	+	+	+	+	+	+	+	+	+	+	+	+	+			+	+	+	+		+							+
Spiraea douglasii														⊕	⊕	+	+	+		+		+	+					
Rubus chamaemorus	+	+	+	+			+																					
Potentilla palustris																+						+			+	+		
Geum calthifolium					+																							
Sanguisorba menziesii	+	+	+		+	+	+	+	+	+	+																	
S. microcephala Presl																		+	+	⊕								

Empetrum nigrum	+	+	+	⊕	+	+	+		+	⊕	+																	
Rhamnus purshiana DC.																		+			+							
Hypericum scouleri Hook.															⊕													
H. anagalloides Cham. & Sch.																		+										
Epilobium angustifolium																	+											
Hippuris vulgaris																							+			+		
Cornus canadensis	+	+	+	+	+	+	+		+	+	+						+	+			+							
Ledum palustre ssp. *groenlandicum*	+	+	+	+	+	+	+		+	⊕	+	+			⊕		⊕	⊕	⊕	+								
L. columbianum Piper																					+		⊕					+
Kalmia polifolia		+	+	+	+	+	+		+	+							+	+	⊕	⊕	+							
Andromeda polifolia	+	+	+	+	+	+	+		+	+	+																	
Gaultheria shallon		+	+	⊕	⊕	+			+								+	+			⊕		⊕					+
Oxycoccus microcarpus	+	+	+	+	+	+	+			+	+							+	+	+	+							
Vaccinium caespitosum		+	+	+																								
V. ovatum Pursh																		+					+					
V. parvifolium																		+										
V. uliginosum		+	+		+																							
V. vitis-idaea ssp. *minus*				+																								
Trientalis europaea ssp. *arctica*	+	+	+		+	+			+	+	+	+			+			+	+		+							
Gentiana douglasiana		+	+	+	+		+		+									+										
G. sceptrum Griseb.								+							+			+	+	+						+		
Fauria crista-galli		+	+		+	+																						
Menyanthes trifoliata		+	+		+	+				+	+																+	
Scutellaria galericulata																	+											
Lycopus uniflorus																+	+											
Mentha arvensis																	+											
Mimulus guttatus																	+											
Veronica americana																+												
Pinguicula vulgaris										+	+																	
Galium boreale																+												
Linnaea borealis ssp. *longiflora*				+			+			+	+							+			+							
Apargidium boreale										+																		

(Sitka spruce, white spruce, and intermediates such as *Picea lutzii* Little) are interspersed in the surrounding area with grass and shrubby alder. Elevation ca 1300 ft.

12. Seward (60°17′N, 149°20′W), a small peat-filled depression, lies 14 mi north of the town of Seward and on the west side of Snow River. Sitka spruce and mountain hemlock compose the surrounding forest. Elevation ca 600 ft.

13. Windy Bay (59°14′N, 151°34′W) is a low-angle slope muskeg situated on the point of land between the upper arms of Windy Bay. This locality and the following one are ca 30 mi south of Homer. Sitka spruce surrounds the site. Elevation ca 50 ft.

14. Port Chatham (59°13′N, 151°41′W) is a large slope muskeg at the head of the northeastern arm of Port Chatham. The section was removed from the southern side of the valley that lies between Port Chatham and Windy Bay. This site is ca 5 mi west of the previous one. Local forest is Sitka spruce. Elevation ca 50 ft.

15. Moose Pass (60°31′N, 149°26′W) is a flat muskeg at Milepost 33 on the Seward-Anchorage Highway, ca 1 mi west of the western arm of Upper Trail Lake. It occurs in the creek bottom on the north side of the road. Black spruce grows at the site. Elevation ca 700 ft.

16. Saxton (60°41′N, 149°28′W) is a small slope muskeg near Milepost 50 on the west side of the Seward-Anchorage Highway, south of Saxton. Elevation ca 1200 ft.

17. Girdwood (60°58′N, 149°08′W) is not actually on Kenai Peninsula but because of its proximity is included in this group of sites. It is a small slope muskeg on the west side of the dirt road that travels up Glacier Creek valley, northeast of the town of Girdwood and ca one-eighth mi below the point where the road crosses California Creek. Forest nearby is largely Sitka spruce and mountain hemlock. Elevation ca 150 ft.

Prince William Sound and Vicinity

18. Perry Island (60°41′N, 147°54′W), in the northwestern part of Prince William Sound, is a slope muskeg associated with a small water-filled depression. It is just east of the larger of the two bays on the southern shore of the island. Elevation ca 50 ft.

19. Montague Island (60°14′N, 147°15′W) is an extensive slope muskeg bordering Port Chalmers and situated on the small peninsula southwest of tiny Wilby Island. Elevation ca 50 ft.

20. Hinchinbrook Island (60°22′N, 146°35′W) is a gently sloping muskeg at the head of the southern arm of Constantine Harbor on the island's west side. Forest on the island is composed mainly of Sitka spruce and mountain hemlock. Elevation ca 20 ft.

21. Cordova (60°34′N, 145°40′W) occurs as a slope muskeg at Mile 4.5 on the west side of Seven Mile Road along Eyak Lake, east of the village of Cordova. Sitka spruce and mountain hemlock comprise the bordering forest. Elevation ca 50 ft.

22. Alaganik 1 (60°27′N, 145°17′W) is near the previous site, at Mile 19 from Cordova. Construction of the road has exposed the section adjacent to upper Alaganik Slough. Elevation ca 20 ft.

23. Alaganik 2 (60°27′N, 145°15′W) is located in an extensive area of slope muskeg interspersed with small pools and colonies, strips, and patches of Sitka spruce-mountain hemlock forest. The site is ca 9 mi beyond Cordova Airport along the north side of the road leading to the Copper River. Elevation ca 100 ft.

Katalla and Vicinity

24. Upper Katalla (60°12′N, 144°32′W) is a slope muskeg ca 0.5 mi north of Katalla. Forest in the vicinity is largely of western hemlock and Sitka spruce. Elevation ca 180 ft.

25. Lower Katalla (60°12′N, 144°32′W) occurs on what is interpreted to be a former strand line. It is a flat muskeg directly below the previous site. Elevation ca 40 ft.

26. Martin Lake (60°21′N, 144°34′W) is a slope muskeg situated on a peninsula on the west side of the lake ca 11 mi north of Katalla. This locality is associated with a parkland where mountain hemlock and Sitka spruce are the principal trees. Elevation ca 100 ft.

27. Bering Lake (60°19′N, 144°20′W), a small slope muskeg, is in dense forest of mountain and western hemlocks and Sitka spruce, ca 0.5 mi from the northwestern shore of the lake and ca 10 northeast of Katalla. Elevation ca 180 ft.

Icy Cape

28. Munday Creek (60°01′N, 141°57′W) is an east-west elongated slope muskeg located just west of Munday Creek and ca 1 mi from the beach between Icy Cape and Cape Yakataga. The muskeg rests on what is considered to be a marine terrace. Ancient forest, largely of western hemlock, occupies the area adjacent to the muskeg. Elevation ca 230 ft.

Cape Fairweather to Icy Point

29. Upper Northwest Lituya Bay (58°43′N, 137°45′W), resting on the upper of a pair of marine terraces, is a slope muskeg ca 4 mi southeast of Fairweather Glacier, ca 7.5 northwest of Lituya Bay, and ca 1.5 from the beach. Lodgepole pine exhibiting poor growth is scattered on the surface while ancient forest upslope from the site consists of western hemlock and Alaska yellow cedar with some Sitka spruce. Elevation ca 300 ft.

30. Lower Northwest Lituya Bay (58°43′N, 137°45′W) is directly below the preceding site on the lower terrace and ca 0.25 mi distant. Forest between the sites consists mostly of western hemlock. Elevation ca 110 ft.

31. Grand Plateau Glacier (58°57′N, 138°00′W) is ca 5 mi northwest of the mouth of Sea Otter Creek and ca 0.5 from the beach. It is a flat muskeg on which lodgepole pine is ca 35 ft in height. The muskeg is separated from the beach by a pure stand of Sitka spruce with a dense understory of devils club. Elevation ca 30 ft.

32. Southeast Lituya Bay (58°36′N, 137°34′W) lies ca 3 mi from the mouth of Lituya Bay, 1.5 from Steelhead Creek, and 0.25 from the ocean. This slope muskeg is the lowest in elevation in this vicinity. It is located on what appears to be the third marine terrace above the present ocean level. Scrubby lodgepole pine is growing on the surface, which is pocketed with many small pools. Elevation ca 100 ft.

33. Icy Point (58°26′N, 137°10′W) muskeg is directly behind the beach at a point 4 mi equidistant from Icy Point to the southeast and the margin of La Perouse Glacier to the northwest. It rests on the lowest marine terrace in the area. Pine and yellow cedar grow on the site. Elevation ca 20 ft.

Alexander Archipelago and Vicinity

34. Upper Montana Creek (58°27′N, 134°40′W) is an extensive slope muskeg situated ca 3 mi by trail from the end of Montana Creek Road, northwest of Juneau. It is on the divide between the drainage of Montana and Windfall Creeks. Elevation ca 750 ft.

35. Lower Montana Creek (58°25′N, 134°37′W) is located on Montana Creek Road ca 1.3 mi northwest of the Loop Road. The surface of the muskeg is domed, but pocketed in places, with small thickets of western and mountain hemlocks and pine. Elevation ca 150 ft.

36. Lemon Creek (58°22′N, 134°32′W) muskeg is domed. The section is from the south side of Glacier Highway at Milepost 7.5, northwest of Juneau. Pine, western and mountain hemlocks, and Sitka spruce grow on the surface. Elevation ca 15 ft.

37. Whitestone Harbor (58°04′N, 135°05′W) slope muskeg is on the north side of the harbor on northeastern Chichagof Island. The site is a short distance from the shore and is covered in part by an open scrub of lodgepole pine growing between numerous small pools (Plate XIII). Elevation ca 125 ft.

38. Gull Cove (58°12′N, 136°09′W) is a slope muskeg just beyond the southern shore of the cove on northwestern Chichagof Island. The surface is somewhat irregular with some small depressions that are filled with water during the very rainy months. Pine constitutes a partial arboreal cover. Elevation ca 50 ft.

39. Mite Cove (58°04′N, 136°27′W) is a slope muskeg that occupies the low part of a small cirque directly above the cove. This locality is on northeastern Yakobi Island, which is

separated from Chichagof Island by Lisianski Inlet. Scrubby trees of mountain hemlock and Alaska yellow cedar border the lower edge of the muskeg and are established on what appears to be a moraine. Elevation ca 150 ft.

40. Threemile Arm (56°36′N, 133°54′W), a slope muskeg, is on the peninsula along the southern shore of upper Threemile Arm on northeastern Kuiu Island. Some low pine contributes to the plant cover. Numerous small shallow pools are present on the surface. Nearby forest is composed of western hemlock and some yellow cedar; Sitka spruce is adjacent to the shore of the arm. Elevation ca 100 ft.

41. Suloia Lake (57°26′N, 135°42′W) is on southwestern Chichagof Island near Baranof and Kruzof Islands. A slope muskeg, it occurs behind the northeastern shore of the lake. Lodgepole is growing on the surface. Elevation ca 200 ft.

42. Port Krestof (57°09′N, 135°35′W), a slope muskeg located on eastern Kruzof Island, is 9 mi northeast of Mt. Edgecumbe volcano and 11 northwest of Sitka. Shallow pools occur on the surface. Low pine grows on the site, and the nearby forest consists of western hemlock with some Alaska yellow cedar. Elevation ca 100 ft.

43. Hasselborg Lake (57°39′N, 134°15′W) is a small bog situated several hundred feet from the southwestern corner of the lake on Admiralty Island, 16 mi northeast of Angoon. The section is from the southern end, which was determined to be the deepest point. A mat, consisting largely of sedge, surrounds open water. Western and mountain hemlocks are the important components of the regional forest. Elevation ca 300 ft.

44. Hobart Bay (57°26′N, 133°23′W) is a domed muskeg on the north shore of an unnamed and unmapped lake, located near the north side of the upper part of the bay, ca one-eighth mi from the shore. No pine occurs on the muskeg. In the nearby forest, western hemlock is predominant. Elevation ca 100 ft.

45. Salmon Bay (56°18′N, 133°09′W) is on a small island south of the bay and near the northeastern corner of Prince of Wales Island. A slope muskeg, it exhibits a surface broken by pools and occupied by lodgepole pine, 8–10 ft in height. Western red cedar is mixed with western hemlock in the bordering forest. Elevation ca 75 ft.

46. Hamilton Bay (56°54′N, 133°46′W) is a small bog ca 8 mi southeast of Kake on the northern shore of the bay on Kupreanof Island. Surface cover is nearly all sedge; western hemlock is the forest dominant. Elevation ca 75 ft.

47. Hollis (55°30′N, 132°43′W) is a domed muskeg on the south side of Maybeso Creek, ca 2.5 mi from the mouth and 2.5 northwest of Hollis on Prince of Wales Island. The site has been recently burned. Elevation ca 180 ft.

48. Sarkar Lake (55°57′N, 133°13′W) is a sphagnum-sedge bog adjacent to the mouth of the lake. The location is northwestern Prince of Wales Island, ca 1 mi southeast of the abandoned village of Deweyville. Elevation ca 5 ft.

49. Kendrick Bay (54°51′N, 132°07′W) is on southern Prince of Wales Island. It is from a peat deposit on the eastern shore of the southern member of two unnamed lakes, situated ca 1 mi east of the upper end of Short Arm on Kendrick Bay. Forest on the lake border is a mixture of western red and Alaska yellow cedars, mountain and western hemlocks, and some lodgepole pine. Elevation ca 300 ft.

50. Southeast Gokachin Lakes (55°23′N, 131°06′W) is a peat deposit at the southeastern corner of the southern lake of this pair. The site is ca 21 mi east of Ketchikan, between the upper ends of Thorne Arm and Princess Bay on southeastern Revillagigedo Island. Forest at this site consists of mountain and western hemlocks and Alaska yellow cedar with occasional Sitka spruce and lodgepole pine. Elevation ca 500 ft.

BRITISH COLUMBIA

Queen Charlotte Islands

51. Masset (54°00′N, 132°07′W) is a classic example of a domed muskeg. The site is on northern Graham Island, ca 1 mi southeast of Masset and ca 0.5 from Delkatla Inlet. Western hemlock and western red cedar are the principal forest components. Elevation ca 50 ft.

Prince Rupert and Vicinity

52. Summit (54°15′N, 130°02′W) is a slope muskeg ca 2.5 mi northeasterly along the road from the Rainbow Lake site. Elevation ca 550 ft.

53. Rainbow Lake (54°14′N, 130°05′W) is a slope muskeg on the south side of the Prince Rupert-Terrace road, ca 0.5 mi northwest of the lake and 11 southeast of Prince Rupert. At this and the preceding site, western hemlock and Alaska yellow cedar were observed growing nearby. Elevation ca 440 ft.

54. Prince Rupert (54°19′N, 130°18′W) is a domed muskeg on the northeastern outskirts of the port on northern Kaien Island. The area was lumbered and burned during settlement. Western hemlock and red and Alaska yellow cedars are important constituents of the forest. Elevation ca 135 ft.

Hecate Strait–Queen Charlotte Sound

55. Pitt Island (53°27′N, 129°28′W) is a small slope muskeg located near the southeastern end of the island on Grenville Channel, ca 70 mi southeast of Prince Rupert and ca 9 east of the village of Hartley Bay. The surface is partly covered with a thick low scrub of Alaska yellow cedar, and outcrops of the country rock appear at places. Nearby forest exhibits a high proportion of red and Alaska yellow cedars. Elevation ca 100 ft.

56. Susan Island (52°29′N, 128°17′W) is on the eastern side of the island bordering Mathieson Channel, 22 mi north of Bella Bella and 28 northwest of Ocean Falls. The area is a complex of muskeg and forest comprised of poor-growth trees of western red and Alaska yellow cedars, western hemlock, and some Sitka spruce. Elevation ca 50 ft.

57. Fitzhugh Sound (51°42′N, 127°52′W) occurs ca 12 mi directly south of the village of Namu and west of Elizabeth Lake. It is a slope muskeg in a forest clearing, a short distance from the shore of the sound. Forest components are the two cedars and western hemlock; western yew was observed near the site. Elevation ca 100 ft.

58. Cape Caution (51°13′N, 127°35′W) is just east of Leonora Lake, 13 mi north of Allison Harbour and 45 south of Namu. The site is a sedge bog in the hemlock-cedar forest. Elevation ca 250 ft.

Vancouver Island and Vicinity

59. Upper Hope Island (50°56′N, 127°55′W) is the upper of a pair of slope muskegs on the northern side of the island ca 0.5 mi east of Bull Harbour. This locality is ca 3 mi from the northern tip of Vancouver Island. Muskeg is intermixed with a low scrub of trees composed largely of Alaska yellow cedar and lodgepole pine. Country rock crops out at many places. Elevation ca 100 ft.

60. Lower Hope Island (50°56′N, 127°55′W) is ca 500 ft distant and downslope from the preceding site and is separated from the beach by a dense tangle of salal, deformed alder, and wind-stripped Sitka spruce. Elevation ca 15 ft.

61. Port Hardy (50°44′N, 127°25′W), a low-angle slope muskeg, is on the northwestern side of the airport, ca 3 mi southeast of the village and near the northern end of Vancouver Island. Lodgepole pine, mainly ca 6–10 ft in height, is established at the site. Elevation ca 20 ft.

62. Harbledown Island (50°35′N, 126°34′W) is an ovate-shaped bog, situated near the midnorthern side of the island ca 0.5 mi from the shore by logging road. It is 11 mi east of the village of Alert Bay and north of the northeastern coast of Vancouver Island. Much of the area has been logged, but the principal components of the forest, western red cedar, western hemlock, and amabilis fir, are still apparent. Elevation ca 250 ft.

63. Menzies Bay (50°10′N, 125°37′W) is an unnamed lake ca 2 mi west of Trout Lake and ca 6 west of the village of Menzies Bay on northeastern Vancouver Island. Large-scale logging operations and accompanying fires have destroyed the forest in this area and that west of Campbell River, as well as the general region northwest of Courtenay. Elevation ca 550 ft.

64. Malahat (48°34′N, 123°35′W) is a small bog located ca 1.5 mi northwest of Malahat

Station, which is on the Esquimalt and Nanaimo Railway, 14 mi northwest of Victoria, southern Vancouver Island. Hydrarch succession is still in progress. The nearby forest has been logged and burned. Douglas fir is dominant in relatively unaffected areas with some lodgepole and western white pines and Alaska yellow cedar. An abundance of madrono is growing on the local outcrops. Elevation ca 1350 ft.

65. Little Qualicum Falls (49°19′N, 124°33′W) is a small sedge bog just east of Little Qualicum Falls Park and ca 2 mi northeast of Cameron Lake, between Alberni and Parksville on southern Vancouver Island. Forest surrounds the site and is a mixture of Douglas fir, western hemlock, and western red and Alaska yellow cedars, and western white pine. Elevation ca 480 ft.

WASHINGTON

66. Pangborn Lake (48°59′N, 122°22′W) occupies a depression, generally oval in outline, ca 4 mi west of Sumas in northwestern Whatcom County, northwestern Washington. Much of the original area of the lake is now covered by a quaking mat of sedge and sweet gale and the open water is ringed with bulrushes. The section was taken toward the eastern end of the lake, after numerous test borings had been made. Most of the original vegetation in the region has been cleared for farming. Elevation ca 130 ft.

67. Whidbey Island (48°24′N, 122°38′W) is at the southern side of Cranberry Lake just south of Deception Pass on the northern end of the island, Island County, northwestern Washington. The site has been burned; both living and fire-killed lodgepole pine occur on the surface of the mat. Forest on the upland consists of Douglas fir, western hemlock, western red cedar, and Sitka spruce. Elevation ca 6 ft.

68. Wessler (48°15′N, 124°38′W) bog is 4.5 mi northeast of Ozette Lake locality, on a trunk road off the main Ozette-Sekiu road. Two bogs occur in proximity to each other and the section was taken from the one located several hundred feet north of the area that has been cultivated for growing cranberries beside the Wessler farmhouse. Such bogs are locally called "prairies." Elevation ca 70 ft.

69. Ozette Lake (48°07′N, 124°40′W) is a wooded bog on the west side of the lake, a short distance south of Ericson Bay. The deposit is 20 mi south of Cape Flattery in Clallam County on the Olympic Peninsula, northwestern Washington. A western red cedar-western hemlock forest, showing evidence of having been burned some time ago, is on the oceanward side. Some of these trees have invaded the site. Elevation ca 40 ft.

70. Humptulips (47°15′N, 123°56′W) bog is on U. S. Highway 101, 4.4 mi north of the village, in Grays Harbor County, western Washington. The red burnet (*Sanguisorba microcephala* Presl) is the principal ground cover. Elevation ca 200 ft.

71. Seaview (46°19′N, 124°03′W) bog is at the end of an abandoned dirt road that leads off the southern side of State Highway 12, ca 1.25 mi east of the town. This location is north of the mouth of the Columbia River in Pacific County in the southwestern corner of the state. Lodgepole pine, up to 20 ft tall, grows on the surface, which has been burned and also utilized as a source of sphagnum moss. The section was collected from a point that appeared to be undisturbed. Elevation ca 10 ft.

OREGON

72. Warrenton (46°09′N, 123°56′W) is a small elongated lake on the northern side of the Ft. Stevens road, 0.4 mi west of U. S. Highway 101. It is south of the mouth of the Columbia River, Clatsop County, northwestern Oregon. Elevation ca 15 ft.

73. Devils Lake (44°58′N, 124°00′W) is a wooded bog on the western shore of the lake, ca 1 mi northeast of the outlet and less than 1 mi east of the village of Oceanlake, Lincoln County, northwestern Oregon. Fire and logging have destroyed much of the original forest along this coast. Sitka spruce occupies the immediate ocean border whereas inland mixtures of Douglas fir, western red cedar, and western hemlock prevail. Some tracts, as that south of Siletz Bay, are covered by almost pure lodgepole pine and are extensive. Elevation ca 15 ft.

The lake level varies, however, on account of rainfall fluctuations. The lake is unaffected by tides, except near the outlet and only once in 4 to 5 yr when a very high tide is running accompanied by strong west wind.

74. Tahkenitch Lake (43°47'N, 124°07'W) is on the southeastern arm of the lake. The locality is north of the lower Umpqua River, 5.5 mi north of the town of Reedsport, and 3.5 east of the ocean, Douglas County, western Oregon. It is ca 2.5 mi from U.S. Highway 101 by logging road that travels up Fivemile Creek, southeast of the lake. Sampling was carried out in early September during a low stage of the surface level when parts of the bottom peat were exposed. Surrounding the site is low mountainous terrain that has been almost totally logged. Moving sand of the extensive dune area, west of the lake and north and south along the ocean, has invaded much of the remaining timber found on these borders. Elevation ca 5 ft.

75. Garrison Lake (42°06'N, 124°31'W) is a bog bordering the northwestern arm of the lake, 6 mi south of Cape Blanco, 1.5 northwest of Port Orford, and less than 0.5 from the ocean, Curry County, southwestern Oregon. Sitka spruce and lodgepole pine occur locally on the upland. Elevation ca 5 ft.

CALIFORNIA

76. Lake Earl (41°48'N, 124°12'W) is at the southwestern arm in a stand of bulrushes. The site is ca 2 mi from the ocean and several hundred feet northeast of the road that leads off U. S. Highway 101, ca 1.5 mi north of Crescent City, Del Norte County, northwestern California. Sitka spruce and some lodgepole grow nearby, although much of the land has been cleared and is used as a pasture. Elevation ca 5 ft.

77. Capetown (40°28'N, 124°22'W) is a small lake located on the farm of Mr. Donald P. Coombe, ca 0.5 mi south of the village and 2.5 northeast of Cape Mendocino, Humboldt County, northwestern California. The lake level has recently been raised artificially. The section was taken in the central part. The surrounding country is mostly treeless, covered by grass, forbs, shrubby plants, and groves of Sitka spruce, Douglas fir, redwood, and lowland white fir. Fire and grazing have altered the original plant cover. Elevation ca 550 ft.

78. Fort Bragg (39°25'N, 123°46'N) is a boggy site in the pygmy forest that prevails in coastal Mendocino County. This station is the southernmost studied and occurs 2.7 mi due east of the village of Noyo, 1.2 due south of the Noyo River, and ca 2 southeast of Fort Bragg. Redwood, western hemlock, Douglas fir, and lowland white fir are the conspicuous members of the surrounding nondwarfed forest. Elevation ca 320 ft.

B. REGIONAL PHYSIOGRAPHY

ALASKA

The treatment used in subdividing the physiographic units of Pacific coastal Alaska follows that recently presented by the U. S. Geological Survey (Williams 1958). The major unit is the Pacific Mountain System, which constitutes the western border of the Americas. The pertinent provinces are the Chugach-Kenai Mountains, the Susitna-Cook Inlet Lowland, the St. Elias Mountains, and Southeastern Alaska (Fig. 49). This latter province has been subdivided using the scheme of Bostock (1948) and boundaries indicated by Buddington and Chapin (1929).

These provinces border 1100 mi of the Pacific. The coast for ca 800 mi, varying in width between 20 and 110 from Kodiak Island to Cross Sound, is part of the Gulf of Alaska area (Miller 1958a); the stretch westward from Icy Bay in this area is included in the Chugach-Kenai Mountains Province whereas that southeastward is in the St. Elias Mountains Province. Approximately 300 mi of the Southeastern Alaska Province, between Cross Sound and Dixon Entrance, front on the ocean.

Chugach-Kenai Mountains Province

Kodiak-Afognak Archipelago

Southwest of the Kenai Peninsula is a string of islands, the Barren Islands, Shuyak, Afognak, Raspberry, Kodiak, and the Trinity Islands, running northeast to southwest in that order, forming the Kodiak-Afognak archipelago (Fig. 2). Several other large islands and many small ones are a part of this group. Kodiak is the dominant island in size and Afognak is next; both are separated from the Alaska Peninsula by Shelikof Strait, which at its narrowest section is 23 mi wide.

Kodiak Island is roughly rectangular in outline, measuring 100 mi long and 60 wide. Its coast line is so strongly irregular in places that in one locality the heads of fiords penetrating from the north and south are less than 8 mi distant. The Kodiak Mountains follow the trend of the island and are topographically and geologically a continuation of the Kenai Mountains (Capps 1937). They reveal a glaciated surface with ridges and summits at ca 4000- to 5000-ft elevation. Ice-free cirques, some observed at elevations as low as 500 to 1000 ft, and U-shaped valleys at 4000 ft attest to intensive glaciation. Capps (1937) reports a small, solitary, unnamed glacier, ca 0.5 mi long and at 4000 ft, on a north valley slope at the Ugak Bay head. Some of the ice-eroded valleys in the western part of the island are occupied by long, narrow lakes. Karluk Lake, the largest, is almost 13 mi in length and 1.9 in maximum width.

Afognak Island also exhibits a generally rectangular form and a topography similar to Kodiak Island. It is ca 40 mi long by 21 to 35 wide, being narrowest in proximity to Kodiak, from which it is separated by straits that are as narrow as 4 mi. Cloud Peak (2332 ft in elevation) is the highest point on Afognak. Shuyak Island, facing the north end of Afognak, is less than a mile away across Shuyak Strait, which is almost 60 ft deep.

It is obvious that a 100-ft transgression of sea level would greatly multiply the number of islands while a 100-ft lowering of sea level would cause considerable extension of the land mass. In fact, glacial deepening of the valleys followed by incursion of marine waters with rise of sea level is responsible for the dissection evident in the present configuration of the archipelago (Capps 1937).

The islands are formed predominantly of Mesozoic or older rock with some Tertiary marine sandstone and nonmarine sandstone and shale. Slate, graywacke, and conglomerate are in abundance, along with greenstone, tuff, chert, and other rock, and the whole has been folded, faulted, and intruded. Several uplifts interspersed with deposition through the Late Tertiary or Pleistocene, and degradation of the mass by glaciation and stream cutting are the important events in their physiographic history (Capps 1937).

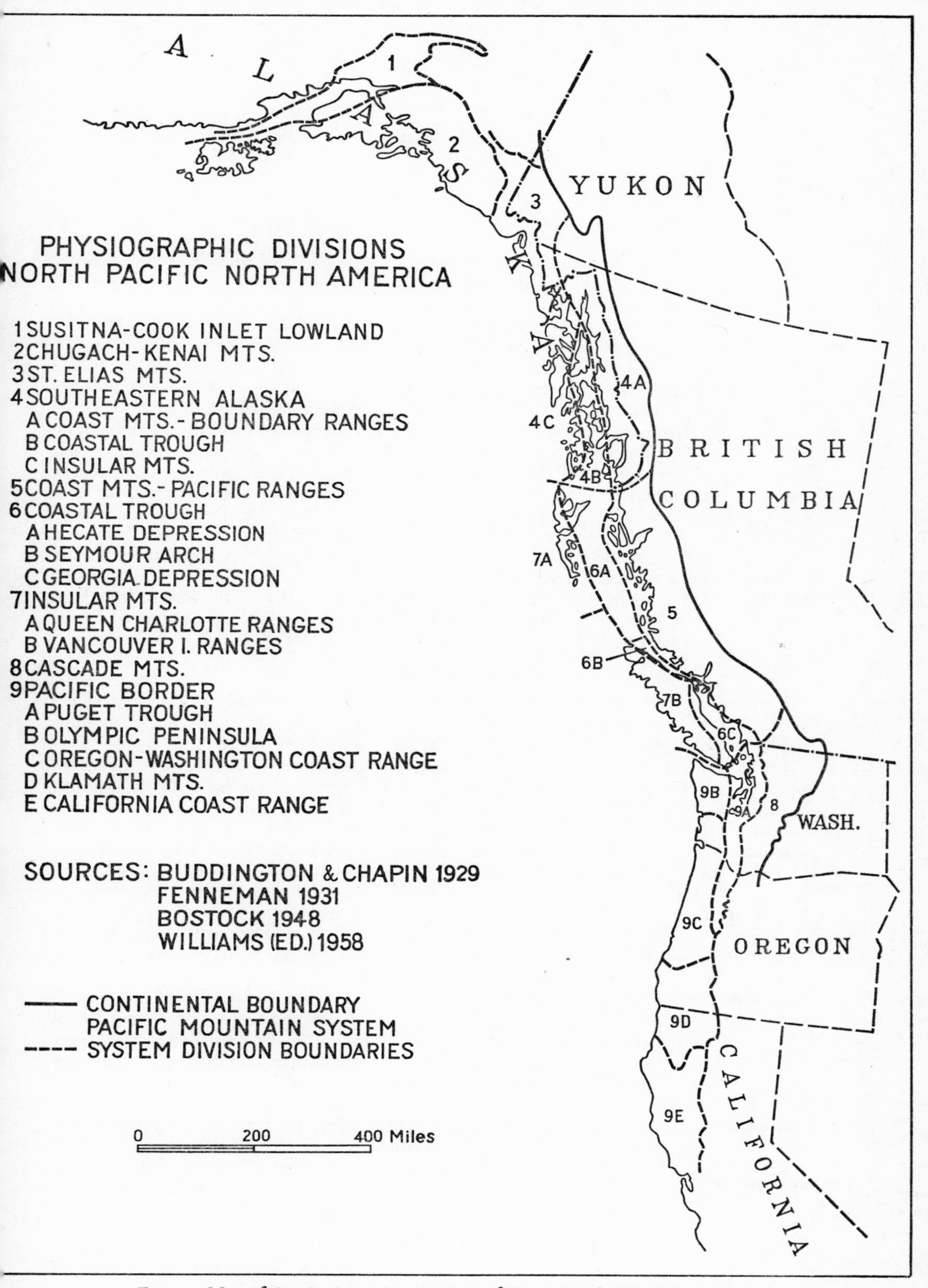

Fig. 49. Map of the physiographic divisions of North Pacific North America.

Kenai Peninsula

On the southern Alaskan coast the Kenai Peninsula projects along the Gulf of Alaska and separates two extensive embayments, Cook Inlet to the northwest and Prince William Sound to the east (Fig. 2). The peninsula is divided into two physiographic provinces: the Susitna-Cook Inlet Lowland to the northwest and the Chugach-Kenai Mountains to the southeast and east. Because of the division, the Kenai Peninsula is treated in two parts; the northwesternmost is described later.

The Kenai Mountains extend the entire 160-mi length of the eastern side of the peninsula and vary in width from 25 to 60 mi. The paramount peaks are over 6000 ft in elevation, the highest being 6800. Geologically and topographically the Kenais are related to the Kodiak Mountains and are continuous with the Chugach Mountains to the northeast (Martin, Johnson, and Grant 1915; Miller 1958a). An arbitrary boundary dividing them from the Chugach Mountains is located at Portage Pass, ca 700 ft high, which separates Portage Canal of Prince William Sound from Turnagain Arm, a branch of Cook Inlet. If it were not for the 7-mi length of the pass, the Kenai Peninsula would lie disconnected from the mainland.

Two large névé tracts and many lesser ones occur in the upper parts of the mountains. The Harding Icefield is the most extensive, located on the south-central part of the peninsula and measuring ca 15–17 by 23 mi; the Sargent Icefield is second in size, ca 10 by 30 mi, and is found on the southeastern part of the peninsula. Two noteworthy valley glaciers, the McCarty and Tustumena, completely drape the central Kenai Mountains from a common névé and flow a total distance of 35 mi. McCarty Glacier drains into the gulf and the Tustumena into Cook Inlet via Tustumena Lake. Fiords indent the entire gulf coast line of the peninsula and reveal a late-Cenozoic, glacial-marine history related to that of the Kodiak-Afognak archipelago. In addition, quite a few valleys gouged out by glaciers toward the eastern end of the subprovince have been partly filled by lakes. Kenai Lake, shaped like a long crooked finger, is the largest of these, measuring 21 mi in length.

Prince William Sound

Included in the Prince William Sound Subprovince are the islands and forelands of the sound, the lofty snow-covered heights of the Chugach Mountains to the north, and the foothills and flatland of the Copper River delta to the east (Fig. 2).

Prince William Sound is a heavily glaciated and drowned valley complex, some parts of which are still above sea level and constitute the islands and promontories in the embayment. It lies in the Chugach Mountains, south of their main axis. The sound is ca 80 mi across from east to west and 50 from north to south. Depths between 600 and 1300 ft are found at the entrance whereas inside they range from 600 to 2400 (Tarr and Martin 1914). Montague, Hinchinbrook, Knight, and Hawkins are the large islands; Latouche, Evans, Elrington, Bainbridge, Green, Chenega, Culross, Esther, Perry, Naked, Glacier, and Bligh Islands make up the remainder worthy of mention. Knight Island is the most rugged and the highest at an elevation of 3261 ft. Montague Island is the largest but is less than 3000 ft above sea level. Hinchinbrook and Hawkins Islands are relatively low. All appear to represent a single preglacial surface.

Between the headlands, fiords of varying length and depth reach inland. Port Nellie Juan is one such extensive fiord on the western side of the sound, cutting 25 mi into the Kenai Mountains. The longest and most impressive is formed by Port Wells-College Fiord, which penetrates over 35 mi of the Chugach Mountains in the northwestern corner of the sound. Two others, Unakwik Inlet off the north-central part and Valdez Arm to the northeast, are over 20 mi in length.

Most fiords in the sound receive the discharge of glaciers. The Chugach Mountains to the north are a tremendous region of glacier alimentation. Here are the highest peaks in the range, Mt. Marcus Baker (13,176 ft) and Mt. Witherspoon (12,023), and the sources of Columbia, Harvard, Yale, and Valdez Glaciers, among numerous less important ones. The eastern

Chugach are lower in altitude, and the glaciers, such as the Scott, Sheriden, Childs, and Miles, are relatively small and scattered.

Where the Copper River reaches tidewater east of the sound, an extensive delta of river alluvium and glacial detritus has formed a broad lowland, broken by a shifting network of sloughs, backwaters, and sand dunes. Low-lying hills, 200 to 400 ft in elevation near Alaganik to the west of the delta, border this expanse of flat country. Some steep-sided bluffs are situated beyond the front of hills and resemble sea stacks.

The rock of the sound is almost entirely slate and graywacke, probably Late Mesozoic in age, interbedded with greenstone and intruded, strongly folded, and locally altered (Grant and Higgins 1910, Moffit 1954). No Tertiary rock has been found. Mountain-building processes that gave rise to the Chugach Mountains appear to have been active during the Late Cretaceous or Early Tertiary. Although Tarr and Martin (1914) are of the opinion that Prince William Sound was excavated by ice erosion of a preglacial lowland and no preglacial sea entered the area, Moffit (1954) believes that various factors, including structure and differential land movement as well as ice degradation, are responsible for its formation.

Copper River—Icy Bay Coast

Extensive tidal flats and estuaries, long stretches of sandy beach, few bays and islands, mountains of low relief, and the giant piedmont lobe of Bering Glacier identify the Copper River-Icy Bay Coast of the Chugach-Kenai Mountains Province (Fig. 2). From the mouth of the Copper River to Cape Suckling, ca 40 mi, the shore line is rather irregular, marked by Controller Bay, Katalla Bay, Okalee Spit, and the tidal marshes of Bering, Campbell, Okalee, and Katalla Rivers, among others. It is in Controller Bay that the only major islands are found: Kanak, Wingham, and Kayak. Ragged Mountain, north of Katalla, reaches 3315-ft elevation. East of Katalla, the upland is near 2000 ft, and in the Suckling Hills, of which Cape Suckling is the southern extremity, the ridges run a maximum close to 1600 ft above sea level.

Between Cape Suckling and Icy Bay, a distance of 80 mi, the shore line is quite even. Yakataga Reef at Cape Yakataga and the tidal mouths of several rivers, notably Seal, Kaliakh, and Duktoth, are the only irregularities. The Robinson Mountains rise steeply a short distance behind the narrow beach between Cape Yakataga and Icy Cape. They reach elevations of over 6400 ft within 6 mi of the coast and farther away are much higher. Inland lies the backbone of the Chugach Mountains, marked by three prominent summits: Mt. Miller (11,000 ft), Mt. Steller (10,267), and Mt. Tom White (10,000).

Bering Glacier, one of the two principal glaciers on the coast, is an imposing feature (Plate I). Its main stream flows from the Bagley Icefield in the heart of the Chugach Mountains, although numerous streams contribute to the piedmont lobe resting on the coastal plain. It is at least 55 mi in length and over 70 along the periphery of the lobe. Large parts are covered with ablation moraine, much of which has been invaded by vegetation along the terminal edge. Many of the lakes found in this sector of the subprovince are along the margin of Bering Glacier.

Guyot Glacier in the Robinson Mountains is derived from a massive ice field northwest of Icy Bay, into which it calves. Yakataga and White River Glaciers originate as overflow on the western side of this névé. Many of the streams draining into the gulf east of Cape Yakataga have small glaciers as their sources. Near Katalla other small glaciers may be found in the high valleys on the western slope of Ragged Mountain (Martin 1908). North of Katalla, Martin River Glacier, draining via Martin River to join the Copper River near its mouth, is perhaps the third longest in this subprovince. Two nearby lakes, Martin and Bering, are probably remnants of former embayments that have been almost entirely filled by glaciofluvial sediments.

Contrasting that forming the divisions of the province to the west and southwest, the rock here is almost entirely Tertiary. Only on Wingham Island and in the hills west of Katalla are pre-Tertiary slate, graywacke, chert, and greenstone to be found (Martin 1908). The tertiary shale, sandstone, conglomerate, and interbedded coal previously assigned to the Upper Oligocene (Taliaferro 1932) are now considered to range from Eocene to Miocene and possibly Pliocene (Gryc, Miller, and Payne 1951; Miller 1957a and b). They are marine and nonmarine, in some places intruded by igneous rock, and were folded and faulted in the Late or Post Tertiary, accompanied or followed by uplift (Martin 1908, Maddren 1914). Glacial outwash gravels comprise most of the overburden in low-lying areas.

Susitna-Cook Inlet Lowland Province

Kenai Peninsula

Cook Inlet Lowland of the Susitna-Cook Inlet Lowland Province forms the northwestern part of the Kenai beyond the western slopes of the Kenai Mountains. Roughly, it is the area northwest of a line between Kachemak Bay off Cook Inlet and Turnagain Arm (Fig. 2). Maximum relief occurs in the vicinity of the Caribou Hills, at elevations of about 3000 ft, and in the upland to the south, all lying between Tustumena Lake and the mouth of Kachemak Bay. Tustumena, the principal lake in this area, measures 23 mi long and more than 6 wide. North of Tustumena, most of the country is below an elevation of 200 ft and is an expanse of swamps, muskegs, and innumerable small lakes—one large water body, Skilak Lake, which measures ca 4 by 15 mi, occurs in this tract. The two principal lakes are the sources of the two major rivers, the Kasilof and the Kenai, which drain into Cook Inlet. The northwestern coast line of the peninsula is remarkably even and no islands occur directly offshore.

This part of the province is underlain by slightly consolidated, gently folded Tertiary beds of sand, clay, and coal, which are buried by till and stratified sand and gravel (Martin, Johnson, and Grant 1915). The entire province is considered a structural depression that already existed toward the end of the Cretaceous or the beginning of the Tertiary (Barnes 1958). It is unknown when and how it was formed, but by the end of the Tertiary it existed much as it is now with the exception of its glacial modification.

St. Elias Mountains Province

Icy Bay—Cross Sound Coast

A low, gently sloping coastal plain, fronting a belt of foothills and attenuating southeastward, characterizes the ocean border of the Icy Bay-Cross Sound Coast of the St. Elias Mountains Province. The subprovince extends from Icy Bay to Cross Sound (Figs. 2, 3). Most of the shore line is regular except for Yakutat, Icy, and Lituya Bays, the mouth of the Alsek River at Dry Bay, and the coast from Icy Point to Cross Sound. Between Icy and Yakutat Bays, Malaspina Glacier occupies most of the low coastal foreland in a basin below sea level inland for ca 28 mi or more (Sharp 1958). Between Yakutat and Dry Bays, muskegs, swamps, lakes, and numerous braided rivers at less than 250-ft elevation drain the foothills that lie 5 to 17 mi behind the coast. Southeastward from Dry Bay the foreland is only 2 to 3 mi broad, and beyond Icy Point the mountains fall abruptly to the coast.

The foothills belt is narrow and low southeastward. Elevations up to 4761 ft occur bordering the main Fairweather Range. The Deception Hills adjacent to Dry Bay reach 3470 ft. The belt bordering the St. Elias Mountains, including the summits of the Chaix Hills, Floral Hills, and Brabazon Range, attains a maximum elevation of 5670 ft. The massive St. Elias Mountains are considered the loftiest coastal mountains in the world, and the largest collection of high peaks in North America. Mt. St. Elias at 18,008-ft elevation is only 20 mi from tidewater. Mt. Logan (19,850 ft) towers above all the others and is followed in order of height by Mt. Lucania (17,150), King Peak (17,130), Mt. Steele (16,439), and a host of peaks over 14,000. Mt. Fairweather (15,300) is the highest in the Fairweather Range with Mt. Quincy Adams (13,650), Mt. Crillon (12,726), and Lituya Mountain (11,750), among several others, above 10,000.

These mountains contain the sources of many glaciers of varying size, and most of the upper valleys are occupied by interconnected ice fields that drain both oceanward and into the interior. Malaspina Glacier, an impressive piedmont sheet fed by Libbey, Agassiz, Seward, Marvine, and Hayden Glaciers, measures 28 by 40 mi and ca 840 sq mi (Plafker and Miller 1958, Sharp 1958). Its outer margin measures over 80 mi and it rivals Bering Glacier in size, probably being the larger. The slopes and heads of Disenchantment Bay and Russell and Nunatak Fiords of inner Yakutat Bay are drained by glaciers, of which Hubbard, Nunatak, and Hidden are worthy of mention. South of the Deception Hills, Grand Plateau, Fairweather, Lituya, Crillon, and La Perouse Glaciers flow seaward from the Fairweather Range. On the continental side of the range, ice drains eastward into Glacier Bay, while to the south, Brady Glacier flows for over 20 mi into Taylor Bay, an arm of Cross Sound.

Most of the low country forming the Yakutat flats and underlying and bordering Malaspina Glacier consists of unconsolidated deposits. These are mainly till and glaciofluvial material on the Malaspina foreland whereas the Yakutat foreland is overlain in addition by tidal and shore sediment (Blackwelder 1909; Tarr and Butler 1909; Plafker and Miller 1957, 1958). Exposures of bedrock are absent over this area except in the foothills, but it is unlikely that rock other than Tertiary and younger underlie the forelands. Farther south about Lituya Bay, Mertie (1933) notes Tertiary sandstone, shale, conglomerate, and a few coal beds occurring except at the head of the bay, where older schist, slate, greenstone, and granitic intrusives are exposed. Blackwelder (1907), working in the Brabazon Range between the Alsek River and Russell Fiord, and Tarr and Butler (1909), in the Yakutat Bay region, indicate that the foothills consist mostly of shale, sandstone, conglomerate, and graywacke that have been greatly folded and faulted.

Little is known about the geology of the St. Elias Mountains, but from all indications they are composed mainly of folded and faulted metamorphic rock derived from sedimentary and volcanic rock of the Paleozoic and Mesozoic (Miller 1958a). These mountains are marked by strong faults trending in a northwesterly direction and owe much of their height to these surfaces of movement. Uplift has affected the Tertiary ocean border so that sections of marine glacial sediments thousands of feet in thickness are perched above sea level (Russell 1893, Miller 1953). Uplift appears to be continuing at present as indicated by the previously noted powerful earthquake in Lituya Bay on 9 July 1958 (Tocher and Miller 1959).

Southeastern Alaska Province

Coast Mountains

Boundary Ranges

The Boundary Ranges Subprovince is the northern member of the Coast Mountains in the Southeastern Alaska Province according to the physiographic systematics of Bostock (1948); it is described by Kerr (1936a). A saddle east of Dixon Entrance, best indicated by the Skeena River valley, separates it from its counterpart, the Pacific Ranges that are mainly in British Columbia (Figs. 3, 4). To the east, the Interior System of the Cordillera adjoins the subprovince, while on the west, boundaries are with the Coastal Trough and the Insular Mountains of the Outer Mountains Area. The Boundary Ranges descend northward to meet the Kluane Plateau in Yukon Territory. Between this terminus and the Skeena River, they run a distance of ca 500 mi; the rest of the Coast Mountains extend an additional 500 mi southward from the Skeena to their southern limit in the vicinity of the Fraser River valley.

Boundary Ranges, forming the back of the Alaska panhandle, are continuous with the exception of transecting valleys occupied by Stikine, Whiting, and Taku Rivers and White and Chilkoot Passes. Fiords penetrate deeply, creating an extremely irregular shore line. Average summit elevations are between 4000 and 6000 ft. Mt. Ratz (10,290 ft), north of Stikine River, is highest in a group including Mussell Peak (10,260), Noel Peak (10,040), Kates Needle (10,002), and Devils Thumb (9077). North of Taku River, the summit level exhibits a secondary rise, topped by Devils Paw (8584 ft).

Two features of the Boundary Ranges are striking: their ruggedness and their mantle of glaciers and ice fields. Glaciation, stream erosion, and weathering, in progress for thousands of years, have sculptured the ranges into the impressively displayed fretted upland. The most extensive névé and glacier complex is that lying between the vicinity of Skagway and the Taku River valley, a distance of ca 90 mi (Plate II). From this névé, Taku Glacier, the longest in the Coast Mountains, flows from ca 6000-ft elevation ca 32 mi to tidewater. South of Taku Inlet the fiords, penetrating the mountain mass, head in glaciers coming off the unnamed ice field north of the Stikine River valley. These glaciers include the Le Conte, Baird, Dawes, and Sawyer. In Stikine valley, Great and Flood Glaciers descend from the high catchment area to the north. Elsewhere in the ranges the névé and glaciers are less extensive.

Intrusives of the Coast Mountains batholith compose most of the Boundary Ranges. These are mainly granodiorite, but with diorite, gabbro, and other igneous rock locally present. The age of this intrusive body is Upper Jurassic or Lower Cretaceous (Buddington and Chapin 1929). Along the western flank of the ranges, metamorphics grade in the direction of the batholith from greenstone through slate to schist and gneiss. Sediments and volcanics are also associated. The area prior to intrusion was a geosyncline that was subjected to downwarping accompanied by sedimentation and vulcanism (Kerr 1936a). The present ranges result from a succession of uplifts in the Tertiary and from late-Cenozoic glaciation.

Coastal Trough

The islands, channels, and inlets of the Alexander Archipelago, which form a narrow wedge along an axis coinciding with Clarence Strait and extending as far as Chatham Strait bordering Admiralty Island, are included in the Coastal Trough division of the Southeastern Alaska Province (Fig. 3). The trough lies juxtaposed between the Boundary Ranges and the Insular Mountains and is in general a low-lying area that owes its configuration to a major synclinorium, striking northwest-southeast, and to powerful glacial corrasion. It is a northwest extension of the Pacific coast downfold, which includes the basins of Hecate Strait, the Strait of Georgia, and Puget Sound to the southeast (Buddington and Chapin 1929). Paleozoic, Mesozoic, and Tertiary sediments and volcanics form most of the rock. Owing to the low relief, no glaciers are found, although the waterways of Frederick Sound–Sumner Strait and Clarence and Chatham Straits were paths of glacier movement at different times during the Pleistocene.

Insular Mountains

The Insular Mountains, in the Southeastern Alaska Province, border directly on the Pacific Ocean. The subprovince includes the mountains of Prince of Wales, Kuiu, Baranof, and Chichagof Islands and extends to Chilkat Peninsula and Glacier Bay, where it joins the St. Elias Mountains Province (Fig. 3). It is considered a continuation of the Queen Charlotte and Vancouver Ranges of coastal British Columbia (Spencer 1903, Bostock 1948). Structurally, it is treated broadly as an anticlinorium composed of Paleozoic and Mesozoic sedimentary and volcanic rock and intrusives of upper-Jurassic or lower-Cretaceous age (Buddington and Chapin 1929).

These mountains, attaining altitudes of 3000 to 5000 ft, resemble the Boundary Ranges in their ruggedness. Cirques, horns, broad valleys, deep fiords, and other glacial features are prevalent and small glaciers may be found at high elevations on Baranof and Chichagof Islands. The fiord system of Southeastern Alaska is one of the most spectacular in the world. The Chatham Strait-Lynn Canal waterway, which separates the subprovince from the Coastal Trough and Boundary Ranges, is ca 225 mi in length. Soundings indicate depths generally in excess of 2000 ft with an extreme of 2900 off Point Caution on Admiralty Island (Martin and Williams 1924). Kruzof Island, northwest of Baranof Island and almost contiguous to it, is formed in part by a cluster of volcanic cones, the highest of which is Mt. Edgecumbe (3271 ft). The volcanic area composes the southern half of the island and consists of ash and lava piled up during the early-postglacial eruption. It is the major seat of vulcanism in the province. The only other localities in Southeastern Alaska border Unuk River on the mainland and occur on southeastern Revillagigedo Island and eastward (Buddington and Chapin 1929).

BRITISH COLUMBIA

Bostock's (1948) classification is applicable to coastal British Columbia and includes the units of his Western System of the Cordillera. His divisions are for the most part a continuation of the Southeastern Alaskan members. From the neighborhood of Cross Sound to the vicinity of Juan de Fuca and Georgia Straits, the Coast Mountains Area, Coastal Trough, and Outer Mountains Area bear the same relationship to one another for 1000 mi or more (Fig. 49).

Coast Mountains

Pacific Ranges

Bostock (1948) points out that the Pacific Ranges of the Coast Mountains, between the Skeena River-Observatory Inlet saddle and the Fraser River valley (Fig. 4), are distinct from the Boundary Ranges to the north for three reasons: (1) Pacific Ranges are broader and their relief is greater, (2) they are more than 90 per cent granitic compared to ca 30 per cent for the Boundary Ranges, and (3) glaciers and ice fields are fewer and less extensive.

North of the lower Fraser valley, Mt. Garibaldi (8787 ft) and SkihistMountain (9660) rise at the south of the ranges. Thus begins a series of high peaks that continues northwesterly, including Mt. Queen Bess (10,700 ft), Mt. Waddington (13,260), Monarch Mountain (11,714), Kalone Peak (8390), and Atna Peak (9040). The district near the head of Knight Inlet, occupied by Mt. Waddington and neighboring summits, reaches a maximum elevation exceeding that of Mt. Robson (12,972 ft), the highest Rocky Mountain peak. The Knight Inlet area contains the Waddington ice field, the largest glacial expanse in the ranges, measuring 20 by 15 mi (Bostock 1948) and feeding Franklin, Tiedemann, and Tellott Glaciers. Another major field lies to the west; dominated by Mt. Silverthrone (9700 ft), it is the source of Klinaklini Glacier. Of the small glaciers that are found in other parts of the ranges, perhaps the best known are the Helm, Warren, and Sphinx, rising in the Garibaldi Névé, as described by Mathews (1951a).

The ranges, which are as much as 120 mi broad, have been cut through by rivers and fiords. Besides the Skeena and the Fraser Rivers, already mentioned, the Dean, Bella Coola, Klinaklini, and Homothko drain the interior plateaux and reach tidewater in deep, lengthy fiords, respectively Dean Channel, Burke Channel, Knight Inlet, and Bute Inlet. The fiords pass far into the ranges. Knight Inlet travels over 70 mi; the course formed by Dean and Fisher Channels and Fitzhugh Sound is over 120 in length; and from the head of Gardner Canal to the coast line is over 160. Grenville Channel, lying between Pitt Island and the mainland, is a remarkably straight waterway, traveling more than 50 mi between bold, massive, granite mountains. The deepest measured fiord of the British Columbia coast is Finlaysen Channel at 2574 ft below sea level (Peacock 1935).

The bulk of the rock underlying this part of the Coast Mountains is composed of batholithic granodiorite and diorite and some gabbro. These are considered Upper Jurassic in age and are associated with both younger and older rock. Mesozoic volcanic and sedimentary material with metamorphic equivalents crops out at places along the flanks as well as within the area of the batholith (Bostock 1948). Pleistocene sand, clay, and gravel are widespread, and Pleistocene lava, ash, and tuff are scattered, appearing, for example, on the Nass River (Hanson 1923) and in Garibaldi Provincial Park (Mathews 1958).

Coastal Trough

Georgia Depression

Within the Coastal Trough Province, the Strait of Georgia rests upon the northern segment of a downfold that Bostock (1948) refers to as the Georgia Depression. This axis of downfolding is continuous with Puget Sound via the intervening islands and waterways and with the lowland that extends from the sound to the southern end of the Willamette Valley in Oregon. Fenneman (1931) calls this southern segment the Puget Trough. Combined, Georgia Depression and Puget Trough travel along the axis of the Coastal Trough for ca 500 mi. The downfold is widest north of Puget Sound between southern Vancouver Island and the lowland fronting on the Washington Cascades, a distance close to 75 mi (Figs. 4, 5). Toward the northwest and to the south of this transect, the downfold narrows.

Georgia Depression includes the submerged area of the strait, and the elevated islands and borderlands along the eastern shore of Vancouver Island as far north as the vicinity of Discovery Passage. Thence its boundary extends southeasterly from the neighborhood of Malaspina Peninsula and nearby islands to the lower Fraser River valley (Bostock 1948). Eastern Vancouver Island and the lower Fraser, including its extensive delta, comprise the largest part of Georgia Depression above sea level. Among the other major land areas in the strait are Texada, Denman, and Lasqueti Islands and the archipelago of Gabriola, Valdes, Galiano, Mayne, Saturna, and Saltspring Islands. With a few exceptions, where they may attain 1000 or 2000 ft, elevations in Georgia Depression are generally ca 500.

Glacial deposits are prevalent, often with marine fossils indicating changes in land–sea-level relations of several hundred feet (Clapp 1912, 1913a, 1917; Johnston 1923). Mesozoic sediments and volcanics including Cretaceous coal lie beneath the depression (Bostock 1948).

Seymour Arch

An upwarped plateau eroded along lines of structural weakness, Seymour Arch is a northwestern extension of Georgia Depression (Bostock 1948). Situated between the Coast Mountains to the northeast and the Insular Mountains to the southwest, the arch consists mainly of the islands and forelands between the Strait of Georgia and Queen Charlotte Strait. Quadra, Sonora, Thurlow, Hardwicke, Cracroft, and Harbledown Islands make up most of the land mass of the emerged Coastal Trough here. The relief covers a wide range of altitude with some islands below 1000 ft in elevation and others with summits ca 5000. Johnstone Strait and Discovery Passage, the principal connecting waterways, separate the islands of the arch from Vancouver Island.

The geology of the coast and islands lying between the Strait of Georgia and Queen Charlotte Sound is discussed by Dawson (1887) and Bancroft (1913). Intrusives that compose the batholith of the Pacific Ranges are exposed over the greater part of the region. Triassic shale and volcanics along with older material form most of the remaining country rock. Glacial sediments, largely stratified sand, clay, and gravel and boulder clay, are irregularly deposited or absent. On the other hand, they form many of the islands along the southern extremity of the arch. Since glaciation, land–sea-level changes have amounted to at least 350 ft (Bancroft 1913).

Hecate Depression

Most of Hecate Depression, a part of the Coastal Trough, is beneath Hecate Strait, but as indicated by its raised borders, the depression is at least 200 mi lengthwise and 100 wide at its broadest sector (Fig. 4). The largest land area occurs as the northern and northeastern lowland beyond the edge of the Queen Charlotte Ranges and central plateau on Graham, Moresby, and Langara Islands, Queen Charlotte Islands (MacKenzie 1916). The northern lowland of Graham Island is west of Naden Harbor, the western embayment of the two on Dixon Entrance (Fig. 3). Langara Island is included in this subprovince, which is, for the most part, a poorly drained muskeg barren at elevations ranging between 500 and 1000 ft (Sheldon 1912). The northeastern lowland forms the upper two-thirds and half the width of Graham Island. Its interior boundary passes from upper Naden Harbor to about halfway through Masset Inlet (the eastern embayment on Dixon Entrance) and then southeast across

Skidegate Inlet to the vicinity of Cumshewa Head on Moresby Island. This low terrain is poorly drained with many shallow lakes and muskegs and with elevations seldom exceeding 500 ft.

The shore line of these lowlands is generally even, and sandy beaches stretch for many miles, particularly along Hecate Strait and between Masset Harbor and Rose Point on Dixon Entrance. Two interesting features of these strands are Spit Point and Rose Spit. MacKenzie (1916) states that Spit Point on Moresby Island has resulted from the northerly tidal currents and the strong southeasterly gales that blow from Hecate Strait; Rose Spit, which terminates Rose Point on northeastern Graham Island, has developed in response to the currents moving eastward through Dixon Entrance running together with those coming northward through Hecate Strait. That Rose Point has been built over a long period seems obvious from the series of long, narrow lakes, *en échelon*, that are apparently former lagoons.

Northeastern Graham Island is overlain with stratified sand, clay, and gravel and unstratified sand and gravel containing striated boulders. These deposits appear to be lacustrine, estuarine, and glacial marine in origin (Dawson 1880, MacKenzie 1916). They are associated with bedrock consisting of Mesozoic argillite, tuff, diabase, and quartz diorite and large amounts of Tertiary sandstone, shale, and conglomerate along with lignite, basalt flows, and agglomerate.

Along the eastern side of Hecate Strait, Hecate Depression has less extensive areas of low, hilly terrain. The majority of these are less than 100 ft above sea level and 10 to 30 mi broad. They occur on parts of Banks, Estevan, Aristazabal, Prince, and Swindle Islands and smaller islands nearby (Dolmage 1922, 1923). The rock here is upper-Jurassic quartz diorite and granodiorite with some older schist and limestone. Glaciation is evident everywhere along this border of the strait.

Insular Mountains

Queen Charlotte Ranges

The major unifying physiographic feature of the Queen Charlotte Islands is the narrow, rugged Queen Charlotte Ranges, a division of the Insular Mountains Province. The ranges, occupying part or all of the islands with the exception of the northernmost island, Langara, reach 170 mi south of the Graham Island lowland and make up most of Moresby Island and all of Louise, Lyell, Burnaby, and Kunghit Islands. Near their northern end they are nearly 30 mi broad but their southern end narrows to a width of ca 10. In this subprovince is the central or Skidegate Plateau, located along the middle lower third of Graham Island between the ranges, the lowland, and Skidegate Inlet (MacKenzie 1916, Bostock 1948). Elevations between 1000 and 1500 ft and low, flat-topped hills and ridges, small lakes, and muskeg characterize the plateau. Fiords and bays have cut into the entire subprovince and have created an exceptionally steep and irregular coast, particularly on Moresby Island. Most of the islands are separated by narrow channels only ca 1 mi wide.

Mt. Needham (4000 ft) on southern Graham Island, Mt. De La Touche (3685) on west-central Moresby Island, and Mt. Kermode (3750) on Louise Island are the major peaks. Other sectors of the ranges are near 3000 ft in elevation, except toward the northern and southern extremities, where summits fall to 2000 and below. The ranges possess many sharp peaks and serrate ridges, although in some places the summits are rounded, noticeably those of northern Graham Island. This subprovince of the Insular Mountains is ca 55 mi from its Alaskan Prince of Wales Ranges counterpart and 140 from its Vancouver Island Ranges counterpart.

Dawson (1880), Ells (1906), Clapp (1913b), and MacKenzie (1914, 1915, 1916) report on the geology. The bedrock consists of basaltic lava flows and agglomerate of Tertiary age and Mesozoic sedimentary and volcanic material. In places upper-Jurassic intrusives of quartz diorite are found. No glaciers are known at present: glacial features are not evident everywhere in the subprovince and are not extensive higher than 3000-ft elevation. It is generally concluded that the ranges were only partly glaciated.

Vancouver Island Ranges

The Vancouver Island Ranges are the southernmost and highest of the Insular Mountains. Running a distance of 225 mi from Quatsino Sound on the north to the Strait of Juan de Fuca on the south, the ranges rise up from the ocean side of Vancouver Island and to the west stand above Georgia Depression and the Puget Trough (Fig. 4). The peaks gain in altitude toward the central part of the island. They reach their maximum elevations on the Golden Hinde (7219 ft), Mt. Elkhorn (7200), and Victoria Peak (7095). In this general locality, marked by the Forbidden Plateau, are the island's glaciers. North of Quatsino Sound, a minor subdivision occurs as an unnamed plateau that is physiographically related to Skidegate Plateau on the Queen Charlotte Islands.

The ranges have been strongly modified by glaciation. The west-coast side has been cut and in part dissected by ice and subsequently drowned. At Barkley Sound and to the northwest, fiords reach into the core of the ranges, particularly from Clayoquot, Nootka, Kyuquot, and Quatsino Sounds but also from between these places. The shore line along this stretch is steep and rocky, except at such localities as Estevan Point and along the bays just northwest of Barkley Sound, where sandy and bouldery beaches are formed (Dolmage 1921). Southeast of Barkley, the coast line is fairly regular with beaches of shingle and boulders (Clapp 1912). Evidence of differential uplift is common. Behind the coast and near the heads of the fiords are many small lakes; inland the lakes are larger, long, and narrow—Buttle, Great Central, and Cowichan are ca 20 mi in length.

The rock constituting the ranges is predominantly Triassic and Paleozoic sedimentary and volcanic (Dawson 1887, Clapp 1912, Dolmage 1921, MacKenzie 1923), invaded by batholiths of upper-Jurassic or lower-Cretaceous age related to the Coast Mountains batholith. Some Tertiary sandstone and conglomerate from the coast southeast of Barkley Sound contain small amounts of lignite (Clapp 1912).

WASHINGTON, OREGON, AND CALIFORNIA

The Washington, Oregon, and California area Fenneman (1931) calls the Pacific Border Province, including the Puget Trough, Olympic Peninsula, Oregon-Washington Coast Range, Klamath Mountains, and California Coast Range, covers the southern stretch of coast under consideration (Fig. 49). In addition, his Cascade-Sierra Mountains Province draws some attention, but comments are limited to the part of the Cascades bordering the Puget Trough from Puget Sound north to the international boundary.

These provinces are divisions of the Pacific Mountain System. They are a continuation of the tripartite sequence of western mountains, trough downfolds, and eastern mountains that has its beginning in southeastern Alaska.

Cascade-Sierra Mountains Province

Cascade Mountains

The Washington sector of the Cascades discussed here concerns an area close to 175 mi long south of the Canadian border and the valley formed by the Fraser River in British Columbia (Fig. 5). It is ca 110 mi broad at the international boundary but decreases to ca 60 in the vicinity of Mt. Rainier (14,408 ft) at the south. Most of this part of the Cascades is composed of metamorphosed and folded Paleozoic and Mesozoic sediments and volcanics that have been intruded by batholithic rock. In the vicinity of Mt. Rainier and east of the southernmost part of Puget Sound, the rock by contrast is almost all volcanic, built up mainly by vast accumulations of Tertiary lava (Fenneman 1931, Bostock 1948). Along the crest of the Cascades stands a series of volcanic cones, the more prominent of which north of Mt. Rainier are Glacier Peak (10,436 ft), Mt. Baker (10,750), and Mt. Shuksan (9038). Glaciers descend from their slopes: Nisqually Glacier on Mt. Rainier and Coleman Glacier on Mt. Baker are perhaps the best known.

Pacific Border Province

Puget Trough

The northernmost sector of the Pacific Border Province is the Puget Trough, which lies between the Cascade Mountains on the east and the Olympic Peninsula and Coast Range on the west. The subprovince is also known as the Puget-Willamette Lowland, since its southern end is at the head of the Willamette Valley in Oregon (Fig. 5). The Cordilleran Ice Sheet pushed south into this trough but did not reach far below the southern edge of Puget Sound (Bretz 1913). The lowland to the south of the terminal moraine formed by this ice sheet was not affected, except by small Cascade glaciers that invaded the eastern border of the Willamette Valley, and ice-rafted erratics and other proglacial deposits that were flushed from the Puget lobe, out of the mountains, or down the Columbia River. Only the glaciated northern Puget Trough, of direct concern, is discussed here.

The trough begins amid the islands and waterways southeast of Georgia Depression. Here between Haro and Rosario Straits lie the San Juan Islands, consisting of three large members, Orcas, San Juan, and Lopez, and several smaller ones. Fidalgo, Whidbey, and Camano Islands are important land masses southeast of the San Juans. All are low lying with the exception of Orcas Island, which is topped by Mt. Constitution, ca 2400-ft elevation.

Southwest of Whidbey Island, Admiralty Inlet connects the Strait of Juan de Fuca with Puget Sound on the east and Hood Canal on the west. Puget Sound is an intricate system of islands and inlets and is almost continuous with Hood Canal. The head of Case Inlet on the inner sound and that of the Canal are separated by a distance of only 2 mi. Bainbridge, Vashon, and Harstine Islands are the principal land areas within this partly drowned trough.

Thick glacial drift covers much of the islands and borderlands of the glaciated Puget Trough. Numerous lakes of varying size occur on the drift; the largest is Lake Washington east of Seattle. Many small rivers crossing the drift are charged with fine glacial sediments, which they transport to tidewater; deltas and tideflats have resulted from the deposition of this alluvium and in some places are extensive. Most of this terrain is not more than 500 ft above sea level. Along steep slopes where the land contacts the waterways or where rivers have cut down into the underlying rock, the glacial material is generally exposed.

The physiographic history of the glaciated Puget Trough is recorded by Fenneman (1931). In general, the trough began as a geosyncline in the Post Cretaceous and received sediments over much of the Tertiary. During and since the Tertiary, it has been uplifted, folded, faulted, and eroded by streams and by glaciers. Four glaciations have modified the area (Crandell, Mullineaux, and Waldron 1958). Following the last, the ocean invaded; since then land–sea-level relations have changed as much as 290 ft (Bretz 1913).

Olympic Peninsula

Northwestern Washington, fronting on the ocean and the Strait of Juan de Fuca and terminating at Cape Flattery, may be regarded in general as the Olympic Peninsula (Fig. 5). From a physiographic standpoint the peninsula is more precisely designated as being situated north of the valleys between the lower Chehalis River and the southwestern inlets at the head of Puget Sound. Grays Harbor, the drowned mouth of the Chehalis River, is the southern limit of the peninsula on the ocean coast. Its central part is dominated by the Olympic Mountains and beyond them is a belt of foothills and lowlands.

The Olympic Mountains, constituting the outstanding topographic feature, trend in a northwesterly direction across the peninsula, and in the central-western sector, a summit complex is topped by Mt. Olympus (7954 ft), which marks their uppermost elevation. Most of the glaciers in the Olympics originate in this group of peaks—the Blue, Hoh, and White

Glaciers flowing northerly and northeasterly are best known. They are, however, small glaciers with drainage systems of only 2 to 3.3 mi in length. Most of the remaining high peaks are in the central-eastern part, where Mt. Deception (7788 ft), Mt. Constance (7743), Mt. Mystery (7631), and Mt. Anderson (7365) are located. To the east the mountains descend steeply to Hood Canal; to the northwest they fall slowly in elevation in a line of low hills, ending near 1400 ft in the vicinity of Cape Flattery. The Olympics completely cross the peninsula, a distance of ca 100 mi. They are only a few miles broad near Cape Flattery but widen to 35 or 40 mi west of Hood Canal.

The glaciers and snow fields in the interior of the mountains are the sources of the many rivers that flow down on all sides of the peninsula: the Dungeness and Elwha on the north; the Soleduck, Bogachiel, Hoh, Queets, and Quinault on the west; the Wynoochee on the south; and the Duckabush and Dosewallips on the east. These cross the lowlands border, where at many places they have cut through the Pleistocene deposits into the underlying bedrock. Much of this low-lying border is terraced, and the Pleistocene deposits are uplifted at least 300 ft (Arnold 1906, Lupton 1914). Several large, deep lakes are present near the outer edge of the mountains: Crescent and Sutherland to the north and Quinault and Cushman to the south. The largest, Ozette, is near the ocean, ca 17 mi south of Cape Flattery.

The northeastern coast is formed by steep bluffs rising ca 300 ft above sea level, intervening bays and inlets, and the well-formed spits near Port Angeles and eastward. The coast along the western part of the Strait of Juan de Fuca and on the ocean north of the vicinity of the Quinault River mouth is rimmed by a wave-cut platform and some small islands. Precipitous cliffs face the ocean along much of this sector, and narrow sandy beaches are discontinuous. Southward to Grays Harbor the borderland is lower and the beach becomes continuous and broad, finally merging at the mouth of the harbor with the spit that terminates at Point Brown.

The most up-to-date description of the geology of the peninsula is presented by Danner (1955). Cretaceous sedimentary and volcanic rock composes a part of the interior of the Olympic Mountains; Eocene sediments and volcanics occupy the outer part of the mountains except on the west, where the remaining area of the peninsula is mainly late-Tertiary and Pleistocene rock. A succession of uplifts, which created a complicated array of faults and folds interspersed with intervals of erosion and marine occupancy, produced the present land mass and set it apart from the depressions of the Chehalis valley, Puget lowland, and the Strait of Juan de Fuca. Glacial erosion by several small valley glaciers is taking place at the present time. At the height of Pleistocene glaciation, the Olympics were a locus from which glaciers flowed outward and made contact with the Cordilleran Ice Sheet on the north and east.

Oregon-Washington Coast Range

The Oregon-Washington Coast Range Subprovince is south of the Chehalis River valley, north of the Klamath Mountains, and west of the Puget Trough, and includes a part of the Cascades south of the trough (Fig. 5). It is a 300-mi-long strip, between 40 and 65 wide, broadest toward the south and narrowest in the middle section. The relief is moderate, generally between 1500 and 2500 ft above sea level. Only the more resistant erosional remnants stand higher. These include Mt. Hebo (3150 ft), Monmouth Peak (3230), Mary's Peak (4097), Grass Mountain (3612), and Prairie Peak (3437). The narrow coastal plain, more or less intermittent and variable in width, is widest in Washington, 15 to 20 mi broad west of the Willapa Hills.

The Coast Range is drained by numerous rivers and several completely cross the subprovince. The largest of the latter is the Columbia, which rises west of the main crest of the Rockies in British Columbia. The Umpqua and Chehalis also cross the range and the Siuslaw, Yaquina, and Nehalem come very close to doing so. The important rivers remaining, the Coquille, Coos, Alsea, Siletz, Nestucca, and Trask, originate in the heart of the range. All these transverse drainage systems have eroded moderately deep valleys along sinuous courses controlled by lithology and structure. The irregular course of the Nehalem, for example, appears to be the result of the regional distribution of resistant igneous rock (Washburne 1914).

The lower reaches of the rivers are drowned for variable distances inland from the ocean: the Chehalis for 30 mi, the Columbia for 140, the Umpqua for 25, and the Coquille for 30 (Fenneman 1931). This drowning is Late Pleistocene as shown by the studies of the lower Columbia by Bretz (1919) and Lowry and Baldwin (1952) and the related work by Allison (1935, 1936); this is revealed also by the investigation of the Coquille by Baldwin (1945). These rivers were eroded along their lower stretches when sea level was down and/or the land higher. Later they became partly drowned as land–sea-level relations changed. More recently uplift and subsequent drowning have differentially reduced the degree of marine inundation.

The lakes in this subprovince are almost all within a few miles of the coast and at elevations close to sea level. Very few occur in the interior of the range; examples are Triangle northwest of Eugene and Meadow southeast of Tillamook. Of the coastal lakes, Devils, Mercer, Woahink, Siltcoos, Tahkenitch, Eel, and Ten Mile are noteworthy. All in this latter group are probably Late Pleistocene in age and owe their origin to a combination of factors, most important of which appears to be the rise of sea level resulting from deglaciation.

The coast is described in detail by Smith (1933a, b, and c), and a detailed study of the coastal sand dunes has been written quite recently by Cooper (1958b). In the broad sense, the coast line is even and is made irregular only by rocky promontories and by small bays at the mouths of rivers. Exceptions are the large embayments of the lower Columbia River and of Willapa Bay and Grays Harbor north of the Columbia. Many of the bays are fronted or bordered by lengthy spits, such as that at Long Beach, which is 17 mi in length on Willapa Bay. The forelands beyond the bays are generally steep and rocky, and Capes Lookout, Meares, Foulweather, and Perpetua, and Tillamook and Yaquina Heads are prominent. Resistant basalt is a common member of the rock composing these and sometimes exhibits a columnar form, such as Seal Rock near Newport. Sandy beaches run for many miles and at a number of localities, in the vicinity of the Umpqua, Siuslaw, Alsea, and Yaquina river mouths, extensive dune areas have developed. The most continuous and widest stretch of dunes, broken only by the Umpqua and Siuslaw Rivers, lies north of Coos Bay for a distance of ca 52 mi (Cooper 1958b). Behind the immediate features on the coast is a series of Pleistocene-age marine terraces.

This Coast Range is made up entirely of Tertiary volcanic rock and sediments, chiefly sandstone and shale, cut by igneous intrusives (Washburne 1914, Smith and Packard 1919, Smith 1933a). Structurally, northwestern Oregon is a low, broad geanticline, but south of the Umpqua River the higher range is synclinal for most of its extent with contiguous anticlines in the upper Umpqua valley and near Coos Bay (Washburne 1914). Fenneman (1931) describes the range as a low anticlinorium with several minor folds. Its geological history is complex, involving a number of adjustments including warping and gentle folding of strata, eustatic sea-level changes coupled with coastal fluctuations, and trenching of streams followed by partial marine drowning.

Klamath Mountains

The Klamath Mountains mass, situated in southwestern Oregon and northwestern California, stands along 150 mi of the Pacific and reaches inland between 75 and 115 (Fig. 5). This subprovince separates the Oregon-Washington Coast Range from the California Coast Range. Diller (1902, 1914) distinguishes it from the former on the basis of rock composition. Whereas the Klamath Mountains are made up largely of Mesozoic and Paleozoic sedimentary and igneous rock, the Coast Range to the north is Tertiary and younger. No such distinction can be made, however, with the California Coast Range. Instead, the manner of drainage is used as the criterion for separation. The rivers draining the Klamath Mountains are transverse and irregular; those of the Coast Range on the south parallel in general the strike of the rocks. The southern border is the South Fork of the Trinity River, a tributary of the Klamath River, and the northern border lies inland from Cape Blanco in the Rogue River Mountains (Diller 1902).

The subprovince is comprised of several subsidiary mountain ranges, and the Klamath Mountains are accordingly considered a complex of these. Included are the Siskiyou, Rogue River, Salmon, Trinity, Scott, Bully Choop, and Yolla Bolly Mountains. They are characterized by gentle relief with summits rounded or somewhat flat. Some of the high peaks are sharp and are generally located in what are called the Salmon-Trinity Alps. Fenneman (1931) considers the upper summits monadnocks. Mt. Eddy (9038 ft) and Thompson Peak (8936) are the uppermost points in the Klamath complex. No glaciers are known to exist in these mountains.

The Klamath River with its tributaries and the Rogue River are the principal streams crossing the province. Some of the minor tributaries rise in small lakes, apparently of the tarn type, in the glaciated heights of the mountains, particularly in the Salmon, Trinity, Scott, and Siskiyou ramparts. A few lakes occur close to sea level along the coast. These include Talawa and Earl near Crescent City and Garrison, Floras, New, Crooks, and Laurel in the vicinity of Cape Blanco.

The greater part of the coast is steep, rugged, and rocky. Diller (1902) points out that the remaining areas of coastal plain are associated with relatively soft rock. These are generally less than 100 ft above sea level and are found north of Cape Blanco, about the mouth of Smith River and near Crescent City, and from Little River near Trinidad to Eel River about Humboldt Bay. Marine terraces occur on this plain to an elevation of 1500 ft.

The late-Cenozoic physiographic history involves submergence followed by uplift and the formation of terraces carrying Pleistocene marine sediments. The relatively extensive drowning of the river mouths north of this subprovince, indicating recent subsidence, is not so manifest here.

California Coast Range

The California Coast Range, the southernmost part of the Pacific Border Province, is north of San Francisco Bay. Weaver (1949) delimits the area as lying between San Francisco Bay and the South Fork Mountains, which stretch northwestward from the upper Sacramento Valley to the mouth of the Klamath River. Its maximum width is 80 mi and its length 300 along the coast. The mountain ranges making up the subprovince run in a nearly parallel series trending obliquely to the coast in a northwesterly direction.

Most of the ridges and summits are between 2000 and 5000 ft above sea level. A few peaks stand above 7000 ft; these are north of Clear Lake and east of the Middle Fork of the Eel River. They appear as a continuation of the upland formed by the southern prong of the Klamath Mountains. The tendency of the component ranges to run parallel has caused most of the rivers to adjust their courses to this control.

The character of the Klamath coast, rising steeply from the ocean and exhibiting terraces, continues in this physiographic unit. The shore line is quite regular except for Point Reyes and nearby Drakes and Tomales Bays near San Francisco, Humboldt and Arcata Bays near Eureka, and the broad headlands of Cape Mendocino and Point Arena. Remaining irregularities can be considered minor. Terraces of marine origin are apparent as reported by Diller (1902), Fenneman (1931), Weaver (1949), and others.

The rock formations are pre-Jurassic and younger, consisting of sedimentary and metamorphic rock along with igneous intrusives and extrusives (Weaver 1949). The ranges are complexly folded and faulted and have been greatly affected by strong displacements along the San Andreas fault, which passes near Point Reyes and continues northwesterly to Point Arena. Important compressional movements north of San Francisco Bay occurred in the Early Pliocene and again during the Late Pliocene and Early Pleistocene. Disturbances have been recurrent up to the present (Weaver 1949).

GLOSSARY

Studies in Pleistocene plant geography, because of the interdisciplinary nature of the field, utilize data and encounter terms from a number of the physical and biological sciences. The terms in most cases are technical, specialized, and often interrelated, so that any attempt to avoid using them by substituting ordinary, more wordy expressions is usually unsuccessful. Because it seems necessary to use certain terms unfamiliar to the specialist or lay reader, the following list has been prepared for reference. These terms have been defined for use specifically with this study and are not intended for application in a general sense. Definitions were written incorporating the views expressed by Wodehouse (1935), Weaver and Clements (1938), Carpenter (1938), Erdtman (1943), Cain (1944), Flint (1947, 1957), Daubenmire (1947), Oosting (1948), Faegri and Iversen (1950), Zeuner (1952), Godwin (1956), and Dansereau (1957).

AGE—The major glacial, interglacial, or pluvial time unit of the Pleistocene.

ALLERÖD—*See* Late-glacial.

ALPINE—Pertaining to the zone above the timber line.

ANEMOPHILY—Pollination by means of wind.

ANNULUS—The single row or ring of elastic thick-walled cells that partly or completely surrounds the fern sporangium.

ANTHESIS—The period during which a flower is in bloom.

ARCUS (pl. arci)—A curved, thickened connection extending from germ pore to germ pore in certain pollen grains; found characteristically in some members of the birch family (Betulaceae).

ASPIS (pl. aspides)—The circular, shield-shaped thickening surrounding the germ pore of pollen grains.

ASSOCIATION—A climax community representing a major subdivision of a formation.

ATLANTIC—*See* Postglacial.

AUTECOLOGY—The study of the interrelations between the individual plant and its environment.

BIOTA—Plants and animals spoken of collectively with regard to a geographic area.

BOG—A natural area, most commonly overlying a depression, where peat has accumulated generally during stages of hydrarch succession and the surface is characteristically occupied by sphagnum moss, sedge, and heath.

BOREAL—*See* Postglacial.

BROAD-SCLEROPHYLL—Characterized by thick, hard, evergreen leaves.

CLAVATE—A type of surface configuration appearing as club-shaped projections found on certain pollen grains.

CLIMATIC CLIMAX—*See* climax.

CLIMAX—The final stage reached during succession whereby the plant community, gaining dynamic adjustment with the prevailing climate, is able to perpetuate itself indefinitely. This is the climatic climax or plant formation which applies to the region as a whole. However, where succession in a late stage is checked by factors such as physiography or soil, a climatic climax cannot be reached. Instead, local conditions cause succession to terminate as a physiographic or edaphic climax.

CLOSED-CONE PINE—A pine whose cones do not open after the seed has ripened.

COLPATE—Of pollen grains possessing colpi.

COLPUS (pl. colpi)—A groove or aperture in the exine of a pollen grain.

COMMUNITY—A general term designating any group of plants having mutual relationships with one another and with the environment.

CONTINENTALITY—The quality of a continental climate, marked by wide ranges of annual and diurnal temperature.

DEFLOCCULATION—The process that takes place during the chemical treatment of peat whereby the plant and animal remains and inorganic fraction composing the peat become separated into particulate constituents.

DIASPORE—A plant reproductive structure, such as a spore, seed, or fruit, which serves as a means for the species of establishing a new member of the species population; also termed a disseminule or propagule.

DIFFERENTIAL UPLIFT—*See* isostasy.

DISSEMINULE—*See* diaspore.

DISTAL—With reference to that surface of the pollen grain or spore facing outward when either is a member of a tetrad.

DISTRIBUTION—*See* range.

ECOLOGICAL AMPLITUDE—The range of tolerance of a plant.

ECOTONE—The transition area between plant communities where representative members grow together. If the environments of each community come into contact sharply, the ecotone is narrow; if, on the other hand, the environments change gradually from one community to the next, the ecotone is broad.

EDAPHIC—Pertaining to the soil as an environmental factor that secondarily controls plant distribution.

ENDEMISM—The condition or quality shown by plants growing confined to a single geographic area.

ENTOMOPHILY—Pollination by means of insects.

EPIPHYTE—A plant that grows attached to another plant and carries out its life functions independent of the other.

ERRATIC—A rock transported by glacier action from a distant source.

EUSTASY—The phenomenon whereby sea level changes in response to the formation and wastage of glacier ice.

EXINE—The outer resistant layer of the pollen or spore wall; the exosporium.

EXOSPORIUM—*See* exine.

FORMATION—*See* climax.

FURROW—*See* germinal furrow.

GERM PORE—The circular opening in the exine of a pollen grain, which serves as a means of egress for the pollen tube.

GERMINAL APERTURE—The opening in the membrane of the germinal furrow through which the pollen tube passes.

GERMINAL FURROW—A groove or opening in the exine of a pollen grain through which directly or by way of an enclosed germ pore the pollen tube emerges.

GERMINATION—The formation and growth of the pollen tube in pollen grains; the emergence of a developing prothallus in spores. It can also include in pollen grains the division of the protoplast in the development of the prothallus prior to tube formation.

GLACIOFLUVIAL—Pertaining to the combined action of glaciers and rivers.

Grenzhorizont—German word for recurrence surface, which see.

HALOPHYTE—A plant restricted to saline soils, such as are found in salt marshes and tide flats.

HOLOCOENOTIC—With reference to the manner in which environmental factors act upon the plant; namely, the factors act in unison and all are mutually interdependent.

HUMIFICATION—The process of organic decomposition that occurs at and near the surface of peat deposits and that is particularly active when the growth of peat-forming plants is decreased, for example, during the latter part of the Hypsithermal or the Sub-Boreal.

HYDRARCH—Adjectival term describing a succession that begins in a lake, pond, swamp, or wherever water can be invaded by plants, and ultimately reaches the climax stage.

HYDROSERE—A succession of plant communities originating in water and terminating with the climax.

HYPSITHERMAL—The time during the Postglacial when mean annual temperatures were higher than those at present; equivalent to the European pollen zones beginning with the Boreal and ending with the Sub-Boreal.

INTERFLUCTUATIONAL—With reference to intervals between glacier advances during glaciation of less than subage rank.

INTERGLACIAL—With reference to the age intervals between glacial ages.

INTERSTADIAL—With reference to intervals between subages of Wisconsin-age glaciation.

ISOSTASY—The theoretical condition of equilibrium in the earth's crust under the action of gravitation, as affected by differences in rock density and the transfer of materials from areas of erosion to areas of deposition. During deglaciation in Pleistocene ice-covered regions, the earth's crust responded isostatically to the loss of the ice load by way of differential uplift or isostatic readjustment, thereby maintaining equilibrium.

ISOSTATIC READJUSTMENT—*See* isostasy.

Krummholz—The gnarled, contorted, and stunted growth form of trees at timber line.

LATE-GLACIAL—The interval following the last ice age during which the amelioration of climate was interrupted by a temporary reversion to cold conditions. In Europe, where the Late-glacial has been carefully studied, it opens with the subdivision Older Dryas (sometimes containing the Bölling, an interval of minor climatic fluctuation), followed by the Alleröd at which time late-glacial temperature reached its highest point, and closes with the Younger Dryas subdivision when temperature decreased.

LATE-PLEISTOCENE—The interval of time representing the Late-glacial and Postglacial; the interval of variable duration that has ensued since ice of the last glacial subage receded from the surface under consideration.

LIGNEOUS—With reference to peat composed of wood.

LIMNIC—Pertaining to lake peat, which consists largely of the microscopic remnants of plants and animals formerly living in the basin and its environs.

MICROFOSSIL—Any microscopic plant or animal preserved beneath the surface of the earth from some time in the past.

MONOCOLPATE—Of pollen grains possessing a colpus.

MONOLETE—Pertaining to a tetrad scar that is a straight line.

MUSKEG—The Indian (Algonquian) term used in Alaska and northwestern Canada to designate a natural area of accumulated peat, the surface cover of which consists principally of sphagnum moss, sedge, heath, and open-growth scrub. Muskeg is classified in a broad sense into three types: slope (soligenous), domed (ombrogenous), and flat (topogenous).

NUNATAK—An Eskimo word that refers to a mountain that projects above an ice sheet, ice field, or glacier.

OCEANITY—The quality of an oceanic climate, as distinguished from a continental climate by less wide ranges of annual and diurnal temperatures and greater humidity.

OLDER DRYAS—*See* Late-glacial.

Ombrogenous—Pertaining to convex or dome-shaped muskeg whose existence is determined by rainfall on its surface.

Paludification—The process governing muskeg formation and enlargement, resulting from congested drainage caused by climatic, physiographic, or biotic changes.

Palynology—The study of pollen grains and spores, particularly with regard to their stratigraphy in Pleistocene peat deposits.

Peat—The partially decayed microscopic and macroscopic remains of plants and animals that have been incorporated with varying amounts of inorganic materials and have accumulated in muskegs, bogs, lakes, and related sites of deposition.

Periporate—Of pollen grains possessing germ pores outside of the equatorial area.

Physiographic climax—*See* climax.

Pleistocene—The epoch of the Cenozoic Era comprising all of post-Pliocene time and characterized by marked climatic changes, intervals of glacial and pluvial conditions, and fluctuations of sea level.

Pluvial—Characterized by rain; with reference to the rainy climate that prevailed in middle latitudes during the ice ages.

Pollen grain—In seed plants the male reproductive body, which results when the nucleus of a microspore divides and which subsequently by means of tube formation transfers the sperm to the female ovule. It is shed from the anther in angiosperms or flowering plants and from the pollen sac or microsporangium in the gynmosperms.

Pollen profile—A graphic presentation depicting the percentages of a single pollen type in spectra at stratigraphic horizons from the surface to the base of the peat section. Profiles for all pollen types in the section when graphed collectively form a pollen diagram.

Pollen spectrum—The percentage representation of the different kinds of pollen and spores found at a stratigraphic horizon in a peat section.

Pollination—The transfer of pollen from the anther (male) to the stigma (female) in the angiosperms or flowering plants; in gymnosperms the transfer is from the microsporangium or pollen sac to the ovule in an ovulate cone.

Pore—*See* germ pore.

Postglacial—The interval of time that has ensued since the Late-glacial. Von Post subdivided the Postglacial into three divisions based on temperature fluctuation: an opening division of increasing warmth, succeeded by one of maximum warmth, and a closing division of decreasing warmth. Blytt and Sernander incorporated moisture and temperature and resolved five zones, which from the earliest to the latest are Pre-Boreal (cool and humid), Boreal (comparatively warm and dry, continental), Atlantic (mild and humid, oceanic), Sub-Boreal (warm and drier, increased continentality), and Sub-Atlantic (cooler with increased oceanity).

Pre-Boreal—*See* Postglacial.

Prisere—A plant succession, beginning on an exposed surface, that has resulted from natural forces.

Proglacial—Pertaining to materials derived from glaciers and deposited beyond the extent of the ice.

Propagule—*See* diaspore.

Proximal—With reference to that surface of a pollen grain or spore facing inward when either is a member of a tetrad.

Range—The geographical area occupied by a species.

Recurrence surface—In muskegs and bogs the contact surface between highly humified or nongenerative peat and slightly humified regenerative sphagnum peat of a regeneration complex. This succession of peat types is interpreted as a result of climatic change, specifically, toward greater humidity or oceanity.

REFUGIUM—A driftless area that was not covered by glaciers during all or part of the Pleistocene, where plants and animals were able to maintain themselves during the intervals of ice-age isolation, and which served as a locus for plant dispersal when glaciers wasted.

REGENERATION COMPLEX—The system of pit ponds and hummocks of growing sphagnum moss found on the surface of domed muskeg during a developmental phase in the history of the peat deposit.

REGRESSION—The retreat of the sea from the land.

Rekurrensyta (pl. *rekurrensytor*)—Swedish word for recurrence surface, which see.

Rekurrenzfläche—German word for recurrence surface, which see.

RELICT—A community or component of one that has been able to survive a major environmental alteration and because of a protective feature or compensating factor remains locally representative of a former environment that prevailed over a more extensive area.

RHIZOPOD—A protozoan belonging to the class Rhizopoda characterized by pseudopods, which serve as the means of locomotion. The remains or tests of these single-celled animals are commonly encountered in sphagnous peat.

SERE—The succession of plant communities beginning with the pioneer stage and terminating with the climax.

SNOW LINE—The altitudinal or latitudinal boundary above or beyond which snow fallen during winter does not disappear the following summer. This is the climatic snow line (in actuality a zone) and can be distinguished from the orographic snow line, which, being determined by snow found in places protected from the agents of ablation (for example, a north-facing cirque), rests at lower elevations.

SOLIGENOUS—Pertaining to muskeg formed on sloping ground where formation and development are controlled by the movement of surface water and by climate.

SPORANGIUM—A structure in which spores are produced.

SPORE—The reproductive body found chiefly in ferns, horsetails, club mosses, quillworts, mosses, and phylogenetically lower groups, sometimes differentiated into a megaspore and microspore (for example, in the club moss *Selaginella* and the quill wort *Isoetes*), which in the relatively higher seed plants occur as the forerunners, respectively, of the embryo sac and the pollen grain.

STAGE—In glacial sediments the stratigraphic equivalent of an age.

STEPHANOCOLPORATE—Of pollen grains possessing more than three meridional colpi, each of which is marked by a germ pore.

STRIATE-RUGULATE—A combination of two sculpture types on certain pollen grains, such that the radial projections are elongated and the elements appear generally parallel (striate) and irregularly distributed (rugulate).

SUBAGE—A subdivision of the Wisconsin glacial age.

SUBALPINE—Pertaining to the zone of the timber line and immediately below.

SUB-ATLANTIC—*See* Postglacial.

SUB-BOREAL—*See* Postglacial.

SUBCLIMAX—A long-enduring stage of succession that immediately precedes the climax but is prevented from succeeding completely by conditions created by soil, physiography, fire, or biota.

SUBSERE—A plant succession beginning on surfaces disturbed or newly exposed, usually by human intervention.

SUBSTAGE—In glacial sediments the stratigraphic equivalent of a subage.

SUCCESSION—The displacement of one community by another. Succession may be primary when started on an exposed surface such as a glacial moraine or a sand dune, or it may be secondary when begun in an area where the plant cover has been disturbed, usually by man, so that any succession in progress is caused to retrogress.

TECTONIC—With reference to the structure of the earth's crust.

TETRAD—The four united pollen grains or spores that have originated from a single mother cell. With comparatively few exceptions (for example, *Typha*, *Drosera*, and Ericales), tetrads break apart at maturity.

THERMOPHILY—The quality demonstrated by plants whose distributions are in low and lower middle latitudes and at low elevations.

TIMBER LINE—The limit of arboreal growth in mountains and at high latitudes, technically forming a zone rather than a line; also known as the tree line.

TOLERANCE—The capacity of an organism to thrive within certain ranges of environmental conditions. Although tolerance can be thought of in connection with particular climatic, edaphic, and biotic factors, it is generally regarded as the ability of a plant to endure shade.

TOPOGENOUS—Pertaining to muskeg formed on level or slightly sloping ground where development is controlled by the level of the water table.

TRANSGRESSION—The encroachment of the sea upon the land.

TRICHOME—A unicellular or multicellular plant hair associated with the epidermis of leaves, stems, flowers, and fruits.

TRILETE—Pertaining to a tetrad scar that is triradiate.

TRICOLPATE—Of pollen grains possessing three colpi.

TRICOLPORATE—Of pollen grains possessing three meridional colpi, each of which is marked by a germ pore.

TUNDRA—Vegetation of arctic and alpine regions beyond the timber or tree line.

VERRUCATE—A type of sculpturing appearing as wartlike projections found on certain pollen grains.

XERIC—Pertaining to dry conditions or a scanty supply of moisture both edaphic and atmospheric.

YOUNGER DRYAS—*See* Late-glacial.

LITERATURE CITED

ABBE, C., JR. 1906. Climate. In: The geography and geology of Alaska, by A. H. Brooks. U. S. Geol. Surv. Prof. Pap. 45: 133–200.

ABBE, E. C. 1936. Botanical results of Grenfell-Forbes northern Labrador expedition 1931. Rhodora 38: 102–164.

ACKERMAN, E. A. 1941. The Köppen classification of climates in North America. Geog. Rev. 31: 105–111.

ALLEN, E. T. 1902. The western hemlock. U. S. Forest Serv. Rept. 33.

ALLISON, I. S. 1935. Glacial erratics in Willamette Valley. Bull. Geol. Soc. Am. 46: 615–632.

———. 1936. Pleistocene alluvial stages in northwestern Oregon. Science 83: 441–443.

American Forestry Association. 1955. These are the champs. Am. Forests 61: 31–40.

———. 1956. These are the champs, Part II. Am. Forests 62: 33–40.

ANDERSEN, B. G. 1954. Rand morener i Sorvest-Norge. Norsk Geografisk Tidsskr. 14: 273–342.

ANDERSEN, H. E. 1953. Range of western redcedar (Thuja plicata) in Alaska. Alaska Forest Res. Center Tech. Note 22.

ANDERSEN, S. T. 1954. A late-glacial pollen diagram from southern Michigan, U. S. A. Danmarks Geologiske Undersøgelse II, 80: 140–155.

ANDERSON, J. P. 1943–1947, 1949, 1950. Flora of Alaska and adjacent parts of Canada. Iowa State College J. Sci. 18: 137–175, 381–445; 19: 133–205; 20: 213–257, 297–347; 21: 363–423; 23: 137–187; 24: 219–271.

ANDERSON, S. T. and T. P. BANK II. 1952. Pollen and radiocarbon studies of Aleutian soil samples. Science 116: 84–86.

ANTEVS, E. 1929. Maps of the Pleistocene glaciations. Bull. Geol. Soc. Am. 40: 631–720.

———. 1952. Climatic history and the antiquity of man in California. Univ. Calif. Archeol. Surv. Rept. 16: 23–31.

———. 1955. Geologic-climatic dating in the west. Am. Antiquity 20: 317–335.

ARMSTRONG, J. E. 1956. Mankato drift in the lower Fraser valley of British Columbia, Canada. Bull. Geol. Soc. Am. 67: 1666–1667.

ARMSTRONG, J. E. and W. L. BROWN. 1954. Late Wisconsin marine drift and associated sediments of the lower Fraser valley, British Columbia, Canada. Bull. Geol. Soc. Am. 65: 349–364.

ARMSTRONG, J. E. and H. W. TIPPER. 1948. Glaciation in north central British Columbia. Am. J. Sci. 246: 283–310.

ARNOLD, J. R. and W. F. LIBBY. 1951. Radiocarbon dates. Science 113: 111–120.

ARNOLD, R. 1906. Geological reconnaissance of the coast of the Olympic Peninsula, Washington. Bull. Geol. Soc. Am. 17: 451–468.

ARTIST, R. C. 1939. Pollen spectrum studies on the Anoka Sand Plain in Minnesota. Ecol. Monog. 9: 493–535.

AUER, V. 1921. Zur Kenntnis der Stratigraphie der mittelösterbottnischen Moore. Acta Forestalia Fennica 18.

———. 1927. Stratigraphical and morphological investigations of peat bogs of southeastern Canada. Comm. ex Instit. Quaestionum Forestalium Finlandiae Editae 12: 1–62.

———. 1930. Peat bogs in southeastern Canada. Can. Dept. Mines Geol. Surv. Mem. 162: 1–32.

———. 1933a. Verschiebungen der Wald- und Steppengebiete Feuerlands in postglazialer Zeit. Acta Geographica 5, Nr. 2.

———. 1933b. Peat bogs of southeastern Canada. Handbuch der Moorkunde 7: 141–223.

———. 1958. The Pleistocene of Fuego-Patagonia. Part II: The history of the flora and vegetation. Ann. Acad. Scient. Fennicae, III. Geologica-Geographica 50.

Bailey, V. 1936. The mammals and life zones of Oregon. U. S. Dept. Agric. North Am. Fauna 55.

Baker, F. S. (chair.). 1945. Forest cover types of western North America. Soc. Am. Foresters, Washington, D. C.

Baldwin, E. M. 1945. Some revisions of the late Cenozoic stratigraphy of the southern Oregon coast. J. Geol. 53: 35–46.

Bancroft, J. A. 1913. Geology of the coast and islands between the Strait of Georgia and Queen Charlotte Sound, B. C. Geol. Surv. Canada Mem. 23.

Barendsen, G. W., E. S. Deevey, and L. J. Gralenski. 1957. Yale natural radiocarbon measurements III. Science 126: 908–919.

Barnes, F. F. 1958. Cook Inlet-Susitna Lowland. In: Landscapes of Alaska: 43–47. Univ. Calif. Press, Berkeley and Los Angeles.

Benninghoff, W. S. 1942. The pollen analysis of the Lower Peat. Papers Peabody Museum Harvard Univ. 2: 96–104.

———. 1958. Quaternary vegetation of central Alaska. 8ème Congr. Intern. de Botanique, Comptes-rendus de Séances et rapports et communications. Sect. 6: 246.

Bertsch, K. 1942. Lehrbuch der Pollenanalyse. Handbücher der praktischen Vorgeschichtsforschung, Bd. 3: 1–195.

Black, R. F. 1958. Wrangell Mountains. In: Landscapes of Alaska: 30–33. Univ. Calif. Press, Berkeley and Los Angeles.

Blackwelder, E. 1907. Reconnaissance on the Pacific coast from Yakutat to Alsek River. U. S. Geol. Surv. Bull. 314d: 82–88.

———. 1909. The Yakutat coastal plain of Alaska; a combined terrestrial and marine formation. Am. J. Sci. 27: 459–466.

Bostock, H. S. 1948. Physiography of the Canadian cordillera, with special reference to the area north of the fifty-fifth parallel. Geol. Surv. Canada Mem. 247.

Bowman, P. W. 1931. Study of a peat bog near the Matamek River, Quebec, Canada, by the method of pollen analysis. Ecology 12: 694–708.

———. 1934. Pollen analysis of Kodiak bogs. Ecology 15: 97–100.

Bradley, W. C. 1957. Origin of marine-terrace deposits in the Santa Cruz area, California. Bull. Geol. Soc. Am. 68: 421–444.

Bretz, J. H. 1913. Glaciation of the Puget Sound region. Wash. Geol. Surv. Bull. 8: 1–244.

———. 1919. The late Pleistocene submergence in the Columbia valley of Oregon and Washington. J. Geol. 27: 489–506.

Brink, V. C. 1959. A directional change in the subalpine forest-heath ecotone in Garibaldi Park, British Columbia. Ecology 40: 10–16.

British Columbia Province Department of Agriculture. 1954. Climate of British Columbia, report for 1953. Victoria.

British Columbia Provincial Museum. 1921. A preliminary catalogue of the flora of Vancouver and Queen Charlotte Islands. Prov. Museum Natural Hist., Victoria.

Brock, R. W. 1928. Volcanoes of the Canadian cordillera. Proc. Third Pan-Pacific Sci. Congr.: 688–710.

Broecker, W. S. 1957. Evidence for a major climatic change close to 11,000 years B. P. Bull. Geol. Soc. Am. 68: 1703–1704.

BROECKER, W. S. and J. L. KULP. 1957. Lamont natural radiocarbon measurements IV. Science 126: 1324–1334.

BROECKER, W. S., J. L. KULP, and C. S. TUCEK. 1956. Lamont natural radiocarbon measurements III. Science 124: 154–165.

BROECKER, W. S. and P. C. ORR. 1958. Radiocarbon chronology of Lake Lahontan and Lake Bonneville. Bull. Geol. Soc. Am. 69: 1009–1032.

BROOKS, C. E. P. 1951. Geological and historical aspects of climatic change. In: Compendium of meteorology: 1004–1018. Am. Meteor. Soc., Boston.

BROWN, S. R. 1956. A piston sampler for surface sediments of lake deposits. Ecology 37: 611–613.

BUDDINGTON, A. F. 1927. Abandoned marine benches in southeastern Alaska. Am. J. Sci. 13: 45–52.

BUDDINGTON, A. F. and T. CHAPIN. 1929. Geology and mineral deposits of southeastern Alaska. U. S. Geol. Surv. Bull. 800.

BUELL, M. F. 1945. Late Pleistocene forests of southeastern North Carolina. Torreya 45: 117–118.

BURWASH, E. M. J. 1914. Pleistocene vulcanism of the Coast Range of British Columbia. J. Geol. 22: 260–267.

BUTTERS, F. K. 1914. The vegetation of the Selkirk Mountains. In: Mountaineering and exploration in the Selkirks: 352–362. Putnam, New York.

BYERS, H. R. 1930. Summer sea fogs of the central California coast. Univ. Calif. Publ. Geog. 3: 291–338.

———. 1953. Coast redwoods and fog drip. Ecology 34: 192–193.

CAIN, S. A. 1939. Pollen analysis as a paleo-ecological research method. Bot. Rev. 5: 627–654.

———. 1944a. Pollen analysis of some buried soils, Spartanburg County, South Carolina. Bull. Torrey Bot. Club 71: 11–22.

———. 1944b. Foundations of plant geography. Harper, New York.

CALDER, J. A. and D. B. O. SAVILE. 1959a. Studies in Saxifragaceae. I. The Heuchera cylindrica complex in and adjacent to British Columbia. Brittonia 11: 49–67.

CALDER, J. A. and D. B. O. SAVILE. 1959b. Studies in Saxifragaceae. II. Saxifraga Sect. Trachyphyllum in North America. Brittonia 11: 228–249.

CAPPS, S. R. 1916. The Chisana-White River district, Alaska. U. S. Geol. Surv. Bull. 630.

———. 1935. The southern Alaska Range. U. S. Geol. Surv. Bull. 862.

———. 1937. Kodiak and adjacent islands, Alaska. U. S. Geol. Surv. Bull. 880C: 111–184.

CARPENTER, J. R. 1938. An ecological glossary. Univ. Okla. Press, Norman.

CARY, N. L. 1922. Sitka spruce. U. S. Dept. Agric. Bull. 1060.

CLAPP, C. H. 1912. Southern Vancouver Island. Geol. Surv. Canada Mem. 13.

———. 1913a. Geology of Victoria and Saanich map-area, Vancouver Island, B. C. Geol. Surv. Canada Mem. 36.

———. 1913b. A geological reconnaissance on Graham Island, Queen Charlotte group, B. C. Geol. Surv. Canada Sum. Rept. 1912: 12–40.

———. 1914. Geology of the Nanaimo map-area. Geol. Surv. Canada Mem. 51.

———. 1917. Sooke and Duncan map-areas, Vancouver Island. Geol. Surv. Canada Mem. 96.

CLARK, H. W. 1937. Association types in the north Coast Ranges of California. Ecology 18: 214–230.

CLISBY, K. H. and P. B. SEARS. 1955. Palynology in southern North America, Part III, Microfossil profiles under Mexico City correlated with sedimentary profiles. Bull. Geol. Soc. Am. 66: 511–520.

———. 1956. San Augustin Plains—Pleistocene climatic changes. Science 124: 537–539.

Connor, A. J. 1938. The climates of North America II. Part 4, Canada. In: Handbuch der Klimatologie, Bd. 2, Teil J2: 332–424. Gebrüder Borntraeger, Berlin.

Coombs, H. A. 1939. Mount Baker, a Cascade volcano. Bull. Geol. Soc. Am. 50: 1493–1510.

Cooper, W. S. 1917. Redwoods, rainfall, and fog. Plant World 20: 179–189.

———. 1922. The broad-sclerophyll vegetation of California. Carnegie Inst. Wash. Publ. 319.

———. 1923. The recent ecological history of Glacier Bay, Alaska. Ecology 4: 93–128, 223–246, 355–365.

———. 1924. The forests of Glacier Bay—present, past, and yet unborn. J. Forestry 22: 16–23.

———. 1931a. A third expedition to Glacier Bay, Alaska. Ecology 12: 61–95.

———. 1931b. The layering habit in Sitka spruce and the two western hemlocks. Bot. Gaz. 91: 441–451.

———. 1931c. The seed-plants and ferns of the Glacier Bay National Monument, Alaska. Bull. Torrey Bot. Club 57: 327–338.

———. 1936. The strand and dune flora of the Pacific coast of North America: a geographic study. In: Essays in geobotany: 141–184. Univ. Calif. Press, Berkeley.

———. 1937. The problem of Glacier Bay, Alaska: a study of glacier variations. Geog. Rev. 27: 37–62.

———. 1939. A fourth expedition to Glacier Bay, Alaska. Ecology 20: 130–155.

———. 1942. Vegetation of the Prince William Sound region, Alaska, with a brief excursion into post-Pleistocene climatic history. Ecol. Monog. 12: 1–22.

———. 1957. Vegetation of the Northwest-American province. Proc. Eighth Pacific Sci. Congr. 4: 133–138.

———. 1958a. Terminology of post-Valders time. Bull. Geol. Soc. Am. 69: 941–945.

———. 1958b. Coastal sand dunes of Oregon and Washington. Geol. Soc. Am. Mem. 72.

———. n.d. The vegetation of the Northwest-American Province. Unpublished Manuscript. Boulder, Colorado.

Crandell, D. R., D. R. Mullineaux, and H. H. Waldron. 1958. Pleistocene sequence in southeastern part of the Puget Sound lowland, Washington. Am. J. Sci. 256: 384–397.

Cranwell, L. and L. von Post. 1936. Post-Pleistocene pollen diagrams from the southern hemisphere. Geog. Ann. 18: 308–347.

Critchfield, W. B. 1957. Geographic variation in Pinus contorta. Maria Moors Cabot Foundation Publ. 3.

Crocker, R. L. and B. A. Dickson. 1957. Soil development on the recessional moraines of the Herbert and Mendenhall Glaciers south-eastern Alaska. J. Ecology 45: 169–185.

Crocker, R. L. and J. Major. 1955. Soil development in relation to vegetation and surface age at Glacier Bay, Alaska. J. Ecology 43: 427–448.

Dachnowski-Stokes, A. P. 1930. Peat profiles in the Puget Sound basin of Washington. J. Wash. Acad. Sci. 20: 193–209.

———. 1936. Peat land in the Pacific coast states in relation to land and water resources. U. S. Dept. Agric. Misc. Publ. 248.

———. 1941. Peat resources in Alaska. U. S. Dept. Agric. Tech. Bull. 769.

Dahl, E. 1946a. On different types of unglaciated areas during the ice ages and their significance to phytogeography. New Phytol. 45: 225–242.

———. 1946b. On the origin of the strand flat. Norsk Geografisk Tidsskr. 11: 159–172.

———. 1955. Biogeographic and geologic indications of unglaciated areas in Scandinavia during the glacial ages. Bull. Geol. Soc. Am. 66: 1499–1520.

Danner, W. R. 1955. Geology of Olympic National Park. Univ. Wash. Press, Seattle.

Dansereau, P. 1957. Biogeography. An ecological perspective. Ronald Press, New York.

Daubenmire, R. F. 1943. Vegetation zonation in the Rocky Mountains. Bot. Rev. 9: 325–393.

———. 1947. Plants and environment. Wiley, New York.

Davis, M. B. 1958. Three pollen diagrams from central Massachusetts. Am. J. Sci. 256: 540–570.

Davis, N. F. G. and W. H. Mathews. 1944. Four phases of glaciation with illustrations from southwestern British Columbia. J. Geol. 52: 403–413.

Dawson, G. M. 1880. Report on the Queen Charlotte Islands. Geol. Surv. Canada Prog. Rept. 1878–1879, III.

———. 1887. Report on a geological examination of the northern part of Vancouver Island and adjacent coasts. Geol. Surv. Canada Ann. Rept. 1886, Part B.

———. 1893. Notes on the geology of Middleton Island, Alaska. Bull. Geol. Soc. Am. 4: 427–431.

Deevey, E. S. 1939. Studies in Connecticut lake sediments. I, A postglacial climatic chronology for southern New England. Am. J. Sci. 237: 691–724.

———. 1944. Pollen analysis and Mexican archaeology: an attempt to apply the method. Am. Antiquity 10: 135–149.

———. 1951. Late-glacial and postglacial pollen diagrams from Maine. Am. J. Sci. 249: 177–207.

———. 1957. Radiocarbon-dated pollen sequences in eastern North America. Veröff. Geobotanisches Institut Rübel in Zürich 34: 30–37.

Deevey, E. S. and R. F. Flint. 1957. Postglacial hypsithermal interval. Science 125: 182–184.

Deevey, E. S. and J. E. Potzger. 1951. Peat samples for radiocarbon analysis: problems in pollen statistics. Am. J. Sci. 249: 473–511.

Dightman, R. A. and M. E. Beatty. 1952. Recent Montana glacier and climate trends. Month. Weath. Rev. 80: 77–81.

Diller, J. S. 1896. A geological reconnaissance in northwestern Oregon. U. S. Geol. Surv. Ann. Rept. 17: 441–520.

———. 1902. Topographic development of the Klamath Mountains. U. S. Geol. Surv. Bull. 196.

———. 1914. Mineral resources of southwestern Oregon. U. S. Geol. Surv. Bull. 546.

———. 1915. The relief of our Pacific coast. Science 41: 48–57.

Doan, D. B. 1957. Sequence of Late Pleistocene and Recent eustatic sea levels of the western Pacific. Bull. Geol. Soc. Am. 68: 1716.

Dolmage, V. 1921. West coast of Vancouver Island between Barkley and Quatsino Sounds. Geol. Surv. Canada Ann. Rept. 1920, Part A: 12–22.

———. 1922. Coast and islands of British Columbia between Burke and Douglas Channels. Geol. Surv. Canada Sum. Rept. 1921, Part A: 22–49.

———. 1923. Coast and islands of British Columbia between Douglas Channel and the Alaskan boundary. Geol. Surv. Canada Sum. Rept. 1922, Part A: 9–34.

Draper, P. 1928. A demonstration of the technique of pollen analysis. Proc. Okla. Acad. Sci. 8: 63–64.

———. 1929. A comparison of pollen spectra of old and young bogs in the Erie basin. Proc. Okla. Acad. Aci. 9: 50–53.

Drury, W. H. 1956. Bog flats and physiographic processes in the upper Kuskokwim River region, Alaska. Contrib. Gray Herbarium Harvard Univ. 178.

Ells, R. W. 1906. Graham Island, B. C. Geol. Surv. Canada Ann. Rept. 1904, 16: 1B–46B.

Emery, K. O. 1958. Shallow submerged marine terraces of southern California. Bull. Geol. Soc. Am. 69: 39–60.

Emiliani, C. 1955. Pleistocene temperatures. J. Geol. 63: 538–578.

———. 1957. Temperature and age analysis of deep-sea cores. Science 125: 383–387.

Erdtman, G. 1931. Worpswede-Wabamun. Ein pollenstatistisches Menetekel. Naturwissenschaftlichen Verein zu Bremen 28: 11–17.

———. 1943. An introduction to pollen analysis. Chronica Botanica, Waltham.

———. 1952. Pollen morphology and plant taxonomy. Angiosperms. Almqvist & Wiksell, Stockholm.

———. 1957. Pollen and spore morphology/plant taxonomy. Gymnospermae, Pteridophyta, Bryophyta. Almqvist & Wiksell, Stockholm.

Erdtman, G. and E. Hultén. 1924. Observations sur quelques tourbières kamtchatiques. Geologiska Föreningens Förhandlinger 46: 279–283.

Ericson, D. B., W. S. Broecker, J. L. Kulp, and G. Wollin. 1956. Late-Pleistocene climates and deep-sea sediments. Science 124: 385–389.

Faegri, K. 1956. Recent trends in palynology. Bot. Rev. 22: 639–664.

Faegri, K. and J. Iversen. 1950. Text-book of modern pollen analysis. Munksgaard, Copenhagen.

Fairbridge, R. W. 1958. Dating the latest movements of the Quaternary sea level. Trans. New York Acad. Sci. 20: 471–482.

Fenneman, N. M. 1931. Physiography of western United States. McGraw-Hill, London.

Fernald, M. L. 1925. Persistence of plants in unglaciated areas of boreal America. Am. Acad. Arts and Sci. Mem. 15: 237–342.

Fernow, B. E. 1902. The forests of Alaska. In: Harriman expedition 2: 235–256. Doubleday, New York.

Firbas, F. 1923. Pollenanalytische Untersuchungen einiger Moore der Ostalpen. Lotos 71.

———. 1949. Waldgeschichte Mitteleuropas. Bd. 1, Allgemeine waldgeschichte. Gustav Fischer, Jena.

Fisher, L. C. 1941. Climate of Washington. In: Climate and man: 1170–1181. U. S. Dept. Agric. Yearbook, Washington, D. C.

Fitton, E. M. 1930. The climates of Alaska. Month. Weath. Rev. 58: 85–103.

Flint, R. F. 1947. Glacial geology and the Pleistocene epoch. Wiley, New York.

———. 1955. Rates of advance and retreat of the margin of the late-Wisconsin ice sheet. Am. J. Sci. 253: 249–255.

———. 1957. Glacial and Pleistocene geology. Wiley, New York.

Flint, R. F., M. Demorest, and A. L. Washburn. 1942. Glaciation of Schickschock Mountains, Gaspé Peninsula. Bull. Geol. Soc. Am. 53: 1211–1230.

Flint, R. F. and E. S. Deevey. 1951. Radiocarbon dating of late-Pleistocene events. Am. J. Sci. 249: 257–300.

Flint, R. F. and W. A. Gale. 1958. Stratigraphy and radiocarbon dates at Searles Lake, California. Am. J. Sci. 256: 689–714.

Flint, R. F. (chair.) *et al.* 1945. Glacial map of North America. Geol. Soc. Am. Spec. Papers 60: 1–37 and map.

Frey, D. G. 1951. Pollen succession in the sediments of Singletary Lake, North Carolina. Ecology 32: 518–533.

———. 1953. Regional aspects of the late-glacial and post-glacial pollen succession of southeastern North Carolina. Ecol. Monog. 23: 289–313.

———. 1955. A differential flotation technique for recovering microfossils from inorganic sediments. New Phytol. 54: 257–258.

FRITZ, E. 1931. The role of fire in the redwood region. J. Forestry 29: 939–950.

FULLER, G. D. 1927. Pollen analysis and postglacial vegetation. Bot. Gaz. 83: 323–325.

GODWIN, H. 1934. Pollen analysis. An outline of the problems and potentialities of the method. New Phytol. 33: 278–305, 325–358.

———. 1954. Recurrence surfaces. In: Studies in vegetational history in honour of Knud Jessen. Danmarks Geologiske Undersøgelse II Nr. 80: 22–30.

———. 1956. The history of the British flora. Cambridge Univ. Press, Cambridge.

GODWIN, H. and R. ANDREW. 1951. A fungal fruit body common in post-glacial peat deposits. New Phytol. 50:179–183.

GODWIN, H., D. WALKER, and E. H. WILLIS. 1957. Radiocarbon dating and post-glacial vegetational history: Scaleby Moss. Proc. Royal Soc. London (B) 147: 352–366.

GODWIN, H. and E. H. WILLIS. 1959. Radiocarbon dating of the late-glacial period in Britain. Proc. Royal Soc. London (B) 150: 199–215.

GOOD, R. 1931. A theory of plant geography. New Phytol. 30: 149–171.

———. 1953. The geography of the flowering plants. Longmans Green, New York.

GRANLUND, E. 1932. De svenska högmossarnas geologi. Sverig. Geol. Undersökn. Årsbok 26: 1–193.

GRANT, U. S. and D. F. HIGGINS. 1910. Reconnaissance of the geology and mineral resources of Prince William Sound. U. S. Geol. Surv. Bull. 443.

GRAVES, H. S. 1916. Forests of Alaska. Am. Forests 22: 24–37.

GRAYSON, J. 1956. The postglacial history of vegetation and climate in the Labrador-Quebec region as determined by palynology. Ph.D. Thesis, Univ. Mich., Ann Arbor.

GREGORY, R. A. 1957. Some silvicultural characteristics of western redcedar in southeast Alaska. Ecology 38: 646–649.

GRIFFIN, J. B. 1960. Some prehistoric connections between Siberia and America. Science 131: 801–812.

GRIGGS, R. F. 1914. Observations on the edge of the forest in the Kodiak region of Alaska. Bull. Torrey Bot. Club 41: 381–385.

———. 1918. The recovery of vegetation at Kodiak. Ohio J. Sci. 19: 1–57.

———. 1922. The Valley of Ten Thousand Smokes. Nat. Geog. Soc., Washington, D. C.

———. 1934. The edge of the forest in Alaska and the reasons for its position. Ecology 15: 80–96.

GRYC, G., D. J. MILLER, and T. G. PAYNE. 1951. Alaska. In: Ball, M. W., *et al.*, Eds., Possible future petroleum provinces of North America. Bull. Am. Assoc. Petroleum Geologists 35: 151–168.

GUNNING, H. C. 1929. Geology and mineral deposits of Quatsino-Nimpkish area, Vancouver Island, British Columbia. Geol. Surv. Canada Sum. Rept.: 94–143.

HAFSTEN, U. 1951. A pollen-analytic investigation of two peat deposits from Tristan da Cunha. Results of the Norwegian Scientific Expedition to Tristan da Cunha 1937–1938. No. 22. Det Norske Videnskaps-Academi, Oslo.

HALLIDAY, W. E. D. and A. W. A. BROWN. 1943. The distribution of some important forest trees in Canada. Ecology 24: 353–373.

HAMMEN, T. VAN DER. 1957. The stratigraphy of the Late-glacial. In: Pleistocene correlations between the Netherlands and adjacent areas: a symposium. Geologie en Mijnbouw 19: 250–254.

HANSEN, H. P. 1937. Pollen analysis of two Wisconsin bogs of different age. Ecology 18: 136–148.

———. 1938. Postglacial forest succession and climate in the Puget Sound region. Ecology 19: 528–542.

———. 1940. Paleoecology of two peat bogs in southwestern British Columbia. Am. J. Bot. 27: 144–149.

———. 1941a. Paleoecology of two peat deposits on the Oregon coast. Ore. State Monog. Studies in Botany 3.

———. 1941b. Paleoecology of a bog in the spruce-hemlock climax of the Olympic Peninsula. Am. Midland Naturalist 25: 290–297.

———. 1941c. Further pollen studies of Post-Pleistocene bogs in the Puget Lowland of Washington. Bull. Torrey Bot. Club 68: 133–148.

———. 1943a. Paleoecology of two sand dune bogs on the southern Oregon coast. Am. J. Bot. 30: 335–340.

———. 1943b. A pollen study of two bogs on Orcas Island, of the San Juan Islands, Washington. Bull. Torrey Bot. Club 70: 236–243.

———. 1944. Further pollen studies of peat bogs on the Pacific coast of Oregon and Washington. Bull. Torrey Bot. Club 71: 627–636.

———. 1947a. Postglacial forest succession, climate, and chronology in the Pacific Northwest. Trans. Am. Philos. Soc. 37: 1–130.

———. 1947b. Climate versus fire and soil as factors in postglacial forest succession in the Puget Lowland of Washington. Am. J. Sci. 245: 265–286.

———. 1948. Postglacial forests of the Glacier National Park region. Ecology 29: 146–152.

———. 1949a. Postglacial forests in west central Alberta, Canada. Bull. Torrey Bot. Club 76: 278–289.

———. 1949b. Postglacial forests in south central Alberta, Canada. Am. J. Bot. 36: 54–65.

———. 1950a. Pollen analysis of three bogs on Vancouver Island, Canada. J. Ecology 38: 270–276.

———. 1950b. Postglacial forests along the Alaska Highway in British Columbia. Proc. Am. Philos. Soc. 94: 411–421.

———. 1952. Postglacial forests in the Grande Prairie-Lesser Slave Lake region of Alberta, Canada. Ecology 33: 31–40.

———. 1953. Postglacial forests in the Yukon Territory and Alaska. Am. J. Sci. 251: 505–542.

———. 1955. Postglacial forests in south-central and central British Columbia. Am. J. Sci. 253: 640–658.

HANSON, G. 1923. Reconnaissance between Kitsault River and Skeena River, B. C. Geol. Surv. Canada Sum. Rept. 1922, Part A: 35–50.

HANZLIK, E. J. 1932. Type successions in the Olympic Mountains. J. Forestry 30: 91–93.

HAURWITZ, B. and J. AUSTIN. 1944. Climatology. McGraw-Hill, New York.

HELLER, E. 1910. Partial list of plants, chiefly trees and shrubs. In: Mammals of the 1908 Alexander expedition. Univ. Calif. Publ. Zoology 5: 349–360.

HENRY, J. K. 1915. Flora of southern British Columbia and Vancouver Island with many references to Alaska and northern species. Toronto.

HERSHEY, O. H. 1900. Ancient alpine glaciers of the Sierra Costa Mountains in California. J. Geol. 8: 42–57.

———. 1903. Some evidence of the two glacial stages in the Klamath Mountains of California. Am. Geol. 31: 139–156.

HEUSSER, C. J. 1952. Pollen profiles from Southeastern Alaska. Ecol. Monog. 22: 331–352.

———. 1953. Radiocarbon dating of the thermal maximum in Southeastern Alaska. Ecology 34: 637–640.

———. 1954a. Alpine fir at Taku Glacier, Alaska, with notes on its postglacial migration to the Territory. Bull. Torrey Bot. Club 81: 83–86.

———. 1954b. Nunatak flora of the Juneau Ice Field, Alaska. Bull. Torrey Bot. Club 81: 236–250.

———. 1954c. Additional pollen profiles from Southeastern Alaska. Am. J. Sci. 252: 106–119.

———. 1955a. Pollen profiles from Prince William Sound and southeastern Kenai Peninsula, Alaska. Ecology 36: 185–202.

———. 1955b. Pollen profiles from the Queen Charlotte Islands, British Columbia. Can. J. Bot. 33: 429–449.

———. 1956. Postglacial environments in the Canadian Rocky Mountains. Ecol. Monog. 26: 263–302.

———. 1957a. Variations of Blue, Hoh, and White Glaciers during recent centuries. Arctic 10: 139–150.

———. 1957b. Pleistocene and postglacial vegetation of Alaska and Yukon Territory. In: Arctic biology. 18th Biological Colloquium. Oreg. State College: 62–72.

———. 1958. Late Pleistocene environments and chronology of Pacific coastal Alaska. Bull. Geol. Soc. Am. 69: 1753–1754.

———. 1959. Radiocarbon dates of peats from North Pacific North America. Am. J. Sci. Radiocarbon Supplement 1: 29–34.

HOFFMAN, B. F. 1912. Sitka spruce of Alaska. Proc. Soc. Am. Foresters 7: 226–238.

HOFMANN, J. V. 1920. The establishment of a Douglas fir forest. Ecology 1: 49–53.

HOLWAY, R. S. 1911. An extension of the known area of Pleistocene glaciation to the Coast Ranges of California. Bull. Geol. Soc. Am. 43: 161–170.

———. 1914. Apparent limits of former glaciation in the northern Coast Ranges of California. Bull. Geol. Soc. Am. 25: 120–121.

HOOGENRAAD, H. R. 1935. Studien über die sphagnicolen Rhizopoden der niederlandischen Fauna. Archiv für Protistenkunde 84.

HOPKINS, D. M. 1959. Cenozoic history of the Bering land bridge. Science 129: 1519–1528.

HOPKINS, D. M. and W. S. BENNINGHOFF. 1953. Evidence of a very warm Pleistocene interglacial interval on Seward Peninsula. Bull. Geol. Soc. Am. 64: 1435–1436.

HOPKINS, D. M. and J. L. GIDDINGS, JR. 1953. Geological background of the Iyatayet archeological site, Cape Denbigh, Alaska. Smithsonian Misc. Collect. 121, No. 11.

HOPKINS, J. S. 1950. Differential flotation and deposition of coniferous and deciduous tree pollen. Ecology 31: 633–641.

HOUDEK, P. K. 1933. Pollen statistics for two Indiana bogs. Proc. Ind. Acad. Sci. 42: 73–77.

HUBLEY, R. C. 1956. Glaciers of the Washington Cascade and Olympic Mountains; their present activity and its relation to local climatic trends. J. Glaciol. 2: 669–674.

HULTÉN, E. 1937a. Flora of the Aleutian Islands and westernmost Alaska Peninsula with notes on the flora of the Commander Islands. Bokförlags Aktiebolaget Thule, Stockholm.

———. 1937b. Outline of the history of arctic and boreal biota during the Quarternary period. Bokförlags Aktiebolaget Thule, Stockholm.

———. 1941–1950. Flora of Alaska and Yukon. Gleerup, Lund.

Hyde, H. A. and D. A. Williams. 1944. In: Pollen Analysis Circ. 8: 6.

Isaac, L. A. 1940. Vegetative succession following logging in the Douglas fir region with special reference to fire. J. Forestry 38: 716–721.

Iversen, J. 1953. Radiocarbon dating of the Alleröd period. Science 118: 4–6.

———. 1954. The late-glacial flora of Denmark and its relations to climate and soil. Danmarks Geologiske Undersøgelse II. Rekke. 80: 87–119.

Iversen, J. and J. Troels-Smith. 1950. Pollenmorfologiske definitioner og typer. Danmarks Geologiske Undersøgelse IV, Nr. 8.

Ives, R. L. 1954. Climatic studies in western North America. In: Proc. Toronto Meteor. Conf. 1953: 218–222.

Jepson, W. L. 1925. A manual of the flowering plants of California. Assoc. Students Store Univ. Calif., Berkeley.

Jessen, K. 1920. Moseundersøgelse i der nordostlige Sjaelland. Danmarks Geologiske Undersøgelse II, 34.

———. 1949. Studies in late Quaternary deposits and flora-history of Ireland. Proc. Royal Irish Acad. 52, Sect. B: 85–290.

Johnson, A. L. and J. A. Sandor. 1957. 1956 Yakutat management survey report. U. S. Forest Serv., Juneau.

Johnson, E. J. 1949. Pollen analysis of peat underlying treeless heath area in the forest-tundra transition near Churchill, Manitoba. M. A. Thesis, McMaster Univ., Ontario.

Johnston, W. A. 1923. Geology of the Fraser River delta map-area. Geol. Surv. Canada Mem. 135.

Jones, G. N. 1936. A botanical survey of the Olympic Peninsula, Washington. Univ. Wash. Publ. Biol. 5.

Jones, S. B. 1932. Classifications of North American climates. Econ. Geog. 8: 205–208.

Judson, S. 1946. Late glacial and postglacial chronology on Adak. J. Geol. 54: 376–385.

Karlstrom, T. N. V. 1953. Upper Cook Inlet region, Alaska. In: Multiple glaciation in Alaska: a progress report. U. S. Geol. Surv. Circ. 289: 3–5.

———. 1957. Tentative correlation of Alaskan glacial sequences, 1956. Science 125: 73–74.

Kellogg, R. S. 1910. The forest of Alaska. U. S. Dept. Agric. Forest Serv. Bull. 81.

Kendrew, W. G. and D. Kerr. 1955. The climate of British Columbia and the Yukon Territory. Edmund Cloutier, Ottawa.

Kerr, F. A. 1934. Glaciation in northern British Columbia. Trans. Royal Soc. Canada, Ser. III, Sect. 4, 28: 17–31.

———. 1936a. Physiography of the Cordilleran region of northern British Columbia and adjacent areas. Trans. Royal Soc. Canada, Ser. III, Sect. 4, 30: 137–154.

———. 1936b. Quaternary glaciation in the coast range, northern British Columbia and Alaska. J. Geol. 44: 681–700.

———. (comp. by H. C. Cooke). 1948a. Taku River map-area, B. C. Geol. Surv. Canada Mem. 248.

———. (comp. by H. C. Cooke). 1948b. Lower Stikine and western Iskut River areas, B. C. Geol. Surv. Canada Mem. 246.

Kincer, J. B. 1941. Climate of Alaska. In: Climate and man: 1211–1215. U. S. Dept. Agric. Yearbook, Washington, D. C.

Knopf, A. 1912. The Sitka mining district. U. S. Geol. Surv. Bull. 504.

Köppen, W. and R. Geiger. 1936. Handbuch der Klimatologie. I., C. Gebrüder Borntraeger, Berlin.

KRAJINA, V. J. 1956. A summary of the nomenclature of Douglas fir, Pseudotsuga Menziesii. Madrono 13: 265–267.

KRIEGER, A. D. 1953. New world culture history: Anglo-America. In: Anthropology today: 238–264. Univ. Chicago Press, Chicago.

KRINSLEY, D. B. 1953. Multiple glaciation in southwest Kenai Peninsula, Alaska. In: Multiple glaciation in Alaska: a progress report. U. S. Geol. Surv. Circ. 289: 5–6.

KULP, J. L., H. W. FEELY, and L. E. TRYON. 1951. Lamont natural radiocarbon measurements I. Science 114: 565–568.

KULP, J. L., L. E. TRYON, W. E. ECKELMAN, and W. A. SNELL. 1952. Lamont natural radiocarbon measurements II. Science 116: 409–414.

LACHAPELLE, E. R. 1959. Annual mass and energy exchange on the Blue Glacier. J. Geophysical Res. 64: 443–449.

LAWRENCE, D. B. 1938. Trees on the march. Mazama Annual, Portland.

———. 1941. The floating island lava flow of Mt. St. Helens. Mazama 23: 56–60.

———. 1948. Mt. Hood's latest eruption and glacier advances. Mazama 30: 22–29.

———. 1950. Glacier fluctuation for six centuries in southeastern Alaska and its relation to solar activity. Geog. Rev. 40: 191–223.

———. 1958. Glaciers and vegetation in southeastern Alaska. Am. Scientist 46: 89–122.

LEOPOLD, E. B. 1956. Two late-glacial deposits in southern Connecticut. Proc. National Acad. Sci. 42: 863–876.

LEWIS, I. F. and E. C. COCKE. 1929. Pollen analysis of Dismal Swamp peat. J. Elisha Mitchell Sci. Soc. 45:37–58.

LIBBY, W. F. 1952. Chicago radiocarbon dates, III. Science 116: 673–681.

———. 1954. Chicago radiocarbon dates, IV. Science 119: 135–140.

LICHTWARDT, R. W. 1952. A new light-weight shaft for peat samplers. Paleobotanist 1: 317–318.

LITTLE, E. L., JR. 1953. A natural hybrid spruce in Alaska. J. Forestry 51: 745–747.

LIVINGSTONE, D. A. 1955a. Some pollen profiles from arctic Alaska. Ecology 36: 587–600.

———. 1955b. A lightweight piston sampler for lake deposits. Ecology 36: 137–139.

———. 1957. Pollen analysis of a valley fill near Umiat, Alaska. Am. J. Sci. 255: 254–260.

LIVINGSTONE, D. A. and B. G. R. LIVINGSTONE. 1958. Late-glacial and postglacial vegetation from Gillis Lake in Richmond County, Cape Breton Island, Nova Scotia. Am. J. Sci. 256: 341–359.

LONGLEY, R. W. 1954. Temperature trends in Canada. In: Proc. Toronto Meteor. Conf. 1953: 207–211.

LOWRY, W. D. and E. M. BALDWIN. 1952. Late Cenozoic geology of the lower Columbia River valley, Oregon and Washington. Bull. Geol. Soc. Am. 63: 1–24.

LUPTON, C. T. 1914. Oil and gas in the western part of the Olympic Peninsula, Washington. U. S. Geol. Surv. Bull. 581: 23–81.

LUTZ, H. J. 1930. Observations on the invasion of glacial moraines by trees. Ecology 11: 562–567.

———. 1953. The effects of forest fires on the vegetation of interior Alaska. Alaska Forest Res. Center Station Paper 1.

MACKENZIE, J. D. 1914. The Queen Charlotte Islands. Geol. Surv. Canada Sum. Rept. 1913: 34–54.

———. 1915. Graham Island, British Columbia. Geol. Surv. Canada Sum. Rept. 1914: 33–37.

———. 1916. Geology of Graham Island, British Columbia. Geol. Surv. Canada Mem. 88.

———. 1923. Alberni area, Vancouver Island, B. C. Geol. Surv. Canada Sum. Rept. 1922, Part A: 51–67.

Mackin, J. H. 1941. Glacial geology of the Snoqualmie-Cedar area, Washington. J. Geol. 49: 449–481.

Maddren, A. G. 1914. Mineral deposits of the Yakataga district, Alaska. U. S. Geol. Surv. Bull. 592E: 119–153.

———. 1919. The beach placers of the west coast of Kodiak Island. U. S. Geol. Surv. Bull. 292E: 299–319.

Martin, A. G. and F. E. Williams. 1924. An ice eroded fiord; the mode of origin of Lynn Canal, Alaska. Geog. Rev. 14: 576–596.

Martin, G. C. 1908. Geology and mineral resources of the Controller Bay region, Alaska. U. S. Geol. Surv. Bull. 335.

Martin, G. C., B. L. Johnson, and U. S. Grant. 1915. Geology and mineral resources of Kenai Peninsula, Alaska. U. S. Geol. Surv. Bull. 587: 39–40, 125–126.

Mason, H. L. 1936. The principles of geographic distribution as applied to floral analysis. Madrono 3: 181–190.

Mathews, W. H. 1947. "Tuyas," flat-topped volcanoes in northern British Columbia. Am. J. Sci. 245: 560–570.

———. 1951a. Historic and prehistoric fluctuations of alpine glaciers in the Mount Garibaldi map-area. J. Geol. 59: 357–380.

———. 1951b. The Table, a flat-topped volcano in southern British Columbia. Am. J. Sci. 249: 830–841.

———. 1952a. Mount Garibaldi, a supraglacial Pleistocene volcano in southwestern British Columbia. Am. J. Sci. 250: 81–103.

———. 1952b. Ice-dammed lavas from Clinker Mountain, southwestern British Columbia. Am. J. Sci. 250: 553–565.

———. 1958. Geology of the Mount Garibaldi map-area, southwestern British Columbia, Canada. Bull. Geol. Soc. Am. 69: 161–198.

Mathias, M. and L. Constance. 1959. New North American Umbelliferae III. Bull. Torrey Bot. Club 86: 374–382.

Matthes, F. E. 1914. Mount Rainier and its glaciers. U. S. Dept. Interior, Washington, D. C.

McAvoy, B. 1929. Successions in the alpine region of British Columbia. Trans. Ill. State Acad. Sci. 22: 332–335.

———. 1931. Ecological surveys of the Bella Coola region. Bot. Gaz. 92: 141–171.

McCabe, T. T. and I. McT. Cowan. 1945. Peromyscus Maniculatus Macrorhinus and the problem of insularity. Trans. Royal Can. Inst. 117–215.

McConnell, R. G. 1913. Portions of Portland Canal and Skeena mining divisions, Skeena district, B. C. Geol. Surv. Canada Mem. 32.

———. 1914. Texada Island, British Columbia. Geol. Surv. Canada Mem. 58.

McMillan, C. 1956. The edaphic restriction of Cupressus and Pinus in the Coast Ranges of central California. Ecol. Monog. 26: 177–212.

Merkle, J. 1951. An analysis of the plant communities of Mary's Peak, western Oregon. Ecology 32: 618–640.

Mertie, J. B., Jr. 1933. Geology and geography of Lituya Bay, Alaska. U. S. Geol. Surv. Bull. 836: 117–135.

Miller, D. J. 1953. Late Cenozoic marine glacial sediments and marine terraces of Middleton Island, Alaska. J. Geol. 61: 17–40.

———. 1957a. Tertiary sequence on the northeast coast of Gulf of Alaska. Bull. Am. Assoc. Petroleum Geologists 41: 353–354.

———. 1957b. Geology of the southeastern part of the Robinson Mountains, Yakataga district, Alaska. U. S. Geol. Surv. Oil and Gas Investigations Map OM 187.

———. 1958a. Gulf of Alaska area. In: Landscapes of Alaska: 19–29. Univ. Calif. Press, Berkeley and Los Angeles.

———. 1958b. Anomalous glacial history of the northeastern Gulf of Alaska region. Bull. Geol. Soc. Am. 69: 1613–1614.

MILLER, M. M. 1952. Scientific observations of the Juneau Ice Field Research Project, Alaska, 1949 field season. Am. Geog. Soc., New York.

MOFFIT, F. H. 1954. Geology of the Prince William Sound region, Alaska. U. S. Geol. Surv. Bull. 989E.

MULLER, E. H., W. JUHLE, and H. W. COULTER. 1954. Current volcanic activity in Katmai National Monument. Science 119: 319–321.

MUNGER, T. T. 1940. The cycle from Douglas fir to hemlock. Ecology 21: 451–459.

MÜNNICH, K. O. 1957. Heidelberg natural radiocarbon measurements I. Science 126: 194–199.

MUNNS, E. N. 1938. The distribution of important forest trees of the United States. U. S. Dept. Agric. Misc. Publ. 287.

MUNZ, P. A. and D. D. KECK. 1949. California plant communities. El Aliso 2: 87–105.

NEILAND, B. J. 1958. Forest and adjacent burn in the Tillamook burn area of northwestern Oregon. Ecology 39: 660–671.

ODELL, N. E. 1938. The great ice age and its effects. In: Northernmost Labrador mapped from the air. Am. Geog. Soc. Spec. Publ. 22: 204–215.

OGDEN, J. G. 1959. A late-glacial pollen sequence from Martha's Vineyard, Massachusetts. Am. J. Sci. 257: 366–381.

OLSON, E. A. and W. S. BROECKER. 1959. Lamont natural radiocarbon measurements V. Am. J. Sci. 257: 1–28 (Radiocarbon Supplement 1: 1–28).

OOSTING, H. J. 1948. The study of plant communities. W. H. Freeman, San Francisco.

OSGOOD, W. H. 1901a. Natural history of the Cook Inlet region, Alaska. U. S. Dept. Agric. North Am. Fauna 21: 51–87.

———. 1901b. Natural history of the Queen Charlotte Islands. U. S. Dept. Agric. North Am. Fauna 21: 7–50.

OSVALD, H. 1933. Vegetation of the Pacific coast bogs of North America. Acta Phytogeog. Suecica 5: 1–12.

———. 1936. Stratigraphy and pollen flora of some bogs of the North Pacific coast of America. Bericht Schweizer Botanische Gesellschaft 46.

PAGE, B. M. 1939. Multiple alpine glaciation in the Leavenworth area, Washington. J. Geol. 47: 785–816.

PALMER, A. H. 1917. Fog along the California coast. Month. Weath. Rev. 45: 496–499.

PEACOCK, M. A. 1935. Fiord land of British Columbia. Bull. Geol. Soc. Am. 46: 633–696.

PECK, M. E. 1925. A preliminary sketch of the plant regions of Oregon. I, Western Oregon. Am. J. Bot. 12: 33–49.

———. 1941. A manual of the higher plants of Oregon. Binfords and Mort, Portland.

PIPER, C. V. 1906. Flora of the state of Washington. Contrib. U. S. National Herbarium 11.

PLAFKER, G. and D. J. MILLER. 1957. Reconnaissance geology of the Malaspina district, Alaska. U. S. Geol. Surv. Oil and Gas Investigations Map OM 189.

PLAFKER, G. and D. J. MILLER. 1958. Glacial features and surficial deposits of the Malaspina district, Alaska. U. S. Geol. Surv. Misc. Geol. Investigations, Map I-271.

PORSILD, A. E. 1938. Earth mounds in unglaciated arctic northwest America. Geog. Rev. 28: 46–58.

POST, L. VON. 1918. Skogsträdspollen i sydsvenska torvmosselagerföljder. Forhandl. 16. Skandinaviske Naturforskermöte 1916.

———. 1946. The prospect for pollen analysis in the study of the earth's climatic history. New Phytol. 45: 193–217.

POTZGER, J. E. 1932. Succession of forests as indicated by fossil pollen from a northern Michigan bog. Science 75: 366.

———. 1953. Nineteen bogs from southern Quebec. Can. J. Bot. 31: 383–401.

———. 1955. A borer for sampling in permafrost. Ecology 36: 161.

———. 1956. Pollen profiles as indicators in the history of lake filling and bog formation. Ecology 37: 476–483.

POTZGER, J. E. and A. COURTEMANCHE. 1956. A series of bogs across Quebec from the St. Lawrence valley to James Bay. Can. J. Bot. 34: 473–500.

POTZGER, J. E., A. COURTEMANCHE, M. SYLVIO, and F. M. HUEBER. 1956. Pollen from moss polsters on the mat of Lac Shaw Bog, Quebec, correlated with a forest survey. Butler Univ. Bot. Studies 13: 24–35.

POWERS, H. A. 1958. Alaska Peninsula-Aleutian Islands. In: Landscapes of Alaska: 61–75. Univ. Calif. Press, Berkeley and Los Angeles.

PRESTON, R. S., E. PERSON, and E. S. DEEVEY. 1955. Yale natural radiocarbon measurements II. Science 122: 954–960.

REED, J. C. 1958. Southeastern Alaska. In: Landscapes of Alaska: 9–18. Univ. Calif. Press, Berkeley and Los Angeles.

RIGG, G. B. 1914. Notes on the flora of some Alaskan sphagnum bogs. Plant World 17: 167–182.

———. 1922. A bog forest. Ecology 3: 207–213.

———. 1925. Some sphagnum bogs of the north Pacific coast of America. Ecology 6: 260–278.

———. 1933. Notes on a sphagnum bog at Fort Bragg, California. Science 77: 535–536.

———. 1937. Some raised bogs of southeastern Alaska with notes on flat bogs and muskegs. Am. J. Bot. 24: 194–198.

———. 1958. Peat resources of Washington. Bull. Wash. Div. Mines and Geology 44.

RIGG, G. B. and H. R. GOULD. 1957. Age of Glacier Peak eruption and chronology of post-glacial peat deposits in Washington and surrounding areas. Am. J. Sci. 255: 341–363.

RIGG, G. B. and C. T. RICHARDSON. 1938. Profiles of some sphagnum bogs of the Pacific coast of North America. Ecology 19: 408–434.

ROACH, A. W. 1952. Phytosociology of the Nash Crater lava flows, Linn County, Oregon. Ecol. Monog. 22: 169–193.

ROOSMA, A. 1958. A climatic record from Searles Lake, California. Science 128: 716.

ROWLEY, J. R. and A. O. DAHL. 1956. Modifications in design and use of the Livingstone piston sampler. Ecology 37: 849–851.

RUBIN, M. and C. ALEXANDER. 1958. U. S. Geological Survey radiocarbon dates IV. Science 127: 1476–1487.

RUBIN, M. and H. E. SUESS. 1955. U. S. Geological Survey radiocarbon dates II. Science 121: 481–488.

———. 1956. U. S. Geological Survey radiocarbon dates III. Science 123: 442–448.

RUSSELL, I. C. 1893. Second expedition to Mount St. Elias in 1891. U. S. Geol. Surv. 13th Ann. Rept.

RUSSELL, R. J. 1926. Climates of California. Univ. Calif. Publ. Geog. 2: 73–84.

ST. AMAND, P. 1957. Geological and geophysical synthesis of the tectonics of portions of British Columbia, the Yukon Territory, and Alaska. Bull. Geol. Soc. Am. 68: 1343–1370.

SCHMIDT, R. L. 1955. Some aspects of western red cedar regeneration in the coastal forests of British Columbia. B. C. Forest Serv. Res. Note 29.

———. 1957. The silvics and plant geography of the genus Abies in the coastal forests of British Columbia. B. C. Forest Serv. Tech. Publ. T. 46.

SCHOFIELD, S. J. and G. HANSON. 1922. Salmon River district, B. C. Geol. Surv. Canada Mem. 32.

SCHULMAN, E. 1951. Tree-ring indices of rainfall, temperature, and river flow. In: Compendium of meteorology: 1024–1029. Am. Meteor. Soc.

———. 1953. Tree-ring evidence for climatic change. In: Climatic change: 207–219. Harvard Univ. Press, Cambridge.

SEARS, P. B. 1930a. Common fossil pollen of the Erie basin. Bot. Gaz. 89: 95–106.

———. 1930b. A record of post-glacial climate in northern Ohio. Ohio J. Sci. 30: 205–217.

SELLING, O. H. 1948. Studies in Hawaiian pollen statistics. Part III, On the late-Quaternary history of the Hawaiian vegetation. Bernice P. Bishop Museum Spec. Publ. 39.

SHARP, R. P. 1958. Malaspina Glacier, Alaska. Bull. Geol. Soc. Am. 69: 617–646.

SHELDON, C. 1912. The wilderness of the North Pacific coast islands. Charles Scribner's Sons, New York.

SIGAFOOS, R. S. 1958. Vegetation of northwestern North America, as an aid in interpretation of geologic data. U. S. Geol. Surv. Bull. 1061-E: 165–185.

SMITH, W. D. 1933a. Geology of the Oregon coast. Pan-Am. Geol. 59: 33–44.

———. 1933b. Physiography of Oregon coast. Pan-Am. Geol. 59: 97–114.

———. 1933c. Special physiographic features of Oregon coast. Pan-Am. Geol. 59: 190–206, 241–258.

SMITH, W. D. and E. PACKARD. 1919. The salient features of the geology of Oregon. J. Geol. 27: 79–120.

SPENCER, A. C. 1903. The Pacific mountain system in Alaska. Bull. Geol. Soc. Am. 14: 117–132.

SPRAGUE, M. 1941. Climate of California. In: Climate and man: 783–797. U. S. Dept. Agric. Yearbook, Washington, D. C.

STEARNS, H. T. 1941. Shore benches on North Pacific islands. Bull. Geol. Soc. Am. 52: 773–780.

———. 1945a. Eustatic shore lines in the Pacific. Bull. Geol. Soc. Am. 56: 1071–1078.

———. 1945b. Late geologic history of the Pacific basin. Am. J. Sci. 243: 614–626.

SUDWORTH, G. B. 1908. Forest trees of the Pacific slope. U. S. Gov. Print. Off., Washington, D. C.

SUESS, H. E. 1954. U. S. Geological Survey radiocarbon dates I. Science 120: 467–473.

———. 1956. Absolute chronology of the last glaciation. Science 123: 355–357.

SVERDRUP, H. U. 1940. Currents of the Pacific Ocean and their bearing on the climates of the coast. Science 91: 273–282.

TALIAFERRO, N. L. 1932. Geology of the Yakataga, Katalla, and Nichawak districts, Alaska. Bull. Geol. Soc. Am. 43: 749–782.

TARR, R. S. 1909. The Yakutat Bay region, Alaska; physiography and glacial geology. U. S. Geol. Surv. Prof. Paper 64: 1–144.

TARR, R. S. and B. S. BUTLER. 1909. The Yakutat Bay region, Alaska. U. S. Geol. Surv. Prof. Paper 64: 145–178.

TARR, R. S. and L. MARTIN. 1906. Recent changes of level in the Yakutat Bay region, Alaska. Bull. Geol. Soc. Am. 17: 29–64.

———. 1912. The earthquakes at Yakutat Bay, Alaska in September 1899. U. S. Geol. Surv. Prof. Paper 69.

———. 1914. Alaskan glacier studies. Nat. Geog. Soc., Washington, D. C.

TAYLOR, R. F. 1929. Pocket guide to Alaska trees. U. S. Dept. Agric. Misc. Publ. 55.

———. 1932. The successional trend and its relation to second-growth forests in southeastern Alaska. Ecology 13: 381–391.

———. 1935. Available nitrogen as a factor influencing the occurrence of Sitka spruce and western hemlock seedlings in the forests of southeastern Alaska. Ecology 16: 580–602.

TAYLOR, W. P. 1922. A distributional and ecological study of Mount Rainier, Washington. Ecology 3: 214–236.

TERASMAE, J. 1959. Terminology of post-Valders time. Bull. Geol. Soc. Am. 70: 665–666.

THOMAS, J. H. 1957. The vascular flora of Middleton Island, Alaska. Contrib. Dudley Herbarium 5: 39–56.

THORNTHWAITE, C. W. 1931. The climates of North America according to a new classification. Geog. Rev. 21: 633–655.

TOCHER, D. and D. J. MILLER. 1959. Field observations on effects of Alaska earthquake of 10 July 1958. Science 129: 394–395.

TSUKADA, M. 1958. On the climatic changes of postglacial age in Japan based on four pollen analyses. Quaternary Res. 1: 48–58.

TURESSON, G. 1916. Lysichiton camtschatcense (L.) Schott, and its behavior in sphagnum bogs. Am. J. Bot. 3: 189–209.

TWENHOFEL, W. S. 1952. Recent shore-line changes along the Pacific coast of Alaska. Am. J. Sci. 250: 523–548.

VALLENTYNE, J. R. 1955. A modification of the Livingstone piston sampler for lake deposits. Ecology 36: 139–141.

VERHOOGEN, J. 1937. Mount Saint Helens, a recent Cascade volcano. Univ. Calif. Publ. Bull. Dept. Geol. Sci. 24: 263–302.

VOSS, J. 1931. Preliminary report on the paleo-ecology of a Wisconsin and an Illinois bog. Trans. Ill. State Acad. Sci. 24: 130–137.

VRIES, H. DE, G. W. BARENDSEN, and H. T. WATERBOLK. 1958. Groningen radiocarbon dates II. Science 127: 129–137.

WALDRON, H. H., D. R. MULLINEAUX, and D. R. CRANDELL. 1957. Age of the Vashon glaciation in the southern and central parts of the Puget Sound basin, Washington. Bull. Geol. Soc. Am. 68: 1849–1850.

WARD, R. D. and C. F. BROOKS. 1936a. The climates of North America I. Part 2, United States. In: Handbuch der Klimatologie, Bd. 2, Teil J1: 80–303. Gebrüder Borntraeger, Berlin.

——— (with E. M. FITTON). 1936b. The climates of North America I. Part 3, Alaska. In: Handbuch der Klimatologie, Bd. 2, Teil J1: 304–325. Gebrüder Borntraeger, Berlin.

WASHBURNE, C. W. 1914. Reconnaissance of the geology and oil prospects of northwestern Oregon. U. S. Geol. Surv. Bull. 590.

WEAVER, C. E. 1949. Geology of the Coast Ranges immediately north of the San Francisco Bay region, California. Geol. Soc. Am. Mem. 35.

WEAVER, J. E. and F. E. CLEMENTS. 1938. Plant ecology. McGraw-Hill, New York.

WELLS, E. L. 1941. Climate of Oregon. In: Climate and man: 1075–1086. U. S. Dept. Agric. Yearbook, Washington, D. C.

WENNER, C. 1947. Pollen diagrams from Labrador. Geog. Ann. 29: 137–374.

WHITFORD, H. N. and R. D. CRAIG. 1918. Forests of British Columbia. Comm. Conserv., Ottawa.

WILLETT, H. C. 1944. Descriptive meteorology. Academic Press, New York.

———. 1953. Atmospheric and oceanic circulation as factors in glacial-interglacial changes of climate. In: Climatic change: 51–71. Harvard Univ. Press, Cambridge.

WILLIAMS, H. 1932. Geology of the Lassen Volcanic National Park. Univ. Calif. Publ. Bull. Dept. Geol. Sci. 21: 195–385.

———. 1942. Geology of Crater Lake National Park, Oregon. Carnegie Inst. Wash. Publ. 540.

———. 1948. The ancient volcanoes of Oregon. Ore. State System Higher Education, Eugene.

——— (Ed.). 1958. Landscapes of Alaska. Univ. Calif. Press, Berkeley and Los Angeles.

WILLIS, B. 1898. Drift phenomena of Puget Sound. Bull. Geol. Soc. Am. 9: 111–162.

WILSON, J. T. (chair.) *et al.* 1958. Glacial map of Canada. Geol. Assoc. Canada, Toronto.

WILSON, L. R. 1934. The spores of the genus Lycopodium in the U. S. and Canada. Rhodora 36: 13–19.

———. 1938. The postglacial history of vegetation in northwestern Wisconsin. Rhodora 40: 137–175.

———. 1944. Spores and pollen as microfossils. Bot. Rev. 10: 499–523.

WODEHOUSE, R. P. 1935. Pollen grains. McGraw-Hill, New York.

WRIGHT, F. E. 1906. The Unuk River mining region of British Columbia. Geol. Surv. Canada Sum. Rept. 1905: 46–53.

WRIGHT, H. E., JR. and M. RUBIN. 1956. Radiocarbon dates of Mankato drift in Minnesota. Science 124: 625–626.

WULFF, E. V. 1950. An introduction to historical plant geography. Chronica Botanica, Waltham.

WYNNE-EDWARDS, V. C. 1937. Isolated arctic-alpine floras in eastern North America; a discussion of their glacial and recent history. Trans. Royal Soc. Canada 31: 1–26.

ZACH, L. 1950. A northern climax, forest or muskeg? Ecology 31: 304–306.

ZEUNER, F. E. 1952. Dating the past. An introduction to geochronology. Methuen, London.

PLATES

PLATE I. Piedmont lobe of Bering Glacier, south-central Alaska, showing ice-front lake and calved icebergs that drain via Seal River in the foreground into the Pacific Ocean. Contortions in the ice are morainal folds. The Chugach Mountains are on the skyline.

PLATE II. View southwesterly across the Juneau Ice Field in southeastern Alaska, taken from a nunatak at 7000 ft near the head of Taku Glacier. Ocean fog over the lower valleys simulates an ice-age landscape.

PLATE III. Deltaic gravels exposed in a pit near Salmon Creek mouth bordering Gastineau Channel, a few miles northwest of Juneau. Foreset beds are clearly in evidence dipping toward the channel. Delta rests at ca 30-ft elevation, indicating change in land and sea-level relations, which are as much as 500 ft in the Juneau sector.

PLATE IV. Sitka spruce snag near the head of Hanning Bay on Montague Island, Prince William Sound. Base is *in situ* and submerged at high tide, indicating very recent subsidence of this part of the island. Photo by H. J. Lutz, 22 May 1925. Courtesy U. S. Forest Service.

PLATE V. Aerial view of Lituya Bay with a part of the coast southeast of the bay in the foreground. End moraine of former Lituya Bay glacier is at the left; Cenotaph Island can be seen, as well as Lituya Glacier on Gilbert Inlet at the head of the bay. Marine terraces are delineated by rows of trees aligned with the beach and are mostly covered by patches of muskeg. The highest terrace is ca 1700-ft elevation. The nonforested land bordering the bay resulted from the destructive, earthquake-related water wave that passed oceanward on 9 July 1958. Photo courtesy Don J. Miller, U. S. Geological Survey.

PLATE VI. South-facing slope bordering upper Salmon Creek drainage near Juneau, elevation ca 2500 ft. Vegetation is alpine tundra in the foreground and Pacific Coastal Forest on the lower slope. Gastineau Channel separates the mainland from Douglas Island in the distance.

PLATE VII. Western hemlock stand at Bond Bay on Behm Canal, southeastern Alaska. Photo by E. S. Schipp taken in 1930. Courtesy U. S. Forest Service.

PLATE VIII. Sitka spruce on southern Chichagof Island, Alexander Archipelago, southeastern Alaska. Photo by H. S. Graves. Courtesy U. S. Forest Service.

PLATE IX. Alaska yellow cedar on marine terrace at ca 350-ft elevation northwest of Lituya Bay. Tree measured a 6.7-ft diameter breast high.

Plate X. Dissected outwash in front of the foot of Mendenhall Glacier near Juneau. Alder and willow are in the foreground, but plants are few and unnoticeable on the newly uncovered outwash. This terrain has been invaded by a host of pioneer plants since the photo was taken, 23 July 1951, from southeast point below the foot.

PLATE XI. Alder and willow being topped by black cottonwood on outwash of Gilkey Glacier, which drains via the South Fork of Antler River into Berners Bay on Lynn Canal, southeastern Alaska.

PLATE XII. Sitka spruce overtopping black cottonwood on a recessional moraine of Mendenhall Glacier near Juneau.

PLATE XIII. Muskeg on gently sloping bench north of Whitestone Harbor, northwestern Chichagof Island, southeastern Alaska. Plant cover consists of lodgepole pine, sedge, and heath.

PLATE XIV. Lodgepole pine growing on slope muskeg near Auke Bay, northwest of Juneau. Tallest tree was ca 55 ft in height, 2 ft in diameter breast high, and 275 yr in age.

PLATE XV. Park-like spruce and poplar in a region of the Kenai Peninsula, where elements of the Interior Forest and Pacific Coastal Forest overlap. Grass and alder are the principal plants between the groves of trees. Location is ca 1300-ft elevation north of Homer.

PLATE XVI. Pure stand of mature Sitka spruce at Seal Bay, Afognak Island. Photo taken 23 May 1927 by M. L. Merritt. Courtesy U. S. Forest Service.

PLATE XVII. Colonies of Sitka spruce that have become established along an arm of Anton Larsen Bay, northeastern Kodiak Island. Spruce in the foreground displays broad bases, characteristic of open-grown species.

PLATE XVIII. Pure stand of mature Sitka spruce surrounding Cape Greville 1 muskeg site, northeastern Kodiak Island. Low, slow-growing spruce is seen on the muskeg surface, principally with grass and sedge.

PLATE XIX. Sitka spruce on the Queen Charlotte Islands. Photo courtesy R. L. Schmidt, British Columbia Forest Service.

PLATE XX. Mature stand of Douglas fir, 300 yr in age, growing in the vicinity of Caycuse River, southwestern Vancouver Island. Photo courtesy R. L. Schmidt, British Columbia Forest Service.

PLATE XXI. Western red cedar stand near Nanaimo River, southeastern Vancouver Island. Photo courtesy R. L. Schmidt, British Columbia Forest Service.

PLATE XXII. Timber-line mountain hemlock and alpine fir of Pacific Subalpine Forest at 4800-ft elevation in the vicinity of Elk River, Strathcona Park, central Vancouver Island. Photo courtesy R. L. Schmidt, British Columbia Forest Service.

PLATE XXIII. Western red cedar forest in Olympic National Park, Olympic Peninsula, western Washington. The cluster of upright branches in front of the automobile represents a single tree, the largest on the Olympic Peninsula.

PLATE XXIV. Sitka spruce showing the effects of salt spray, sand abrasion, and wind. Locality is the mouth of the Raft River, western Olympic Peninsula.

PLATE XXV. Active dune area north of Reedsport, Oregon. Foreground dune has almost completely interred the Sitka spruce shown with only its upper crown exposed. Living trees become buried by moving dunes, and decades or centuries later are unearthed as sand-polished skeletons.

INDEX

Bold-face type indicates figures, tables, or plates.

A

D

T

U

V

W

72996
QE
931
.H43
HEUSSER
LATE-PLEISTOCENE
ENVIRONMENTS OF NORTH
PACIFIC NORTH AMERICA